A CHARLTON STANDARD CATALOGUE

BESWICK ANIMALS

TENTH EDITION

Diana Callow
John Callow

Marilyn Sweet
Peter Sweet

Publisher
W. K. Cross

The Charlton Press
TORONTO, ONTARIO ❖ PALM HARBOR, FLORIDA

Library and Archives of Canada has Catalogued this Publication as follows:

The Charlton standard catalogue of Beswick Animals

2nd ed. (1996) -
Continues: Charlton price guide to Beswick animals, ISSN 1202-9831.
ISSN 1203-8318
ISBN 978-0-88968-346-4 (10th edition)

1. Beswick (Firm)--Catalogs.   2. Porcelain animals--Catalogs.
I. Charlton Press   II. Title: Beswick Animals

NK4660.C48 2- 1996-   738.8'2'0294   C96-900264-5

The Charlton Press

VISIT OUR WEB SITE
www.charltonpress.com

EDITORIAL

Editors	W. K. Cross, Jean Dale
Graphic Technician	Davina Rowan

ACKNOWLEDGMENTS

The Charlton Press wishes to thank those who have helped and assisted with the tenth edition of Beswick Animals (A Charlton Standard Catalogue).

Contributors to the Tenth Edition

The Publisher would like to thank the following individuals and companies who graciously supplied pricing, photographs or information, or allowed us access to their collections for photographic purposes: **Richard Andrews**, UK; **Janet Butcher**, UK; **Mark Diegutis**, AU; **Jim Fitzell**, UK; **William Forter**, UK; **Karen Grimm, Black Horse Ranch**, USA; **John Lee**, UK; **Stuart Octhoff**, UK; **Joe Schenberg**, USA

A SPECIAL NOTE TO COLLECTORS

We welcome and appreciate any comments or suggestions in regard to **Beswick Animals (A Charlton Standard Catalogue)**. If any errors or omissions come to your attention, please do not hesitate to write to us, or if you would like to participate in pricing or supply previously unavailable data or information, please contact Jean Dale at (416) 488-1418, or e-mail us at chpress@charltonpress.com.

**Printed in Canada
in the Province of Quebec**

The Charlton Press

Editorial Office
P.O. Box 820, Station Willowdale B
North York, Ontario M2K 2R1
Telephone (416) 488-1418 Fax: (416) 488-4656
Telephone (800) 442-6042 Fax: (800) 442-1542
E-mail: chpress@charltonpress.com www.charltonpress.com

HOW TO USE THIS CATALOGUE

THE PURPOSE

The tenth edition of this price guide covers the complete range of animals produced at the John Beswick Studios.

As with other catalogues in Charlton's Beswick reference library, this publication has been designed to serve two specific purposes. First, to furnish the collector with accurate and detailed listings that provide the essential information needed to build a rewarding collection. Second, to provide collectors and dealers with an indication of current market prices for the complete line of Beswick animal figures.

VARIETY CLASSIFICATIONS

In developing the series of Beswick catalogues, we found it necessary to divide the model changes into three classifications based on the degree of complexity.

STYLES: When two or more animal figures have the same name - but different physical modelling characteristics - they are listed as **Style One, Style Two** and so after their names. Such figures will also have different model numbers.

VERSIONS: Versions are modifications in a minor style element, such as the Siamese Cat, model 1559. In the first version, the head of the cat shows puffed out cheeks, with the body being fleshy and having a short neck. The second version shows the cat with a sleek tapering face, a long neck and a lean body. Another example of a version change is model 1014 the Welsh Cob (rearing) where the first version has the tail of the horse attached the the ceramic base whilst in the second version the tail of the horse hangs loose.

VARIATIONS: A change in colour is a variation; for example, almost any of the horses or cats with the lists of colourways and finishes are variations.

PRICING AND THE INTERNET

Over the past thirty years we have gathered pricing information from auctions, dealer submissions, direct mail catalogues and newsletters, all contributed prices on one of two levels, wholesale or retail. We, at the Charlton Press, consider auctions basically a dealer affair, while price lists, naturally retail. To equate both prices, we needed to adjust the auction results upward by a margin of 30% to 40%, allowing for dealer markups, before comparing and then looking for a consensus on a retail price.

The marketplace has changed, the Internet and on-line auctions are now a major source of pricing information. True, there still are problems such as condition, improper descriptions, and the potential for fraudulent sales, but overall online auctions have many more pluses than minuses.

TABLE OF CONTENTS

INTRODUCTION

An article entitled "Equestrian Figures for Collectors —Growth of the House of Beswick," in the "Pottery Gazette and Glass Trade Review" of September 1961, ended with this paragraph: "Among the potters of the present day yet to reach the one hundred-year mark, and whose products are already highly prized, none is more likely to be of future interest to collectors and antique dealers than the House of Beswick." How prophetic this has proved to be. In 1985 the Beswick Collector's Circle was formed by Diana and John Callow to stimulate interest in the products of the Beswick factory was aroused. The Circle flourished as more and more people worldwide joined the search to add to their collections and to seek information in order to enjoy their finds to the full. Diana and John retired in 1995 and the Circle was wound up. Later the Beswick Collectors Club was set up in conjunction with Collecting Doulton Magazine. This book represents the most comprehensive attempt to date to form as complete a guide as possible to the Beswick animal collection.

In 1994 the John Beswick factory celebrated its centenary—a hundred years of producing an unbelievably wide variety of pottery items, from mundane household earthenware right through to the intricate ornamental ware and pure ornaments of all shapes and sizes.

Initially the factory produced plain and decorated ware. An advertisement from about 1900 lists "jugs, tea ware, dinner ware, toilet ware, flower pots, pedestals, novelties, vases, figures, bread trays, cheese dishes, etc., etc." The figures included the traditional Old Staffordshire dogs, but hares and hounds, horses, generals, a cow and calf, milkmaids, gardeners and Puss in Boots are also mentioned. Unfortunately many of these pieces were not marked Beswick.

From the start the Beswick factory was very much a family-run firm. James Wright Beswick, the founder, and his sons, John and Gilbert, and John's son, John Ewart, were all very committed to the factory's success. In 1934 ,when John Ewart Beswick became chairman and managing director and his uncle, Gilbert Beswick, was sales manager, several new pieces were introduced to the range, and recorded in the "shape book."

This was the start of shape numbers being impressed into the base whenever possible and also the more widespread use of a Beswick backstamp.

Arthur Gredington in his studio

Five years later Arthur Gredington took up his appointment as the first full-time modeller. His influence was enormous, for he had a great talent for modelling not only accurate and realistic animals of all kinds , but also ones of the comical variety, for example the very appealing "Grebie," number 1006. Consequently his name appears more than that of any other person in this book.

James Hayward also made an outstanding contribution to the high quality associated with the Beswick name. As decorating manager from 1934 and art director from 1957, he was responsible for designing almost three thousand different decorations and patterns. He also designed new shapes, such as the 720 "Panda Cub," and was an outstanding glaze chemist. His experience with glazes was fundamental in the development of the matt glaze used initially on the top of the range Connoisseur Series.

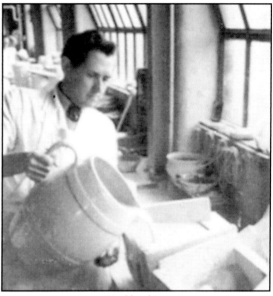

Mould making

When a complex model, such as an animal, is being manufactured, the mould it will be produced from is of vital importance. In this department Albert Hallam had exceptional skill. He joined Beswick in 1926 at age 14 as an apprentice mouldmaker and went on to become head of the mouldmaking department and also a modeller. The series of butterflies are Albert Hallam's creations, as are a number of horses, dogs and cats, which were modelled after Arthur Gredingtons retirement. These include at least one model that is very sought after today, number 2282 "Norwegian Fjord Horse."

Graham Tongue began work at Beswick in 1966, and became head modeller in 1973, when Albert Hallam retired. He concentrated on the modelling of animals, and his modelling skill is apparent in almost all the sections here.

Graham Tongue has the distinction of modelling the piece which holds the world-record price for a piece of Beswick, appropriately an equine model entitled the "Spirit of Whitfield." In 1987 he was commissioned by the Chatterley Mining Museum to model Kruger, the last pit pony used at the Staffordshire mine. The resulting

Graham Tongue at work

significant contributions were also made by Alan Maslankowski, whose 2578 "Shire Horse" is quite magnificent, Colin Melbourne, who besides the unique "C.M." series also modelled most of the Peter Scott ducks, Graham Orwell whose models included the 1374 "Galloping Horse" and 1391 "Mounted Indian," and Pal Zalman whose one equine model, the 1549 "Horse, Head tucked," is still in production.

By the late 1960's, Ewart and Gilbert Beswick were nearing retirement, and as there was not another generation to follow them into the family business, the decision was made in 1969 to sell to Royal Doulton. Beswick animals continued to be produced, and although much rationalization took place, such as reducing the number of colourways of the horses and withdrawing many pieces, the ranges were also expanded by the regular introduction of new pieces.

Then in August 1989, the decision was implemented to make the vast majority of the remaining animals produced at the Beswick factory into Doulton Animals, and the pieces were all issued with DA numbers. At the same time, grey and palomino matts were withdrawn from the horses' colourways, and only a few continued to be available in grey and palomino glosses.

In September 1999, Royal Doulton moved their complete range of animals (with the exception of the limited edition models) to the Beswick backstamp. Confusion in pricing will exist for a while until the secondary market catches up.

This book illustrates the animal kingdom as seen through the eyes of the Beswick designers since the early 1930s. Cats and kittens with appealing eyes, birds and butterflies to fly across walls, a well-stocked zoo with animals from all over the world, everyday farm animals, animals which make you laugh, champion dogs, sleek horses and fish leaping from their pools are all lasting reminders of the Beswick story.

The End of the Line

Sadly at the end of 2002 Royal Doulton ceased the manufacture of all Beswick products.

A bad day for the employees and beleaguered pottery industry in Staffordshire.

The factory at Gold Street in Longton was sold to property developers in 2003.

Beswick, Longton, Staffordshire 1894 - 2002

model, based on the 2541 "Welsh Mountain Pony," was considerably adapted with incredible attention to detail. The result was superb. Only four models were made, one each for the Beswick and Chatterley Whitfield museums, one presented to HRH Princess Anne when she visited the museum, and one was auctioned in aid of the Princesss favourite charity. In April 1994 the mining museum was closed and everything was auctioned. The "Spirit of Whitfield" sold for £2,750, a far cry from one hundred years ago when Beswick was advertising pieces for 6 ½d.

There are several other modellers whose work is featured in this book. Very little is known about some of them as they tended to be employed on a freelance basis, for example, Mr. Garbet, who contributed cats, dogs and a sheep. Although small in number,

BACKSTAMPS AND SEALS

BACKSTAMPS

Backstamp 1, is the earliest printed stamp found.

SEALS

In addition to the first small gummed seal, green with gold lettering, an alternative oval style with gold lettering on a green background was used. The small green seal was replaced by the oval style.

1. Script Beswick Ware Made In England

1. Small gummed seal
(first style) green with gold lettering

2. Circular BESWICK ENGLAND

2. Small gummed seal
(second style) green with gold lettering

3. Oval BESWICK ENGLAND

Note: Beswick backstamps give no indication of the year in which a model was issued.

The ones shown on this page were in common use over the years. Some series had their own special backstamps – most of them are shown in this book.

The smallest Beswick models, due to lack of space have no backstamp and some have just the word "England".

4. Semi circular BESWICK ENGLAND

5. BESWICK CREST ENGLAND

Chapter One
BIRDS

The models of our "feathered friends" are a delight for any bird enthusiast, and there are plenty here to choose from.

They come in all sizes, from very small birds, such as the little wren, to the impressive and large pheasant from the Connoisseur Series. The figures cover a wide range from the comic Fun Models to wall plaques to the precise realism of the Peter Scott Wildfowl collection. When displayed in groups, the colours of their plumage create an impressive display.

Among the birds in this group are species that you could see any day of the week in your garden and also more exotic or rare varieties, such as the bald eagle, penguin and kookaburra.

Model No. 317
DUCK - On pottery base

Designer:	Miss Greaves
Height:	8 ¼", 21.0 cm
Colours:	See below
Issued:	c.1936-1954
Series:	Fun Models

Colourway	U.K. £	U.S. $	Can. $
1. Blue - gloss	85.00	130.00	130.00
2. Blue/green - matt	70.00	110.00	110.00
3. Green - gloss	70.00	110.00	110.00
4. Natural - satin	85.00	130.00	130.00
5. White - gloss	65.00	100.00	100.00

Model No. 450A
PENGUIN – Large

Designer:	Mr. Owen
Height:	8", 20.3 cm
Colours:	1. Black and white - gloss
	2. Blue - gloss
Issued:	1936-by 1954

Colourway	U.K. £	U.S. $	Can. $
1. Black	300.00	450.00	450.00
2. Blue	300.00	450.00	450.00

Model No. 450B
PENGUIN – Small

Designer:	Mr. Owen
Height:	3 ½", 8.9 cm
Colours:	1. Black and white - gloss
	2. Blue - gloss
Issued:	1936-by 1954

Colourway	U.K. £	U.S. $	Can. $
1. Black	125.00	200.00	200.00
2. Blue	90.00	140.00	140.00

Model No. 618
PUFFIN

Designer:	Mr. Owen
Height:	9", 22.9 cm
Colours:	Blue - gloss
Issued:	1938-by 1954

Colourway	U.K. £	U.S. $	Can. $
Blue - gloss	350.00	550.00	550.00

Model No. 749
MALLARD DUCK - Rising

Designer:	Arthur Gredington
Height:	6 ½", 16.5 cm
Colours:	Browns, teal green and white - gloss
Issued:	1939-by 1965

Description	U.K. £	U.S. $	Can. $
Gloss	100.00	150.00	150.00

Note: Pair with Model No. 750.

Model No. 750
MALLARD DUCK - Settling

Designer:	Arthur Gredington
Height:	6 ½", 16.5 cm
Colours:	Browns, teal green and white - gloss
Issued:	1939-by 1965

Description	U.K. £	U.S. $	Can. $
Gloss	100.00	150.00	150.00

Note: Pair with Model No. 749.

Model No. 756
MALLARD DUCK - Standing

Designer:	Mr. Watkin
Height:	756/1 - 7", 17.8 cm
	756/2 - 5 ¾", 14.6 cm
	756/2A - 4 ½", 11.9 cm
	756/3 - 3 ½", 8.9 cm
Colours:	1. Brown, teal green and white - gloss
	2. Blue - gloss
Issued:	1939-1973

Colourway	U.K. £	U.S. $	Can. $
1. 756/1 Brown	35.00	55.00	55.00
2. 756/1 Blue	75.00	115.00	115.00
3. 756/2 Brown	25.00	40.00	40.00
4. 756/2 Blue	60.00	95.00	95.00
5. 756/2A Brown	20.00	30.00	30.00
6. 756/2A Blue	50.00	80.00	80.00
7. 756/3 Brown	15.00	25.00	25.00
8. 756/3 Blue	45.00	70.00	70.00

Note: Model no. 756/3 has grass around feet.
Model no. 902 makes a set of five pieces.

Model No. 760
DUCK WITH LADYBIRD ON BEAK

Designer:	Mr. Watkin
Height:	3 ¾", 9.5 cm
Colours:	White with yellow beak, ladybird on beak - gloss
Issued:	1939-1971
Series:	Fun Models

Description	U.K. £	U.S. $	Can. $
Gloss	20.00	30.00	30.00

Model No. 765
DUCK FAMILY

Designer:	Arthur Gredington
Height:	2 ¾" x 7", 7.0 x 17.8 cm
Colours:	White with yellow beaks - gloss
Issued:	1939-1971

Description	U.K. £	U.S. $	Can. $
Gloss	25.00	40.00	40.00

Model No. 767A
PHEASANT
First Version - Curved tail

Designer:	Mr. Watkin
Height:	3", 7.6 cm
Colours:	Red brown, teal green - gloss
Issued:	1939-1971

Description	U.K. £	U.S. $	Can. $
Gloss	15.00	25.00	25.00

Note: This model was used on 754 (pheasant ashtray).

Model No. 767B
PHEASANT
Second Version - Straight tail

Designer:	Mr. Watkin
Height:	3", 7.6 cm
Colours:	Red, brown and teal green - gloss or matt
Issued:	1. Gloss - 1971-1995
	2. Matt - 1983-1989

Description	U.K. £	U.S . $	Can. $
1. Gloss	15.00	25.00	25.00
2. Matt	15.00	25.00	25.00

Model No. 768
SEAGULL ON ROCK

Designer: Arthur Gredington
Height: 8 ½", 21.6 cm
Colours: Cream and dark brown,
green and yellow base - gloss
Issued: 1939-by 1954

Description	U.K. £	U.S. $	Can. $
Gloss	1,000.00	1,500.00	1,500.00

Model No. 800
PENGUIN - Chick

Designer: Arthur Gredington
Height: 2". 5.0 cm
Colours: Black and white with yellow
markings - gloss
Issued: 1940-1973

Description	U.K. £	U.S. $	Can. $
Gloss	10.00	15.00	15.00

Note: Set with model numbers 801, 802 and 803. For
other models in this set see "Beswick Collectables."

Model No. 801
PENGUIN - Chick

Designer: Arthur Gredington
Height: 2", 5.0 cm
Colours: Black and white with yellow
markings - gloss
Issued: 1940-1973

Description	U.K. £	U.S. $	Can. $
Gloss	10.00	15.00	15.00

Note: Set with model numbers 800, 802 and 803. For other
models in this set see "Beswick Collectables."

Model No. 817/1
MALLARD DUCK - Squatting

Designer: Mr. Watkin
Height: 7 ½", 19.1 cm
Colours: 1. Brown, teal green and white - gloss
2. Cream - satin matt
Issued: 1940-1954
Set: 817/2

Colourway	U.K. £	U.S. $	Can. $
1. Brown/green/white	175.00	275.00	275.00
2. Cream	125.00	200.00	200.00

Model No. 817/2
MALLARD DUCK - Squatting

Designer:	Mr. Watkin		
Height:	6 ¾", 17.2 cm		
Colours:	Brown, teal green and white - gloss		
Issued:	1940-1970		
Set:	817/1		

Description	U.K. £	U.S. $	Can. $
Gloss	100.00	150.00	150.00

Model No. 820
GEESE (Pair)

Designer:	Arthur Gredington		
Height:	4", 10.1 cm		
Colours:	White with orange feet and beaks - gloss		
Issued:	1940-1971		
Series:	Fun Models		
Set:	821, 822		

Description	U.K. £	U.S. $	Can. $
Gloss	15.00	25.00	25.00

Model No. 821
GOSLING - Facing left

Designer:	Arthur Gredington		
Height:	2 ¼", 5.7 cm		
Colours:	White with orange beak - gloss		
Issued:	1940-1971		
Series:	Fun Models		
Set:	820, 822		

Description	U.K. £	U.S. $	Can. $
Gloss	10.00	15.00	15.00

Model No. 822
GOSLING - Facing right

Designer:	Arthur Gredington		
Height:	1 ¾", 4.3 cm		
Colours:	White with orange beak - gloss		
Issued:	1940-1971		
Series:	Fun Models		
Set:	820, 821		

Description	U.K. £	U.S. $	Can. $
Gloss	10.00	15.00	15.00

Model No. 827
HARDY'S DUCK - Standing

Designer:	Mr. Watkin
Height:	Large - 7 ½", 19.1 cm
	Medium - 6", 15.0 cm
	Small - 5", 12.7 cm
Colours:	1. White; brown and yellow - gloss
	2. White; solid decorated wing - gloss
	3. White; solid decorated neck, wing - gloss
	4. White; yellow bill, feet - gloss
Issued:	1940-by 1954

Description	U.K. £	U.S. $	Can. $
1. Large	85.00	130.00	130.00
2. Large	85.00	130.00	130.00
3. Large	85.00	130.00	130.00
4. Large	85.00	130.00	130.00
1. Medium	75.00	115.00	115.00
2. Medium	75.00	115.00	115.00
3. Medium	75.00	115.00	115.00
4. Medium	75.00	115.00	115.00
1. Small	65.00	100.00	100.00
2. Small	65.00	100.00	100.00
3. Small	65.00	100.00	100.00
4. Small	65.00	100.00	100.00

Model No. 849
PHEASANT ON BASE - Flying upwards

Designer:	Arthur Gredington
Height:	6", 15.0 cm
Colours:	Browns, teal green and yellow - gloss
Issued:	1940-1971

Description	U.K. £	U.S. $	Can. $
Gloss	70.00	110.00	110.00

Note: Pair with model number 850.

Model No. 850
PHEASANT ON BASE - Settling

Designer:	Arthur Gredington
Height:	5 ¾", 14.6 cm
Colours:	Browns, teal green and yellow - gloss
Issued:	1940-1971

Description	U.K. £	U.S. $	Can. $
Gloss	70.00	110.00	110.00

Note: Pair with model number 849.

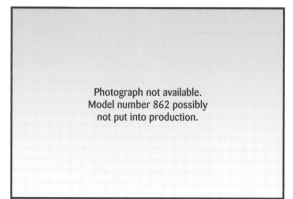

Photograph not available.
Model number 862 possibly
not put into production.

Model No. 862
FANTAIL PIGEON

Designer: Miss Joachin
Height: Unknown
Colours: Unknown
Issued: 1940-Unknown

Description	U.K. £	U.S. $	Can. $
Fantail Pigeon	Possibly not put into production		

Model No. 902
MALLARD DUCK - Standing

Designer: Arthur Gredington
Height: 10", 25.4 cm
Colours: 1.   Brown and teal green - gloss
             2.   Brown, teal green or white - gloss
Issued: 1940-1970

Colourway	U.K. £	U.S. $	Can. $
1. Brown	85.00	130.00	130.00
2. Brown/white	85.00	130.00	130.00

Note: Makes a set of five with 756/1, 756/2, 756/2A,
            756/3.

Model No. 919A
DUCK - Large

Designer: Mr. Watkin
Height: 3 ¾", 9.5 cm
Colours: 1.   Brown, teal green, white and pink - gloss
             2.   White with yellow beak and feet - gloss
Issued: 1941-1971

Colourway	U.K. £	U.S. $	Can. $
1. Brown	15.00	25.00	25.00
2. White	15.00	25.00	25.00

Note: Makes a set of three with model numbers 919b and
            919c.

Model No. 919B
DUCK - Medium

Designer: Mr. Watkin
Height: 2 ½", 6.4 cm
Colours: 1.   Brown, teal green, white and pink - gloss
             2.   White with yellow beak and feet - gloss
Issued: 1941-1971

Colourway	U.K. £	U.S. $	Can. $
1. Brown	15.00	25.00	25.00
2. White	15.00	25.00	25.00

Note: Makes a set of three with model numbers 919a and
            919c.

Model No. 919C
DUCK - Small

Designer:	Mr. Watkin
Height:	2", 5.0 cm
Colours:	1. Brown, teal green, white and pink - gloss
	2. White with yellow beak and feet - gloss
Issued:	1941-1971

Colourway	U.K. £	U.S. $	Can. $
1. Brown	15.00	25.00	25.00
2. White	15.00	25.00	25.00

Note: Makes a set of three with model numbers 919a and 919b.

Model No. 925
AMERICAN BLUE JAYS

Designer:	Arthur Gredington
Height:	5", 12.7 cm
Colours:	Blue and white - gloss
Issued:	1941-by 1965

Description	U.K. £	U.S. $	Can. $
Gloss	75.00	115.00	115.00

Model No. 926
BALTIMORE ORIOLES

Designer:	Arthur Gredington
Height:	5", 12.7 cm
Colours:	1. Chestnut brown, green claws - gloss
	2. Golden/dark brown/blue markings - gloss
	3. Yellow/black/blue markings - gloss
Issued:	1941-by 1965

Colourway	U.K. £	U.S. $	Can. $
1. Chestnut	60.00	95.00	95.00
2. Golden	70.00	110.00	110.00
3. Yellow	70.00	110.00	110.00

Model No. 927
CARDINAL

Designer:	Arthur Gredington
Height:	5 ¾", 14.6 cm
Colours:	1. Dark red - gloss
	2. Pinkish-purple - gloss
Issued:	1941-by 1959

Colourway	U.K. £	U.S. $	Can. $
1. Dark red	55.00	85.00	85.00
2. Pinkish-purple	65.00	100.00	100.00

Model No. 928
TANAGER

Designer:	Arthur Gredington
Height:	5 ¾", 14.6 cm
Colours:	1. Red - gloss
	2. Various - gloss
	3. Yellow, green and orange - gloss
Issued:	1941-1959

Colourway	U.K. £	U.S. $	Can. $
1. Red	85.00	130.00	130.00
2. Various	85.00	130.00	130.00
3. Yellow/green	85.00	130.00	130.00

Model No. 929
CHICKADEE

Designer:	Arthur Gredington
Height:	5 ¾", 14.6 cm
Colours:	Dark and light blue, white and
	yellow - gloss or lustre
Issued:	1941-1968

Description	U.K. £	U.S. $	Can. $
1. Gloss	40.00	60.00	60.00
2. Lustre	45.00	70.00	70.00

Model No. 930
PARAKEET

Designer:	Arthur Gredington
Height:	6", 15.0 cm
Colours:	Green and yellow - gloss
Issued:	1941-1975

Description	U.K. £	U.S. $	Can. $
Gloss	45.00	70.00	70.00

Model No. 980A
ROBIN
First Version - Base is a green mound

Designer:	Arthur Gredington
Height:	3", 7.6 cm
Colours:	Brown and red - gloss
Issued:	1942-1973

Description	U.K. £	U.S. $	Can. $
Gloss	25.00	40.00	40.00

Model No. 980B
ROBIN
Second Version - Base is a branch and leaf

Designer: Arthur Gredington
Remodelled: Albert Hallam
Height: 3", 7.6 cm
Colours: Brown and red - gloss or matt
Issued: 1. Gloss - 1973-2002
              2. Matt - 1983-1992

Description	U.K. £	U.S. $	Can. $
1. Gloss	20.00	30.00	30.00
2. Matt	20.00	30.00	30.00

Model No. 991A
CHAFFINCH
First Version - Base is a green mound

Designer: Arthur Gredington
Height: 2 ¾", 7.0 cm
Colours: Pink, brown and black - gloss
Issued: 1943-1973

Description	U.K. £	U.S. $	Can. $
Gloss	30.00	45.00	45.00

Model No. 991B
CHAFFINCH
Second Version - Base is a branch

Designer: Arthur Gredington
Remodelled: Albert Hallam
Height: 2 ¾", 7.0 cm
Colours: Pink, brown, black - gloss or matt
Issued: 1. Gloss - 1973-2002
              2. Matt - 1983-1992

Description	U.K. £	U.S. $	Can. $
1. Gloss	20.00	30.00	30.00
2. Matt	20.00	30.00	30.00

Model No. 992A
BLUE TIT
First Version - Base is a green mound

Designer: Arthur Gredington
Height: 2 ½", 6.4 cm
Colours: White, blue and green - gloss
Issued: 1943-1973

Description	U.K. £	U.S. $	Can. $
Gloss	30.00	45.00	45.00

Model No. 992B
BLUE TIT
Second Version - Base is branch and leaves with ladybug

Designer:	Arthur Gredington
Remodelled:	Unknown
Height:	2 ¼", 5.7 cm
Colours:	White, blue and green - gloss or matt
Issued:	1. Gloss - 1973-2002
	2. Matt - 1983-1992

Description	U.K. £	U.S. $	Can. $
1. Gloss	20.00	30.00	30.00
2. Matt	20.00	30.00	30.00

Model No. 993A
WREN
First Version - Base is a green mound

Designer:	Arthur Gredington
Height:	2 ¼", 5.7 cm
Colours:	Light brown, pink breast - gloss
Issued:	1943-1973

Description	U.K. £	U.S. $	Can. $
Gloss	30.00	45.00	45.00

Model No. 993B
WREN
Second Version - Base is a green leaf

Designer:	Arthur Gredington
Remodelled:	Graham Tongue
Height:	2 ¼", 5.7 cm
Colours:	Dark and light brown - gloss or matt
Issued:	1. Gloss - 1973-2002
	2. Matt - 1983-1992

Description	U.K. £	U.S. $	Can. $
1. Gloss	20.00	30.00	30.00
2. Matt	20.00	30.00	30.00

Model No. 994
SHELLDRAKE - Rising (beak closed)

Designer:	Arthur Gredington
Height:	6", 15.0 cm
Colours:	White, brown and green - gloss
Issued:	1943-1965

Description	U.K. £	U.S. $	Can. $
Gloss	100.00	150.00	150.00

Note: Pair with model number 995.

Model No. 995
SHELLDRAKE - Settling (beak open)
Designer: Arthur Gredington
Height: 6 ¼", 15.9 cm
Colours: White, brown and green - gloss
Issued: 1943-1965

Description	U.K. £	U.S. $	Can. $
Gloss		100.00	150.00	150.00

Note: Pair with model number 994.

Model No. 1001
COCKEREL
Designer: Arthur Gredington
Height: 5 ¾", 14.6 cm
Colours: Green, red and yellow - gloss
Issued: 1944-by 1959
Series: Stylistic Models

Description	U.K. £	U.S. $	Can. $
Gloss	175.00	275.00	275.00

Model No. 1004
ROOSTER
Designer: Arthur Gredington
Height: 7", 17.8 cm
Colours: White, green, red, blue and black - gloss
Issued: 1944-by 1959
Series: Stylistic Model

Description	U.K. £	U.S. $	Can. $
Gloss	160.00	250.00	250.00

Model No. 1006
GREBIE
Designer: Arthur Gredington
Height: 5 ¼", 13.3 cm
Colours: Green and browns - gloss
Issued: 1945-by 1954
Series: Stylistic Model

Description	U.K. £	U.S. $	Can. $
Gloss	600.00	950.00	950.00

Model No 1015
COURTING PENGUINS

Designer:	Arthur Gredington
Height:	5 ½", 14.0 cm
Colours:	1. Black and white with yellow markings - gloss
	2. Blue - gloss
Issued:	1945-1965

Colourway	U.K. £	U.S. $	Can. $
1. Black/white	175.00	275.00	275.00
2. Blue	125.00	200.00	200.00

Model No. 1018
BALD EAGLE

Designer:	Arthur Gredington
Height:	7 ¼", 18.4 cm
Colours:	1. Brown and white - gloss or matt
	2. Bronze with black - satin
Issued:	1a. Gloss - 1945-1995
	1b. Matt - 1983-1989
	2. Britannia Collection - 1989-1992

Description	U.K. £	U.S. $	Can. $
1a. Gloss	65.00	100.00	100.00
1b. Matt	55.00	85.00	85.00
2. Satin	55.00	85.00	85.00

Model No. 1022
TURTLE DOVES

Designer:	Arthur Gredington
Height:	7 ½", 19.1 cm
Colours:	Browns, pale blue and pink, light brown and green base - gloss
Issued:	1945-1970

Description	U.K. £	U.S. $	Can. $
Gloss	150.00	225.00	225.00

Model No. 1041A
GREY WAGTAIL
First Version - Head down, light green base

Designer:	Arthur Gredington
Height:	2 ½", 6.4 cm
Colours:	Yellow, grey and black - gloss
Issued:	1945-1973

Description	U.K. £	U.S. $	Can. $
Gloss	35.00	55.00	55.00

Model No. 1041B
GREY WAGTAIL
Second Version - Head up, dark blue and green base

Designer: Arthur Gredington
Remodelled: Albert Hallam
Height: 2 ½", 6.4 cm
Colours: Yellow, grey and black - gloss or matt
Issued: 1. Gloss - 1973-2002
              2. Matt - 1983-1989

Description	U.K. £	U.S. $	Can. $
1. Gloss	20.00	30.00	30.00
2. Matt	20.00	30.00	30.00

Model No. 1042A
BULLFINCH
First Version - Yellow base and flowers

Designer: Arthur Gredington
Height: 2 ½", 6.4 cm
Colours: Red breast, dark brown feathers,
              yellow flowers and base - gloss
Issued: 1945-1973

Description	U.K. £	U.S. $	Can. $
Gloss	30.00	50.00	50.00

Model No. 1042B
BULLFINCH
Second Version - Base is a twig

Designer: Arthur Gredington
Remodelled: Graham Tongue
Height: 2 ½", 6.4 cm
Colours: Red, dark brown - gloss or matt
Issued: 1. Gloss - 1973-1998
              2. Matt - 1983-1989

Description	U.K. £	U.S. $	Can. $
1. Gloss	15.00	25.00	25.00
2. Matt	15.00	25.00	25.00

Model No. 1046A
BARN OWL
First Version - Split tail feathers

Designer: Arthur Gredington
Height: 7 ¼", 18.4 cm
Colours: Golden brown and white - gloss
Issued: 1946-Unknown

Description	U.K. £	U.S. $	Can. $
Gloss	50.00	75.00	75.00

Model No. 1046B
BARN OWL
Second Version - Closed tail feathers
Designer: Arthur Gredington
Height: 7 ¼", 18.4 cm
Colours: Golden brown and white - gloss or matt
Issued: 1.   Gloss - Unknown-1997
              2.   Matt - 1983-1989

Description	U.K. £	U.S. $	Can. $
1. Gloss	30.00	45.00	45.00
2. Matt	45.00	70.00	70.00

Model No. 1052
BARNACLE GOOSE
Designer: Arthur Gredington
Height: 6 ½", 16.5 cm
Colours: Dark grey-blue and white - gloss
Issued: 1943-1968

Description	U.K. £	U.S. $	Can. $
Gloss	650.00	1,000.00	1,000.00

Model No. 1159
KOOKABURRA
Designer: Arthur Gredington
Height: 5 ¾", 14.6 cm
Colours: Brown, blue and fawn - gloss
Issued: 1949-1976

Description	U.K. £	U.S. $	Can. $
Gloss	100.00	150.00	150.00

Model No. 1178
GOULDIAN FINCH - Wings out
Designer: Arthur Gredington
Height: 4", 10.1 cm
Colours: Purple, green and yellow - gloss
Issued: 1949-by 1959

Description	U.K. £	U.S. $	Can. $
Gloss	200.00	300.00	300.00

Model No. 1179
GOULDIAN FINCH - Wings in

Designer: Arthur Gredington
Height: 4 ½", 11.9 cm
Colours: Purple, green and yellow - gloss
Issued: 1949-by 1959

Description	U.K. £	U.S. $	Can. $
Gloss	200.00	300.00	300.00

Model No. 1180
COCKATOO - Small

Designer: Arthur Gredington
Height: 8 ½", 21.6 cm
Colours: 1. Pink and grey - gloss
2. Turquoise and yellow - gloss
Issued: 1949-1975

Colourway	U.K. £	U.S. $	Can. $
1. Pink/grey	85.00	125.00	125.00
2. Turquoise/yellow	85.00	125.00	125.00

Note: For Cockatoo - large, see page 27.

Model No. 1216A
BUDGERIGAR - Facing left
First Version - Flowers in high relief on base

Designer: Arthur Gredington
Height: 7", 17.8 cm
Colours: 1. Blue with dark brown markings - gloss
2. Green with yellow markings - gloss
Issued: 1951-1967

Colourway	U.K. £	U.S. $	Can. $
1. Blue	400.00	625.00	625.00
2. Green	900.00	1,400.00	1,400.00

Model No. 1216B
BUDGERIGAR - Facing left
Second Version - No flowers on base

Designer: Arthur Gredington
Height: 7", 17.8 cm
Colours: Blue, green or yellow - gloss
Issued: 1. Blue - 1967-1975
2. Green - 1967-1972
3. Yellow - 1970-1972

Colourway	U.K. £	U.S. $	Can. $
1. Blue	100.00	150.00	150.00
2. Green	300.00	450.00	450.00
3. Yellow	1,300.00	2,000.00	2,000.00

Model No. 1217A
BUDGERIGAR - Facing right
First Version - Flowers in high relief on base

Designer: Arthur Gredington
Height: 7", 17.8 cm
Colours: 1.   Blue - gloss
              2.   Green - gloss
Issued: 1951-1967

Colourway	U.K. £	U.S. $	Can. $
1. Blue	650.00	1,000.00	1,000.00
2. Green	800.00	1,250.00	1,250.00

Model No. 1217B
BUDGERIGAR - Facing right
Second Version - No flowers on base

Designer: Arthur Gredington
Height: 7", 17.8 cm
Colours: 1.   Blue - gloss
              2.   Green - gloss
              3.   Yellow - gloss
Issued: 1967-1970

Colourway	U.K. £	U.S. $	Can. $
1. Blue	125.00	200.00	200.00
2. Green	400.00	625.00	625.00
3. Yellow	2,500.00	3,750.00	3,750.00

Model No. 1218A
GREEN WOODPECKER
First Version - Flowers in high relief on base

Designer: Arthur Gredington
Height: 9", 22.9 cm
Colours: Green, red and white - gloss
Issued: 1951-1967

Description	U.K. £	U.S. $	Can. $
Gloss	400.00	625.00	625.00

Model No. 1218B
GREEN WOODPECKER
Second Version - No flowers on base

Designer: Arthur Gredington
Height: 9", 22.9 cm
Colours: Green, red and white - gloss or matt
Issued: 1.   Gloss - 1967-1989
              2.   Matt - 1983-1988

Description	U.K. £	U.S. $	Can. $
1. Gloss	90.00	140.00	140.00
2. Matt	90.00	140.00	140.00

Model No. 1219A
JAY
First Version - Flowers in high relief on base

Designer:	Arthur Gredington
Height:	6", 15.0 cm
Colours:	Rust, blue, black and grey - gloss
Issued:	1951-1967

Description	U.K. £	U.S. $	Can. $
Gloss	275.00	425.00	425.00

Model No. 1219B
JAY
Second Version - No flowers on base

Designer:	Arthur Gredington
Height:	6", 15.0 cm
Colours:	Pink, blue and white - gloss
Issued:	1967-1971

Description	U.K. £	U.S. $	Can. $
Gloss	200.00	300.00	300.00

Model No. 1225A
PHEASANT
First Version - Flowers in high relief on base

Designer:	Arthur Gredington
Height:	7 ¾", 19.7 cm
Colours:	Red-brown, teal green, green base - gloss
Issued:	1951-1967

Description	U.K. £	U.S. $	Can. $
Gloss	225.00	350.00	350.00

Model No. 1225B
PHEASANT
Second Version - No flowers on base

Designer:	Arthur Gredington
Height:	7 ¾", 19.7 cm
Colours:	Red-brown, teal green, green base - gloss
Issued:	1967-1977

Description	U.K. £	U.S. $	Can. $
Gloss	75.00	115.00	115.00

Model No. 1226A
PHEASANT
First Version - Flowers in high relief on base
Designer: Arthur Gredington
Height: 6", 15.0 cm
Colours: Red-brown, teal green, green base - gloss
Issued: 1951-1967

Description	U.K. £	U.S. $	Can. $
Gloss	300.00	450.00	450.00

Model No. 1226B
PHEASANT
Second Version - No flowers on base
Designer: Arthur Gredington
Height: 6", 15.0 cm
Colours: Red-brown, teal green, green base - gloss
Issued: 1967-1977

Description	U.K. £	U.S. $	Can. $
Gloss	75.00	115.00	115.00

Model No. 1383A
PIGEON
First Version - Three stripes on wings
Designer: Mr. Orwell
Height: 5 ½", 14.0 cm
Colours: 1.   Blue - gloss
             2.   Red - gloss
Issued: 1955-1972

Colourway	U.K. £	U.S. $	Can. $
1. Blue - gloss	150.00	225.00	225.00
2. Red - gloss	150.00	225.00	225.00

Model No. 1383B
PIGEON
Second Version - Two stripes on wings
Designer: Mr. Orwell
Height: 5 ½", 14.0 cm
Colours: Blue or red - gloss or matt
Issued: 1.   Gloss - 1955-1989
             2.   Matt - 1983-1988

Colourway	U.K. £	U.S. $	Can. $
1a. Blue - gloss	85.00	125.00	125.00
1b. Blue - matt	85.00	125.00	125.00
2a. Red - gloss	85.00	125.00	125.00
2b. Red - matt	85.00	125.00	125.00

Model No. 1518
MALLARD DUCK

Designer: Arthur Gredington
Length: See below
Colours: Teal green, brown, white, yellow beak - gloss
Issued: See below
Series: Peter Scott Wildfowl

Description	Issued	Length	U.K. £	Price U.S. $	Can. $
1. Large	1958-1971	6 ½", 16.5 cm	125.00	195.00	195.00
2. Medium	1958-1971	5 ½", 14.0 cm	85.00	125.00	125.00
3. Small - First Version	1958-1962	4 ½", 11.9 cm	50.00	75.00	75.00
4. Small - Second Version	1962-1971	3 ¾", 11.9 cm	50.00	75.00	75.00

Model No. 1519
MANDARIN DUCK

Designer: Arthur Gredington
Length:
1. Large – 4 ½", 11.9 cm
2. Medium – 3 ¾", 9.5 cm
3. Small – 3", 7.6 cm
Colours: Tan-brown and blue with red beak - gloss
Issued: 1958-1971
Series: Peter Scott Wildfowl

Description	U.K. £	U.S. $	Can. $
1. Large	500.00	750.00	750.00
2. Medium	300.00	450.00	450.00
3. Small	110.00	165.00	165.00

Model No. 1520
POCHARD DUCK

Designer: Arthur Gredington
Length:
1. Large – 5 ½", 14.0 cm
2. Medium – 4 ½", 11.9 cm
3. Small – 3 ½", 8.9 cm
Colours: Brown, grey and black - gloss
Issued: 1958-1971
Series: Peter Scott Wildfowl

Description	U.K. £	U.S. $	Can. $
1. Large	225.00	350.00	350.00
2. Medium	175.00	275.00	275.00
3. Small	165.00	250.00	250.00

Model No. 1521
KING EIDER DUCK

Designer:	Colin Melbourne
Length:	4", 10.1 cm
Colours:	Dark grey with tan, brown, green and white - gloss
Issued:	1958-1971
Series:	Peter Scott Wildfowl

Description	U.K. £	U.S. $	Can. $
Gloss	125.00	190.00	190.00

Model No. 1522
SMEW DUCK

Designer:	Colin Melbourne
Length:	3", 7.6 cm
Colours:	Grey, black and white - gloss
Issued:	1958-1971
Series:	Peter Scott Wildfowl

Description	U.K. £	U.S. $	Can. $
Gloss	125.00	190.00	190.00

Model No. 1523
TUFTED DUCK

Designer:	Colin Melbourne
Length:	2 ¾", 7.0 cm
Colours:	Black and white - gloss
Issued:	1958-1971
Series:	Peter Scott Wildfowl

Description	U.K. £	U.S. $	Can. $
Gloss	125.00	190.00	190.00

Model No. 1524
GOLDENEYE DUCK

Designer:	Colin Melbourne
Length:	3 ½", 8.9 cm
Colours:	Black, white and green - gloss
Issued:	1958-1971
Series:	Peter Scott Wildfowl

Description	U.K. £	U.S. $	Can. $
Gloss	225.00	350.00	350.00

Model No. 1525
GOOSANDER

Designer:	Colin Melbourne
Length:	4 ½", 11.9 cm
Colours:	Pink, black and white, orange beak - gloss
Issued:	1958-1971
Series:	Peter Scott Wildfowl

Description	U.K. £	U.S. $	Can. $
Gloss	225.00	350.00	350.00

Model No. 1526
WIDGEON DUCK

Designer:	Colin Melbourne
Length:	3 ½", 8.9 cm
Colours:	Pink, brown yellow, black and white - gloss
Issued:	1958-1971
Series:	Peter Scott Wildfowl

Description	U.K. £	U.S. $	Can. $
Gloss	100.00	150.00	150.00

Model No. 1527
SHELDUCK

Designer:	Colin Melbourne
Length:	4", 10.1 cm
Colours:	Dark grey, tan, white, green and brown - gloss
Issued:	1958-1971
Series:	Peter Scott Wildfowl

Description	U.K. £	U.S. $	Can. $
Gloss	125.00	190.00	190.00

Model No. 1528
SHOVELER

Designer:	Colin Melbourne
Length:	3 ½", 8.9 cm
Colours:	Tan, blue, white and dark brown - gloss
Issued:	1958-1971
Series:	Peter Scott Wildfowl

Description	U.K. £	U.S. $	Can. $
Gloss	125.00	190.00	190.00

Model No. 1529
TEAL DUCK

Designer:	Colin Melbourne
Length:	2 ¾", 7.0 cm
Colours:	Tan, yellow, black, white with blue beak - gloss
Issued:	1958-1971
Series:	Peter Scott Wildfowl

Description	U.K. £	U.S. $	Can. $
Gloss	125.00	190.00	190.00

Model No. 1614
FANTAIL PIGEON

Designer:	Arthur Gredington
Height:	5", 12.7 cm
Colours:	White - gloss
Issued:	1959-1969

Description	U.K. £	U.S. $	Can. $
Gloss	400.00	625.00	625.00

Model No. 1684
SWAN - Head up

Designer:	Arthur Gredington
Height:	3", 7.6 cm
Colours:	White - gloss
Issued:	1960-1973
Set:	1685, 1686, 1687

Description	U.K. £	U.S. $	Can. $
Gloss	35.00	55.00	55.00

Model No. 1685
SWAN - Head down

Designer:	Arthur Gredington
Height:	2", 5.0 cm
Colours:	White - gloss
Issued:	1960-1973
Set:	1684, 1686, 1687

Description	U.K £	U.S. $	Can. $
Gloss	35.00	55.00	55.00

Model No. 1686
CYGNET - Facing left

Designer:	Arthur Gredington	
Height:	1", 2.5 cm	
Colours:	Grey - gloss	
Issued:	1960-1971	
Set:	1684, 1685, 1687	

Description	U.K. £	U.S. $	Can. $
Gloss	40.00	60.00	60.00

Model No. 1687
CYGNET - Facing right

Designer:	Arthur Gredington	
Height:	1", 2.5 cm	
Colours:	Grey - gloss	
Issued:	1960-1971	
Set:	1684, 1685, 1686	

Description	U.K. £	U.S. $	Can. $
Gloss	40.00	60.00	60.00

Model No. 1774
PHEASANT - On pottery base

Designer:	Albert Hallam
Height:	4 ¾", 12.1 cm
Colours:	Red-brown, teal green and beige - gloss
Issued:	1961-1975

Description	U.K. £	U.S. $	Can. $
Gloss	45.00	70.00	70.00

Model No. 1818
COCKATOO - Large

Designer:	Albert Hallam	
Height:	11 ½", 29.2 cm	
Colours:	1. Pink and grey - gloss	
	2. Turquoise and yellow - gloss	
Issued:	1962-1973	

Colourway	U.K. £	U.S. $	Can. $
1. Pink/grey	135.00	200.00	200.00
2. Turquoise/yellow	175.00	275.00	275.00

Note: For Cockatoo - small, see page 19.

Model No. 1892
LEGHORN COCKEREL

Designer:	Arthur Gredington	
Height:	9", 22.9 cm	
Colours:	Teal green, red, orange and yellow - gloss	
Issued:	1963-1983	

Description	U.K. £	U.S. $	Can. $
Gloss	225.00	350.00	350.00

Model No. 1899
SUSSEX COCKEREL

Designer:	Arthur Gredington	
Height:	7", 17.8 cm	
Colours:	Black, white and pink - gloss	
Issued:	1963-1971	

Description	U.K. £	U.S. $	Can. $
Gloss	950.00	1,475.00	1,475.00

Model No. 1957
TURKEY

Designer:	Albert Hallam	
Height:	7 ¼", 18.4 cm	
Colours:	1. Bronze - gloss	
	2. White - gloss	
Issued:	1964-1969	

Colourway	U.K. £	U.S. $	Can. $
1. Bronze	1,000.00	1,500.00	1,500.00
2. White	600.00	900.00	900.00

Model No. 2026
OWL

Designer:	Albert Hallam	
Height:	4 ½", 11.9 cm	
Colours:	Golden brown and white - gloss or matt	
Issued:	1965-2002	

Description	U.K. £	U.S. $	Can. $
1. Gloss	25.00	35.00	35.00
2. Matt	25.00	35.00	35.00

Model No. 2059
GAMECOCK

Designer:	Arthur Gredington
Height:	9 ½", 24.0 cm
Colours:	Brown, teal green, cream and red - gloss
Issued:	1966-1975

Description	U.K. £	U.S. $	Can. $
Gloss	600.00	900.00	900.00

Model No. 2062
GOLDEN EAGLE

Designer:	Graham Tongue
Height:	9 ½", 24.0 cm
Colours:	Dark brown - gloss, matt, or satin matt
Issued:	1. 1966-1974 - Gloss
	2. 1970-1972 - Matt
	3. 1973-1989 - Satin matt
Series:	3. Connoisseur

Description	U.K. £	U.S. $	Can. $
1. Gloss	125.00	190.00	190.00
2. Matt	75.00	115.00	115.00
3. Satin matt	75.00	115.00	115.00

Model No. 2063
GROUSE (Pair)

Designer:	Albert Hallam
Height:	5 ½", 14.0 cm
Colours:	Red-brown - gloss
Issued:	1966-1975

Description	U.K. £	U.S. $	Can. $
Gloss	425.00	650.00	650.00

Model No. 2064
PARTRIDGE (Pair)

Designer:	Albert Hallam
Height:	5 ½", 14.0 cm
Colours:	Brown and blue - gloss
Issued:	1966-1975

Description	U.K. £	U.S. $	Can. $
Gloss	500.00	750.00	750.00

Model No. 2067
TURKEY

Designer: Albert Hallam
Height: 2 ½", 6.4 cm
Colours: 1.   White and red - gloss
            2.   Bronze - gloss
Issued: 1966-1969

Colourway	U.K. £	U.S. $	Can. $
1. White	200.00	300.00	300.00
2. Bronze	175.00	275.00	275.00

Photograph not available.
Model number 2071 possibly
not put into production.

Model No. 2071
OWL (Contemporary)

Designer: Graham Tongue
Height: 5", 12.7 cm
Colours: Green and dark grey - matt
Issued: 1966-Unknown
Series: Contemporary Models

Description	U.K. £	U.S. $	Can. $
Owl		Possibly not put into production

Model No. 2078
PHEASANTS (Pair)

Designer: Arthur Gredington
Height: 6 ¾", 17.2 cm
Colours: Red-brown and teal green with
            yellow markings - gloss
Issued: 1966-1975

Description	U.K. £	U.S. $	Can. $
Gloss	400.00	600.00	600.00

Model No. 2105A
GREENFINCH
First Version - Without flower on base

Designer: Graham Tongue
Height: 3", 7.6 cm
Colours: Natural - gloss
Issued: 1967-1973

Description	U.K. £	U.S. $	Can. $
Gloss	35.00	55.00	55.00

Model No. 2105B
GREENFINCH
Second Version - With flower on base

Designer:	Graham Tongue
Remodelled:	Albert Hallam
Height:	3", 7.6 cm
Colours:	Green and yellow - gloss or matt
Issued:	1. Gloss - 1973-1998
	2. Matt - 1983-1992

Description	U.K. £	U.S. $	Can. $
1. Gloss	25.00	40.00	40.00
2. Matt	20.00	30.00	30.00

Model No. 2106A
WHITETHROAT
First Version - Mouth open, base is a green mound

Designer:	Graham Tongue
Height:	3", 7.6 cm
Colours:	Dark grey, white and pink - gloss
Issued:	1967-1973

Description	U.K. £	U.S. $	Can. $
Gloss	100.00	150.00	150.00

Model No. 2106B
WHITETHROAT
Second Version - Mouth closed, base is a leaf

Designer:	Graham Tongue
Remodelled:	Albert Hallam
Height:	3", 7.6 cm
Colours:	Natural - gloss or matt
Issued:	1. Gloss - 1973-1996
	2. Matt - 1983-1992

Description	U.K. £	U.S. $	Can. $
1. Gloss	20.00	30.00	30.00
2. Matt	15.00	25.00	25.00

Model No. 2183
BALTIMORE ORIOLE

Designer:	Albert Hallam
Height:	3 ½", 8.9 cm
Colours:	Black and red - gloss or matt
Issued:	1. Gloss - 1968-1973
	2. Matt - 1970-1972

Description	U.K. £	U.S. $	Can. $
1. Gloss	125.00	200.00	200.00
2. Matt	100.00	150.00	150.00

Model No. 2184
CEDAR WAXWING

Designer:	Graham Tongue
Height:	4 ½", 11.9 cm
Colours:	Brown, black and yellow - gloss or matt
Issued:	1. Gloss - 1968-1973
	2. Matt - 1970-1972

Description	U.K. £	U.S. $	Can. $
1. Gloss	200.00	300.00	300.00
2. Matt	100.00	150.00	150.00

Model No. 2187
AMERICAN ROBIN

Designer:	Graham Tongue
Height:	4", 10.1 cm
Colours:	Dark grey and red - gloss or matt
Issued:	1. Gloss - 1968-1973
	2. Matt - 1970-1972

Description	U.K. £	U.S. $	Can. $
1. Gloss	200.00	300.00	300.00
2. Matt	100.00	150.00	150.00

Model No. 2188
BLUE JAY

Designer:	Albert Hallam
Height:	4 ½", 11.9 cm
Colours:	Blue and white - gloss or matt
Issued:	1. Gloss - 1968-1973
	2. Matt - 1970-1972

Description	U.K. £	U.S. $	Can. $
1. Gloss	200.00	300.00	300.00
2. Matt	100.00	150.00	150.00

Model No. 2189
BLACK CAPPED CHICADEE

Designer:	Graham Tongue
Height:	4 ½", 11.9 cm
Colours:	Yellow, white, grey, green and black - gloss or matt
Issued:	1. Gloss - 1968-1973
	2. Matt - 1970-1972

Description	U.K. £	U.S. $	Can. $
1. Gloss	200.00	300.00	300.00
2. Matt	100.00	150.00	150.00

Model No. 2190
EVENING GROSBEAK

Designer: Albert Hallam
Height: 4", 10.1 cm
Colours: Black and yellow - gloss or matt
Issued: 1. Gloss - 1968-1973
2. Matt - 1970-1972

Description	U.K. £	U.S. $	Can. $
1. Gloss	200.00	300.00	300.00
2. Matt	100.00	150.00	150.00

Model No. 2191
QUAIL

Designer: Albert Hallam
Height: 5", 12.7 cm
Colours: Browns, black and white - gloss or matt
Issued: 1. Gloss - 1968-1971
2. Matt - 1970-1972

Description	U.K. £	U.S. $	Can. $
1. Gloss	325.00	500.00	500.00
2. Matt	200.00	300.00	300.00

Model No. 2200
CHICKEN - Running

Designer: Graham Tongue
Height: 1 ¼", 3.2 cm
Colours: Yellow - gloss
Issued: 1968-1973
Set: 2201, 2202

Description	U.K. £	U.S. $	Can. $
Gloss	50.00	75.00	75.00

Model No. 2201
CHICKEN - Pecking

Designer: Graham Tongue
Height: 1", 2.5 cm
Colours: Yellow - gloss
Issued: 1968-1973
Set: 2200, 2202

Description	U.K. £	U.S. $	Can. $
Gloss	50.00	75.00	75.00

Model No. 2202
CHICKEN - Seated

Designer:	Graham Tongue
Height:	1 ½", 3.8 cm
Colours:	Yellow - gloss
Issued:	1968-1973
Set:	2200, 2201

Description	U.K. £	U.S. $	Can. $
Gloss	50.00	75.00	75.00

Model No. 2238
OWL

Designer:	Harry Sales
Height:	6 ¾", 17.2 cm
Colours:	Dark and light brown - matt
Issued:	1968-1971
Series:	Moda Range

Description	U.K. £	U.S. $	Can. $
Owl	300.00	450.00	450.00

Model No. 2239
BIRD

Designer:	Harry Sales
Height:	5", 12.7 cm
Colours:	Brown - matt
Issued:	1968-1971
Series:	Moda Range

Description	U.K. £	U.S. $	Can. $
Bird	350.00	525.00	525.00

Model No. 2240
COCKEREL

Designer:	Harry Sales	
Height:	6", 15.0 cm	
Colours:	1.	Blue - gloss
	2.	Brown - matt
Issued:	1968-1971	
Series:	Moda Range	

Colourway	U.K. £	U.S. $	Can. $
1. Blue	175.00	275.00	275.00
2. Brown	150.00	225.00	225.00

Model No. 2273
GOLDFINCH

Designer: Graham Tongue
Height: 3", 7.6 cm
Colours: Brown, white, red and yellow - gloss or matt
Issued: 1. Gloss - 1969-1995
         2. Matt - 1983-1992

Description	U.K. £	U.S. $	Can. $
1. Gloss	20.00	30.00	30.00
2. Matt	20.00	30.00	30.00

Model No. 2274
STONECHAT

Designer: Albert Hallam
Height: 3", 7.6 cm
Colours: Dark brown and white, red breast - gloss or matt
Issued: 1. Gloss - 1969-1997
         2. Matt - 1983-1992

Description	U.K. £	U.S. $	Can. $
1. Gloss	20.00	30.00	30.00
2. Matt	20.00	30.00	30.00

Model No. 2305
MAGPIE

Designer: Albert Hallam
Height: 5", 12.7 cm
Colours: Black and white - gloss
Issued: 1970-1982

Description	U.K. £	U.S. $	Can. $
Gloss	95.00	150.00	150.00

Model No. 2307
EAGLE ON ROCK

Designer: Graham Tongue
Height: 3 ¾", 9.5 cm
Colours: Browns - gloss
Issued: 1970-1975

Description	U.K. £	U.S. $	Can. $
Gloss	100.00	150.00	150.00

Model No. 2308
SONGTHRUSH

Designer:	Albert Hallam
Height:	5 ¾", 14.6 cm
Colours:	Brown with yellow speckled breast - gloss and matt
Issued:	1. Gloss - 1970-1989
	2. Matt - 1983-1989

Description	U.K. £	U.S. $	Can. $
1. Gloss	75.00	110.00	110.00
2. Matt	75.00	110.00	110.00

Model No. 2315
CUCKOO

Designer:	Albert Hallam
Height:	5", 12.7 cm
Colours:	Blue - gloss
Issued:	1970-1982

Description	U.K. £	U.S. $	Can. $
Gloss	100.00	150.00	150.00

Model No. 2316
KESTREL

Designer:	Graham Tongue
Height:	6 ¾", 17.2 cm
Colours:	Browns, white and blue - gloss or matt
Issued:	1. Gloss - 1970-1989
	2. Matt - 1983-1989

Description	U.K. £	U.S. $	Can. $
1. Gloss	60.00	90.00	90.00
2. Matt	60.00	90.00	90.00

Model No. 2357
PENGUIN

Designer:	Albert Hallam
Height:	12", 30.5 cm
Colours:	Black and white - gloss
Issued:	1971-1976
Series:	Fireside Model

Description	U.K. £	U.S. $	Can. $
Gloss	850.00	1,300.00	1,300.00

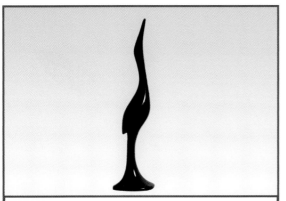

Model No. 2359
HERON - Stylistic

Designer:	Albert Hallam
Height:	10 ½", 26.7 cm
Colours:	Black - satin
Issued:	1971-Unknown

Description	U.K. £	U.S. $	Can. $
Satin	45.00	70.00	70.00

Note: This item was produced for use with bowls for flower arrangements. See the "Charlton Standard Catalogue of Beswick Pottery".

Model No. 2371
KINGFISHER

Designer:	Albert Hallam
Height:	5", 12.7 cm
Colours:	Blue and brown - gloss or matt
Issued:	1. Gloss - 1971-1998
	2. Matt - 1983-1989

Description	U.K. £	U.S. $	Can. $
1. Gloss	40.00	60.00	60.00
2. Matt	50.00	75.00	75.00

Photograph not available.
Model number 2399 possibly
not put into production.

Model No. 2398
PENGUIN CHICK - Standing

Designer:	Graham Tongue
Height:	7", 17.8 cm
Colours:	Blue, black and white - gloss
Issued:	1971-1976

Description	U.K. £	U.S. $	Can. $
Gloss	400.00	600.00	600.00

Note: Pair with model number 2434.

Model No. 2399
PENGUIN CHICK

Designer:	Albert Hallam
Height:	6 ¾", 17.2 cm
Colours:	Black and white - gloss
Issued:	1972-Unknown

Description	U.K. £	U.S. $	Can. $
Gloss	Possibly not put into production		

Model No. 2413
NUTHATCH

Designer: Graham Tongue
Height: 3", 7.6 cm
Colours: Dark blue and white - gloss or matt
Issued: 1. Gloss - 1972-1995
2. Matt - 1983-1989

Description	U.K. £	U.S. $	Can. $
1. Gloss	25.00	40.00	40.00
2. Matt	25.00	40.00	40.00

Model No. 2415
GOLDCREST

Designer: Graham Tongue
Height: 3", 7.6 cm
Colours: Green, yellow and grey - gloss or matt
Issued: 1. Gloss - 1972-2002
2. Matt - 1983-1989

Description	U.K. £	U.S. $	Can. $
1. Gloss	25.00	40.00	40.00
2. Matt	25.00	40.00	40.00

Model No. 2416A
LAPWING
First Version - Tail feathers split;
leg not attached to stump

Designer: Albert Hallam
Height: 5 ½", 14.0 cm
Colours: Black, dark green and white - gloss
Issued: 1972-c.1975

Description	U.K. £	U.S. $	Can. $
Gloss	200.00	300.00	300.00

Note: A version is known with the leg attached to the base, and the tail feathers split.

Model No. 2416B
LAPWING
Second Version - Tail feathers together;
leg moulded to stump

Designer: Albert Hallam
Height: 5 ½", 14.0 cm
Colours: Black, dark green and white - gloss
Issued: c.1975-1982

Description	U.K. £	U.S. $	Can. $
Gloss	100.00	150.00	150.00

Model No. 2417
JAY

Designer:	Graham Tongue
Height:	5", 12.7 cm
Colours:	Brown, white and blue - gloss
Issued:	1972-1982

Description	U.K. £	U.S. $	Can. $
Gloss	90.00	140.00	140.00

Model No. 2420
LESSER SPOTTED WOODPECKER

Designer:	Graham Tongue
Height:	5 ½", 14.0 cm
Colours:	Red, white and black - gloss
Issued:	1972-1982

Description	U.K. £	U.S. $	Can. $
Gloss	125.00	200.00	200.00

Model No. 2434
PENGUIN CHICK - Sliding

Designer:	Graham Tongue
Height:	3 ¾" x 8", 9.5 x 20.3 cm
Colours:	Blue, black and white - gloss
Issued:	1972-1976

Description	U.K. £	U.S. $	Can. $
Gloss	350.00	525.00	525.00

Note: Pair with model number 2398.

Model No. 2760
PHEASANT

Designer:	Graham Tongue	
Height:	10 ½", 26.7 cm	
Colours:	1.	Tan and brown - satin matt
	2.	Bronze; black shading - matt
Issued:	1.	1982-1989
	2.	1989-1992
Series:	1.	Connoisseur
	2.	Britannia Collection

Description	U.K. £	U.S. $	Can. $
1. Connoisseur	350.00	525.00	525.00
2. Britannia	175.00	275.00	275.00

Model No. 3272
TAWNY OWL

Designer:	Mr. Sutton
Height:	3 ¼", 8.3 cm
Colours:	Brown and white - gloss
Issued:	1990-2002

Description	U.K. £	U.S. $	Can. $
Gloss	15.00	25.00	25.00

Model No. 3273
BARN OWL

Designer:	Martyn Alcock
Height:	3 ¼", 8.3 cm
Colours:	Light brown and white - gloss
Issued:	1990-1998

Description	U.K. £	U.S. $	Can. $
Gloss	20.00	30.00	30.00

Model No. 3274
GREAT TIT

Designer:	Martyn Alcock
Height:	3", 7.6 cm
Colours:	Black, yellow, white and grey - gloss
Issued:	1990-1995

Description	U.K. £	U.S. $	Can. $
Gloss	150.00	225.00	225.00

Model No. 3275
KINGFISHER

Designer:	Mr. Sutton
Height:	2 ¾", 7.0 cm
Colours:	Blue head and wings, orange breast - gloss
Issued:	1990-1998

Description	U.K. £	U.S. $	Can. $
Gloss	75.00	110.00	110.00

BIRD WALL PLAQUES

INDEX BY MODEL NUMBER

Model No. 596

MALLARD

Designer: Mr. Watkin
Length: See below
Issued: See below
Colours: 1. Brown, teal green and white - gloss
             2. White with yellow beaks - matt

Model No./Finish	Issued	Length	U.K. £	Price U.S. $	Can. $
1. 596/0 Gloss	1938-1971	11 ¾", 29.8 cm	200.00	300.00	300.00
2. 596/0 Matt	1938-1971	11 ¾", 29.8 cm	200.00	300.00	300.00
3. 596/1 Gloss	1938-1973	10", 25.4 cm	50.00	75.00	75.00
4. 596/1 Matt	1938-1973	10", 25.4 cm	50.00	75.00	75.00
5. 596/2 Gloss	1938-1973	8 ¾", 22.2 cm	40.00	60.00	60.00
6. 596/2 Matt	1938-1973	8 ¾", 22.2 cm	40.00	60.00	60.00
7. 596/3 Gloss	1938-1973	7", 17.8 cm	25.00	40.00	40.00
8. 596/3 Matt	1938-1973	7", 17.8 cm	25.00	40.00	40.00
9. 596/4 Gloss	1938-1971	5 ¾", 14.6 cm	40.00	60.00	60.00
10. 596/4 Matt	1938-1971	5 ¾", 14.6 cm	40.00	60.00	60.00

Note: These also exist with a small "pocket" between the wings.

Model No. 658

SEAGULL
Style One - Wings up, apart

Designer: Mr. Watkin
Length: See below
Colours: 1. White, black and yellow - gloss
              2. White and yellow - matt
              3. White - matt
Issued: 1938-1967

Model No./Finish	Colourway	Length	U.K. £	Price U.S. $	Can. $
1. 658/1 Gloss	White/black/yellow	14", 35.5 cm	85.00	130.00	130.00
2. 658/1 Matt	White/yellow	14", 35.5 cm	85.00	130.00	130.00
3. 658/1 Matt	White	14", 35.5 cm	75.00	115.00	115.00
4. 658/2 Gloss	White/black/yellow	11 ¾", 29.8 cm	75.00	115.00	115.00
5. 658/2 Matt	White/yellow	11 ¾", 29.8 cm	70.00	110.00	110.00
6. 658/2 Matt	White	11 ¾", 29.8 cm	50.00	75.00	75.00
7. 658/3 Gloss	White/black/yellow	10", 25.4 cm	45.00	70.00	70.00
8. 658/3 Matt	White/yellow	10", 25.4 cm	40.00	60.00	60.00
9. 658/3 Matt	White	10", 25.4 cm	25.00	40.00	40.00
10. 658/4 Gloss	White/black/yellow	8", 20.3 cm	40.00	60.00	60.00
11. 658/4 Matt	White/yellow	8", 20.3 cm	35.00	55.00	55.00
12. 658/4 Matt	White	8", 20.3 cm	25.00	40.00	40.00

Model No. 661

PHEASANT

Designer: Mr. Watkin
Length: See below
Colours: 1. Teal green, browns and white - gloss
             2. White - matt
Issued: 1938-1971

Model No./Size		Finish	Length	U.K. £	Price U.S. $	Can. $
1. 661/1	Large	Gloss	12", 30.5 cm	85.00	130.00	130.00
2. 661/1	Large	Matt	12", 30.5 cm20	75.00	115.00	115.00
3. 661/2	Medium	Gloss	10 ¼", 26.0 cm	60.00	90.00	90.00
4. 661/2	Medium	Matt	10 ¼", 26.0 cm	60.00	90.00	90.00
5. 661/3	Small	Gloss	8 ½", 21.6 cm	40.00	60.00	60.00
6. 661/3	Small	Matt	8 ½", 21.6 cm	40.00	60.00	60.00

Model No. 705
BLUE TIT - Flying to the right

Designer: Mr. Watkin
Height: 4 ½", 11.9 cm
Size: Large
Colours: Blue and browns - gloss
Issued: 1939-1967
Set: 706, 707

Description	U.K. £	U.S. $	Can. $
Gloss	75.00	125.00	125.00

Model No. 706
BLUE TIT - Flying to the left

Designer: Mr. Watkin
Height: 4 ½", 11.9 cm
Size: Medium
Colours: Blue and browns - gloss
Issued: 1939-1967
Set: 705, 707

Description	U.K. £	U.S. $	Can. $
Gloss	75.00	125.00	125.00

Model No. 707
BLUE TIT - Wings up, flying to the left

Designer: Mr. Watkin
Height: 4 ½", 11.9 cm
Size: Small
Colours: Blue and browns - gloss
Issued: 1939-1967
Set: 705, 706

Description	U.K. £	U.S. $	Can. $
Gloss	125.00	200.00	200.00

Model No. 729

KINGFISHER - Flying to the right

Designer: Arthur Gredington
Height: See below
Colours: 1. Green and yellow - gloss
            2. Blue - gloss
Issued: 1939-1971

Model No./Size	Colourway	Height	U.K. £	Price U.S. $	Can. $
1. 729/1 Large	Green	7 ½", 19.1 cm	65.00	100.00	100.00
2. 729/1 Large	Blue	7 ½", 19.1 cm	65.00	100.00	100.00
3. 729/2 Medium	Green	6", 15.0 cm	65.00	100.00	100.00
4. 729/2 Medium	Blue	6", 15.0 cm	65.00	100.00	100.00
5. 729/3 Small	Green	5", 12.7 cm	65.00	100.00	100.00
6. 729/3 Small	Blue	5", 12.7 cm	65.00	100.00	100.00

Note: Model no. 729/2 can be paired with no. 743 to make a facing pair.

Model No. 731
FLAMINGO

Designer: Mr. Watkin
Length: 15", 38.1 cm
Colours: 1. Pearl orange and black - gloss
2. White, yellow and black wing
tips - satin
Issued: 1939-1954

Description	U.K. £	U.S. $	Can. $
1. Gloss	500.00	750.00	750.00
2. Satin	500.00	750.00	750.00

Model No. 743
KINGFISHER - Flying to the left

Designer: Arthur Gredington
Height: 6", 15.0 cm
Colours: Greens and yellow - gloss
Issued: 1939-1954

Description	U.K. £	U.S. $	Can. $
Gloss	200.00	300.00	300.00

Note: Model no. 743 can be paired with no. 729/2 to make
a facing pair.

Model No. 757

SWALLOW

Designer:	Arthur Gredington
Height:	See below
Colours:	1. Blues - gloss
	2. Golden brown; yellow tail - gloss
Issued:	1939-1973

Model No./Colourway	Size	Height	U.K. £	Price U.S. $	Can. $
1. 757/1 Blue	Large	7 ½", 19.1 cm	50.00	75.00	75.00
2. 757/1 Brown	Large	7 ½", 19.1 cm		Extremely Rare	
3. 757/2 Blue	Medium	6 ¼", 15.9 cm	40.00	60.00	60.00
4. 757/2 Brown	Medium	6 ¼", 15.9 cm		Extremely Rare	
5. 757/3 Blue	Small	5", 12.7 cm	40.00	60.00	60.00
6. 757/3 Brown	Small	5", 12.7 cm		Extremely Rare	

Model No. 922
SEAGULL
Style Two - Wings up, together

Designer:	Arthur Gredington
Height:	Large - 12", 30.5 cm
	Medium - 10 ½", 26.7 cm
	Small - 9 ½", 24.0 cm
Colours:	White, grey and black - gloss or matt
Issued:	1941-1971

Description	U.K. £	U.S. $	Can. $
1. Large - gloss	80.00	125.00	125.00
2. Large - matt	80.00	125.00	125.00
3. Medium - gloss	70.00	110.00	110.00
4. Medium - matt	70.00	110.00	110.00
5. Small - gloss	65.00	100.00	100.00
6. Small - matt	65.00	100.00	100.00

Model No. 1023
HUMMING BIRD

Designer:	Arthur Gredington
Height:	Large - 5 ¾", 14.6 cm
	Medium - 5", 12.7 cm
	Small - 3 ¾", 9.5 cm
Colours:	Browns, grey and red - gloss
Issued:	1944-1967

Description	U.K. £	U.S. $	Can. $
1. Large - gloss	115.00	175.00	175.00
2. Medium - gloss	100.00	150.00	150.00
3. Small - gloss	80.00	120.00	120.00

Model No. 1188

PINK LEGGED PARTRIDGE

Designer: Arthur Gredington
Length: See below
Colours: Browns, white and grey - gloss
Issued: 1950-1967

Model No.	Size	Length	U.K. £	Price U.S. $	Can. $
1. 1188/1	Large	10 ½", 26.7 cm	115.00	175.00	175.00
2. 1188/2	Medium	9", 22.9 cm	100.00	150.00	150.00
3. 1188/3	Small	7 ½", 19.1 cm	80.00	120.00	120.00

Model No. 1344

GREEN WOODPECKER

Designer:	Mr. Orwell
Length:	See below
Colours:	Greens and brown, red head - gloss
Issued:	1954-1968

Model No.	Size	Length	U.K. £	Price U.S. $	Can. $
1. 1344/1	Large	7 ½", 19.1 cm	150.00	225.00	225.00
2. 1344/2	Medium	6", 15.0 cm	125.00	200.00	200.00
3. 1344/3	Small	5", 12.7 cm	100.00	150.00	150.00

Model No. 1530

TEAL

Designer:	Arthur Gredington
Length:	See below
Colours:	Brown, grey and green - gloss
Issued:	1958-1968

Model No.	Size	Length	U.K. £	Price U.S. $	Can. $
1. 1530/1	Large	8 ¼", 21.0 cm	115.00	175.00	175.00
2. 1530/2	Medium	7 ¼", 18.4 cm	100.00	150.00	150.00
3. 1530/3	Small	6 ¼", 15.9 cm	80.00	120.00	120.00

Chapter Two

BUTTERFLY PLAQUES

Butterflies are an unusual choice for the medium of pottery, and these few wall plaques tend to be rare. It is also unusual to find them in perfect condition, as often the antennae have suffered from the passage of time. These butterfly wall plaques were modelled in large, medium and small sizes. The Beswick attention to detail is very apparent here.

At the present time, there have been no catalogues found in which these models are illustrated. Fortunately, each model is impressed on the back with the name of the butterfly and the shape number. If this were not the case, then identification would be a problem.

INDEX BY MODEL NUMBER

Model No. 1487

PURPLE EMPEROR BUTTERFLY

Designer: Albert Hallam
Height: 6 ¼" x 4", 15.9 x 10.1 cm
Size: Large

Colourway	Issued	U.K. £	Price U.S. $	Can. $
Blue and white - gloss	1957-by 1963	400.00	600.00	600.00

Note: Butterflies are priced as having the antennae intact, without them the price must be much lower.

Model No. 1488
RED ADMIRAL BUTTERFLY

Designer: Albert Hallam
Dimensions: 6 ¼" x 4", 15.9 x 10.1 cm
Size: Large
Colours: Browns, blue and white - gloss
Issued: 1957-by 1963

Description	U.K. £	U.S. $	Can. $
Gloss	350.00	525.00	525.00

Model No. 1489
PEACOCK BUTTERFLY

Designer: Albert Hallam
Dimensions: 6 ¼" x 4", 15.9 x 10.1 cm
Size: Large
Colours: Browns, black and yellow - gloss
Issued: 1957-by 1963

Description	U.K. £	U.S. $	Can. $
Gloss	350.00	525.00	525.00

Model No. 1490
CLOUDED YELLOW BUTTERFLY

Designer: Albert Hallam
Dimensions: 5 ¼" x 3 ½", 13.3 x 8.9 cm
Size: Medium
Colours: Yellow, black and red - gloss
Issued: 1957-by 1963

Description	U.K. £	U.S. $	Can. $
Gloss	300.00	450.00	450.00

Model No. 1491
TORTOISESHELL BUTTERFLY

Designer: Albert Hallam
Dimensions: 5 ¼" x 3 ½", 13.3 x 8.9 cm
Size: Medium
Colours: Yellow, blue and black - gloss
Issued: 1957-by 1963

Description	U.K. £	U.S. $	Can. $
Gloss	300.00	450.00	450.00

Model No. 1492
SWALLOW-TAIL BUTTERFLY
Designer: Albert Hallam
Dimensions: 5 ¼" x 3 ½", 13.3 x 8.9 cm
Size: Medium
Colours: Brown, green and blue wings - gloss
Issued: 1957-by 1963

Description	U.K. £	U.S. $	Can. $
Gloss	300.00	450.00	450.00

Model No. 1493
SMALL COPPER BUTTERFLY
Designer: Albert Hallam
Dimensions: 3 ¾" x 2 ¼", 9.5 x 5.7 cm
Size: Small
Colours: Browns - gloss
Issued: 1957-by 1963

Description	U.K. £	U.S. $	Can. $
Gloss	300.00	450.00	450.00

Model No. 1494
PURPLE HAIRSTREAK BUTTERFLY
Designer: Albert Hallam
Dimensions: 3 ¾" x 2 ¼", 9.5 x 5.7 cm
Size: Small
Colours: Browns and grey - gloss
Issued: 1957-by 1963

Description	U.K. £	U.S. $	Can. $
Gloss	300.00	450.00	450.00

Model No. 1495
SMALL HEATH BUTTERFLY
Designer: Albert Hallam
Dimensions: 3 ¾" x 2 ¼", 9.5 x 5.7 cm
Size: Small
Colours: Browns - gloss
Issued: 1957-by 1963

Description	U.K. £	U.S. $	Can. $
Gloss	350.00	525.00	525.00

Chapter Three

CATS

Cat lovers will appreciate the variety of felines offered here. Colours listed under individual cats are those on which they could be found.

The Swiss roll decoration is very distinctive. The markings are in clear black and the circles, one on the hip and the other on the shoulder, have a solid spot in the centre. The circles are completely round and the cat's coat has a slight tinge of ginger.

Colourways	Dates of Issue
Black gloss	1986 - 1989
Black matt	1984 - 1988
British Blue (lead grey gloss)	1964 - 1966
Chocolate point gloss	1953 - 1963
Copper lustre	1971 only
Ginger matt	1984 - 1988
Ginger (dark) gloss	1945 - 1970
Ginger (pale) gloss	1959 - 1963
Ginger striped gloss	1965 - 1989
Ginger Swiss roll gloss	1964 - 1966
Grey matt	1984 - 1988
Grey (shaded) gloss	1965 - 1989
Grey (smokey blue) gloss	1945 - 1970
Grey striped gloss	1962 - 1973
Grey Swiss roll gloss	1964 - 1966
Royal blue gloss	Only one example known
Seal point gloss	1963 - 1989
Seal point matt	1984 - 1988
White (large eyes) gloss	1963 - 1989
White (small eyes) gloss	1945 - 1963
White matt	1984 - 1988
White Zodiac cat	1958 - 1970

INDEX BY MODEL NUMBER

Persian Kitten - Standing, Model No. 1885

Model No. 1030
CAT - Seated, head looks up

Designer: Arthur Gredington
Height: 6 ¼", 15.9 cm

Colourway	Finish	Issued	U.K. £	Price U.S. $	Can. $
1. British Blue (lead grey)	Gloss	1964-1966	115.00	175.00	175.00
2. Ginger (dark)	Gloss	1945-1970	30.00	45.00	45.00
3. Ginger (pale)	Gloss	1959-1963	30.00	45.00	45.00
4. Ginger striped	Gloss	1965-1973	55.00	80.00	80.00
5. Ginger Swiss roll	Gloss	1964-1966	95.00	150.00	150.00
6. Grey (shaded)	Gloss	1971-1973	25.00	40.00	40.00
7. Grey (smokey blue)	Gloss	1945-1970	20.00	30.00	30.00
8. Grey striped	Gloss	1962-1973	50.00	75.00	75.00
9. Grey Swiss roll	Gloss	1964-1966	125.00	200.00	200.00
10. Royal blue	Gloss			Unique*	
11. White (small eyes)	Gloss	1945-1963	25.00	40.00	40.00
12. White (large eyes)	Gloss	1963-1973	20.00	30.00	30.00

Note: * Only one example known.

Model No. 1031
CAT - Seated, head looks forward

Designer: Arthur Gredington
Height: 4 ½", 11.9 cm

Colourway	Finish	Issued	U.K. £	Price U.S. $	Can. $
1. British Blue (lead grey)	Gloss	1964-1966	95.00	150.00	150.00
2. Ginger (dark)	Gloss	1945-1970	25.00	40.00	40.00
3. Ginger (pale)	Gloss	1959-1963	20.00	30.00	30.00
4. Ginger striped	Gloss	1965-1973	25.00	40.00	40.00
5. Ginger Swiss roll	Gloss	1964-1966	95.00	150.00	150.00
6. Grey (shaded)	Gloss	1971-1973	25.00	40.00	40.00
7. Grey (smokey blue)	Gloss	1945-1970	20.00	30.00	30.00
8. Grey striped	Gloss	1962-1973	25.00	40.00	40.00
9. Grey Swiss roll	Gloss	1964-1966	150.00	225.00	225.00
10. White (small eyes)	Gloss	1945-1963	20.00	30.00	30.00
11. White (large eyes)	Gloss	1963-1971	20.00	30.00	30.00

Model No. 1296 / K1296
SIAMESE KITTENS - Curled together

Designer: Miss Granoska
Length: 2 ¾", 7.0 cm

Colours	Model Number	Issued	U.K. £	Price U.S. $	Can. $
1. Chocolate point, gloss	1296	1953-1963	15.00	25.00	25.00
2. Copper lustre, gloss (1)	1296	1971	25.00	40.00	40.00
3. One white/one pale grey, gloss (2)	1296	Unknown		Unique	
4. Seal point, gloss					
a. Original issue	1296	1964-1989	15.00	25.00	25.00
b. Reissued	K1296	1999-2002	15.00	25.00	25.00
5. Seal point - matt		1984-1989	25.00	40.00	40.00

Note: 1. Copper lustre was produced for export only.
       2. Only one example known.

Model No. 1316
PERSIAN KITTENS - Seated

Designer: Miss Granoska
Height: 3 ½", 8.9 cm

Colourway	Finish	Issued	U.K. £	Price U.S. $	Can. $
1. British Blue (lead grey)	Gloss	1964-1966	70.00	110.00	110.00
2. Ginger (dark)	Gloss	1953-1970	20.00	30.00	30.00
3. Ginger (pale)	Gloss	1959-1963	15.00	25.00	25.00
4. Ginger striped	Gloss	1971-1973	25.00	40.00	40.00
5. Ginger Swiss roll	Gloss	1964-1966	55.00	85.00	85.00
6. Grey (shaded)	Gloss	1965-1973	15.00	25.00	25.00
7. Grey striped	Gloss	1962-1973	25.00	40.00	40.00
8. Grey Swiss roll	Gloss	1964-1966	100.00	150.00	150.00
9. White (large eyes)	Gloss	1963-1973	15.00	25.00	25.00

Model No. 1435
CAT - Seated

Designer: Colin Melbourne
Height: 5 ¼", 13.3 cm
Colours: Grey striped - gloss
Issued: 1956-1963

Colourway	U.K. £	U.S. $	Can. $
Grey striped, gloss	175.00	275.00	275.00

Note: A pewter example is known to exist.

Model No. 1436
KITTEN - Seated

Designer: Colin Melbourne
Height: 3 ¼", 8.3 cm

				Price	
Colourway	Finish	Issued	U.K. £	U.S. $	Can. $
1. Black	Matt	1984-1989	15.00	25.00	25.00
2. British Blue (lead grey)	Gloss	1964-1966	55.00	80.00	80.00
3. Ginger	Matt	1984-1989	10.00	15.00	15.00
4. Ginger (dark)	Gloss	1956-1970	15.00	25.00	25.00
5. Ginger (pale)	Gloss	1959-1963	10.00	15.00	15.00
6. Ginger striped	Gloss	1965-1989	15.00	25.00	25.00
7. Ginger Swiss roll	Gloss	1964-1966	55.00	80.00	80.00
8. Grey	Matt	1984-1989	15.00	25.00	25.00
9. Grey (shaded)	Gloss	1965-1989	10.00	15.00	15.00
10. Grey striped	Gloss	1962-1973	15.00	25.00	25.00
11. Grey Swiss roll	Gloss	1964-1966	70.00	100.00	100.00
12. White (small eyes)	Gloss	1956-1963	15.00	25.00	25.00
13. White (large eyes)	Gloss	1963-1989	10.00	15.00	15.00
14. White	Matt	1984-1989	15.00	25.00	25.00

Model No. 1437
CAT - Seated, looking up
Designer: Colin Melbourne
Height: 3 ¼", 8.3 cm
Colours: Grey striped - gloss
Issued: 1956-1963

Colourway		Price	
	U.K. £	U.S. $	Can. $
Grey striped	175.00	275.00	275.00

Note: A ginger striped colourway is known to exist.

Model No. 1438
CAT - Standing, looking back
Designer: Colin Melbourne
Height: 3 ¾", 9.5 cm
Colours: Grey striped - gloss
Issued: 1956-1963

Colourway		Price	
	U.K. £	U.S. $	Can. $
Grey striped	250.00	375.00	375.00

Model No. 1541
CAT - Seated

Designer: Mr. Garbet
Height: 5 ½", 14.0 cm
Colours: Dark pewter - Satin gloss
Issued: 1958-1961

Description	U.K. £	U.S. $	Can. $
Satin gloss	1,000.00	1,500.00	1,500.00

Model No. 1542
CAT - Lying, left front paw up

Designer: Mr. Garbet
Height: 2", 5.0 cm
Colours: Dark pewter - Satin gloss
Issued: 1958-1961

Description	U.K. £	U.S. $	Can. $
Satin gloss	500.00	750.00	750.00

Model No. 1543
CAT - Seated, left front paw up

Designer: Mr. Garbet
Height: Unknown
Colours: Dark pewter- Satin gloss
Issued: 1958-1961

Description	U.K. £	U.S. $	Can. $
Satin gloss	500.00	750.00	750.00

Model No. 1558A
SIAMESE CAT - Lying, facing left
First Version -
Puffed out cheeks, short neck, fleshy body

Designer: Pal Zalmen
Length: 7 ¼", 18.4 cm
Colours: Chocolate point - gloss
Issued: 1958-c.1963

Description	U.K. £	U.S. $	Can. $
Gloss	25.00	40.00	40.00

Model No. 1558B / K1558
SIAMESE CAT - Lying, facing left
Second Version -
Sleek, tapering face, long neck and body

Designer: Pal Zalmen
Remodelled: Albert Hallam
Length: 7 ¼", 18.4 cm
Colours: 1. Copper lustre - gloss
              2. Seal point - gloss or matt
Issued: 1. Copper lustre
                  a. Gloss - 1971 (export only)
              2. Seal point - gloss
                  a. Model 1558B - c.1963-1989
                  b. Model K1558 - 1999-2002
              3. Seal point
                  a. Matt - 1984-1989

Description	U.K. £	U.S. $	Can. $
1. Copper lustre	50.00	75.00	75.00
2. Seal point - gloss			
a. Model 1558B	20.00	30.00	30.00
b. Model K1558	20.00	30.00	30.00
3. Seal point - matt	20.00	30.00	30.00

Model No. 1559A
SIAMESE CAT - Lying, facing right
First Version -
Puffed out cheeks, short neck, fleshy body

Designer: Pal Zalmen
Length: 7 ¼", 18.4 cm
Colours: Chocolate point - gloss
Issued: 1958-c.1963

Description	U.K. £	U.S. $	Can. $
Gloss	25.00	40.00	40.00

Model No. 1559B / K1559
SIAMESE CAT - Lying, facing right
Second Version -
Sleek, tapering face, long neck and body

Designer: Pal Zalmen
Remodelled: Albert Hallam
Length: 7 ¼", 18.4 cm
Colours: 1. Copper lustre - gloss
              2. Seal Point - gloss or matt
Issued: 1. Copper lustre
                  a. Gloss - 1971 (export only)
              2. Seal point - gloss
                  a. Model 1559B - c.1963-1989
                  b. Model K1559 - 1999-2002
              3. Seal point
                  a. Matt - 1984-1989

Description	U.K. £	U.S. $	Can. $
1. Copper lustre	50.00	75.00	75.00
2. Seal point - gloss			
a. Model 1559B	20.00	30.00	30.00
b. Model K1559	20.00	30.00	30.00
3. Seal point - matt	20.00	30.00	30.00

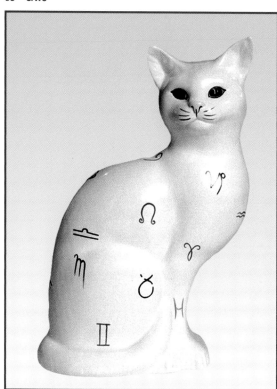

Model No. 1560
ZODIAC CAT - Seated, facing right

Designer:	Pal Zalmen
Length:	11", 27.9 cm
Colours:	1. Black with gold details - gloss
	2. White with zodiac symbols - gloss
Issued:	1958-1967
Set:	Stylized model forming a pair with 1561

Colourway	U.K. £	U.S. $	Can. $
1. Black	175.00	275.00	275.00
2. White	110.00	175.00	175.00

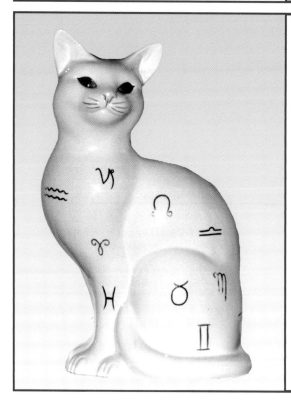

Model No. 1561
ZODIAC CAT - Seated, facing left

Designer:	Pal Zalmen
Length:	11", 27.9 cm
Colours:	1. Black with gold details - gloss
	2. White with zodiac symbols - gloss
Issued:	1958-1967
Set:	Stylized model forming a pair with 1560

Colourway	U.K. £	U.S. $	Can. $
1. Black	175.00	275.00	275.00
2. White	110.00	175.00	175.00

Model No. 1677
SIAMESE CAT - Climbing

Designer: Albert Hallam
Length: 6 ½", 16.5 cm
Colours: Seal point - gloss
Issued: 1960-1997

Description	U.K. £	U.S. $	Can. $
Gloss	10.00	15.00	15.00

Model No. 1803
CAT - Seated, looking up

Designer: Albert Hallam
Height: 1 ¼", 3.2 cm
Colours: Ginger striped - gloss
Issued: 1962-1971
Series: Bedtime Chorus

Description	U.K. £	U.S. $	Can. $
Gloss	20.00	30.00	30.00

Photograph not
available at press time

Model No. 1857
SIAMESE CAT - Climbing

Designer: Albert Hallam
Length: 5 ½", 14.0 cm
Colours: Seal point - gloss
Issued: 1962-Unknown

Description	U.K. £	U.S. $	Can. $
Gloss	Extremely Rare		

Note: Similar in shape to model no. 1677.

Model No. 1867
PERSIAN CAT - Seated, looking up

Designer: Albert Hallam
Height: 8 ½", 21.6 cm

				Price	
Colourway	Finish	Issued	U.K. £	U.S. $	Can. $
1. Black	Matt	1984-1989	30.00	45.00	45.00
2. British Blue (lead grey)	Gloss	1964-1966	175.00	275.00	275.00
3. Ginger	Matt	1984-1989	30.00	45.00	45.00
4. Ginger (dark)	Gloss	1963-1970	30.00	45.00	45.00
5. Ginger striped	Gloss	1965-1989	85.00	130.00	130.00
6. Ginger Swiss roll	Gloss	1964-1966	110.00	175.00	175.00
7. Grey (shaded)	Gloss	1963-1989	25.00	40.00	40.00
8. Grey	Matt	1984-1989	30.00	45.00	45.00
9. Grey striped	Gloss	1963-1973	110.00	175.00	175.00
10. Grey Swiss roll	Gloss	1964-1966	225.00	350.00	350.00
11. White (large eyes)	Gloss	1963-1989	30.00	45.00	45.00
12. White	Matt	1984-1989	25.00	40.00	40.00

Model No. 1876
PERSIAN CAT - Lying

Designer: Albert Hallam
Height: 3 ½" x 6 ½", 8.0 x 6.5 cm

Colourway	Finish	Issued	U.K. £	Price U.S. $	Can. $
1. British Blue (lead grey)	Gloss	1964-1966	160.00	250.00	250.00
2. Ginger (dark)	Gloss	1963-1970	90.00	140.00	140.00
3. Ginger striped	Gloss	1965-1971	90.00	140.00	140.00
4. Ginger Swiss roll	Gloss	1964-1966	160.00	250.00	250.00
5. Grey (shaded)	Gloss	1963-1971	95.00	150.00	150.00
6. Grey striped	Gloss	1963-1971	90.00	140.00	140.00
7. Grey Swiss roll	Gloss	1964-1966	175.00	275.00	275.00
8. White (large eyes)	Gloss	1963-1971	55.00	85.00	85.00

Model No. 1877
CAT - Seated, scratching ear

Designer:	Albert Hallam
Height:	6 ½", 16.5 cm
Issued:	British Blue (lead grey), gloss – 1964-1966
	Ginger (dark), gloss –1963-1970
	Ginger striped, gloss –1965-1971
	Ginger Swiss roll, gloss – 1964-1966
	Grey (shaded), gloss – 1963-1971
	Grey striped, gloss – 1963-1971
	Grey Swiss roll, gloss – 1964-1966
	White (large eyes), gloss – 1963-1971

Colourway	U.K. £	U.S. $	Can. $
1. British Blue (lead grey)	250.00	375.00	375.00
2. Ginger (dark)	125.00	200.00	200.00
3. Ginger striped	175.00	275.00	275.00
4. Ginger Swiss roll	250.00	375.00	375.00
5. Grey (shaded)	150.00	230.00	230.00
6. Grey striped	225.00	350.00	350.00
7. Grey Swiss roll	300.00	450.00	450.00
8. White (large eyes)	100.00	150.00	150.00

Model No. 1880
PERSIAN CAT - Seated, looking up

Designer:	Albert Hallam
Height:	5 ¼", 13.3 cm
Issued:	1. Black, gloss - Unknown
	2. British Blue (lead grey), gloss – 1964-1966
	3. Ginger (dark), gloss –1963-1970
	4. Ginger striped, gloss – 1965-1971
	5. Ginger Swiss roll, gloss –1964-1966
	6. Grey (shaded), gloss – 1963-1971
	7. Grey striped, gloss –1963-1971
	8. Grey Swiss roll, gloss –1964-1966
	9. White (large eyes), gloss –1963-1971

Colourway	U.K. £	U.S. $	Can. $
1. Black	100.00	150.00	150.00
2. British Blue (lead grey)	175.00	275.00	275.00
3. Ginger (dark)	100.00	150.00	150.00
4. Ginger striped	100.00	150.00	150.00
5. Ginger Swiss roll	125.00	200.00	200.00
6. Grey (shaded)	90.00	140.00	140.00
7. Grey striped	100.00	150.00	150.00
8. Grey Swiss roll	175.00	27500	275.00
9. White (large eyes)	75.00	115.00	115.00

Model No. 1882
SIAMESE CAT - Seated, head forward

Designer: Albert Hallam
Height: 9 ½", 24.0 cm
Issued: 1.   Black, gloss – 1986-1989
              2.   Black, matt – 1986-1989
              3.   Copper lustre, gloss – 1971-1971
              4.   Seal point, gloss 1963-1989
              5.   Seal point, matt – 1984-1989
Series: Fireside Model

Colourway	U.K. £	U.S. $	Can. $
1. Black, gloss	30.00	45.00	45.00
2. Black, matt	35.00	55.00	55.00
3. Copper lustre, gloss	55.00	85.00	85.00
4. Seal point, gloss	30.00	45.00	45.00
5. Seal point, matt	35.00	55.00	55.00

Note: Copper lustre issued for export only.

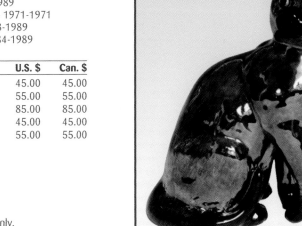

Model No. 1883
PERSIAN CAT - On hind legs

Designer: Albert Hallam
Height: 6", 15.0 cm
Issued: 1.   British Blue (lead grey),
                   gloss – 1964-1966
              2.   Ginger (dark), gloss –1963-1970
              3.   Ginger striped, gloss – 1965-1971
              4.   Ginger Swiss roll, gloss – 1964-1966
              5.   Grey (shaded), gloss – 1963-1971
              6.   Grey striped, gloss – 1963-1971
              7.   Grey Swiss roll, gloss – 1964-1966
              8.   White (large eyes), gloss – 1963-1971

Colourway	U.K. £	U.S. $	Can. $
1. British Blue (lead grey)	175.00	275.00	275.00
2. Ginger (dark)	100.00	150.00	150.00
3. Ginger striped	125.00	200.00	200.00
4. Ginger Swiss roll	150.00	230.00	230.00
5. Grey (shaded)	175.00	275.00	275.00
6. Grey striped	110.00	175.00	175.00
7. Grey Swiss roll	200.00	300.00	300.00
8. White (large eyes)	90.00	140.00	140.00

Model No. 1885
PERSIAN KITTEN - Standing

Designer: Albert Hallam
Height: 4 ¾", 12.1 cm

Colourway	Finish	Issued	U.K. £	Price U.S. $	Can. $
1. British Blue (lead grey)	Gloss	1964-1966	150.00	230.00	230.00
2. Ginger (dark)	Gloss	1963-1970	30.00	45.00	45.00
3. Ginger striped	Gloss	1965-1973	85.00	130.00	130.00
4. Ginger Swiss roll	Gloss	1964-1966	110.00	175.00	175.00
5. Grey (shaded)	Gloss	1963-1973	25.00	40.00	40.00
6. Grey striped	Gloss	1963-1973	70.00	110.00	110.00
7. Grey Swiss roll	Gloss	1964-1966	160.00	250.00	250.00
8. White (large eyes)	Gloss	1963-1973	25.00	40.00	40.00

Model No 1886 / K1886
PERSIAN KITTEN - Seated, looking up

Designer: Albert Hallam
Height: 4", 10.1 cm

Colourway	Finish	Issued	U.K. £	Price U.S. $	Can. $
1. Black	Matt	1984-1989	15.00	25.00	25.00
2. British Blue (lead grey)	Gloss	1964-1966	100.00	150.00	150.00
3. Ginger	Matt	1984-1989	15.00	25.00	25.00
4. Ginger (dark)	Gloss	1963-1970	15.00	25.00	25.00
5. Ginger striped	Gloss	1965-1989	15.00	25.00	25.00
6. Ginger Swiss roll	Gloss	1964-1966	110.00	175.00	175.00
7. Grey					
a. Model 1886	Gloss	1965-1989	10.00	15.00	15.00
b. Model K1886	Gloss	1999-2002	10.00	15.00	15.00
8. Grey	Matt	1984-1989	15.00	25.00	25.00
9. Grey striped	Gloss	1962-1973	25.00	40.00	40.00
10. Grey Swiss roll	Gloss	1964-1966	125.00	200.00	200.00
11. White					
a. Model 1886	Gloss	1963-1989	10.00	15.00	15.00
c. Model K1886	Gloss	1999-2002	10.00	15.00	15.00
12. White	Matt	1984-1989	10.00	15.00	15.00

Note: Used on model number 4677, deco in black and white.

Model No. 1887 / K1887
SIAMESE CAT - Seated, head turned back

Designer: Albert Hallam
Height: 4", 10.1 cm
Issued:
1. Copper lustre, gloss – 1971-1971
2. Seal point, gloss
   a. Model 1887 – 1971-1989
   b. Model K1887 – 1999-2002
3. Seal point, matt – 1984-1989

Colourway	U.K. £	U.S. $	Can. $
1. Copper lustre	50.00	75.00	75.00
2. Seal point, gloss			
a. Model 1887	10.00	15.00	15.00
b. Model K1887	10.00	15.00	15.00
3. Seal point, matt	15.00	25.00	25.00

Note: Copper lustre produced for export only.

Model No. 1897
SIAMESE CAT - Standing

Designer: Albert Hallam
Height: 6 ½", 16.5 cm
Series: Fireside Model
Issued:
1. Black, gloss – 1987-1989
2. Black, matt – 1987-1989
3. Copper lustre, gloss – 1971-1971
4. Seal point, gloss – 1963-1980
5. Seal point, matt – 1984-1989

Colourway	U.K. £	U.S. $	Can. $
1. Black, gloss	25.00	40.00	40.00
2. Black, matt	25.00	40.00	40.00
3. Copper lustre, gloss	90.00	140.00	140.00
4. Seal point, gloss	20.00	30.00	30.00
5. Seal point, matt	20.00	30.00	30.00

Note: 1. In 1987 introduced as "Lucky Black Cat."
         2. Copper lustre produced for export only.

Model No. 1898
PERSIAN CAT - Standing, tail erect

Designer: Albert Hallam
Height: 5", 12.7 cm

Colourway	Finish	Issued	U.K. £	Price U.S. $	Can. $
1. Black	Matt	1984-1989	30.00	45.00	45.00
2. British Blue (lead grey)	Gloss	1964-1966	160.00	250.00	250.00
3. Ginger	Matt	1984-1989	25.00	40.00	40.00
4. Ginger striped	Gloss	1965-1989	30.00	45.00	45.00
5. Ginger Swiss roll	Gloss	1964-1966	160.00	250.00	250.00
6. Grey	Matt	1984-1989	15.00	25.00	25.00
7. Grey (shaded)	Gloss	1963-1989	15.00	25.00	25.00
8. Grey Swiss roll	Gloss	1964-1966	275.00	425.00	425.00
9. White (large eyes)	Gloss	1963-1989	15.00	25.00	25.00
10. White	Matt	1984-1989	15.00	25.00	25.00

Model No. 2100
CAT WITH MOUSE

Designer:	Albert Hallam
Height:	3", 7.6 cm
Colours:	Brown cat, white mouse - gloss
Issued:	1967-1973
Series:	Fun Models

Description	U.K. £	U.S. $	Can. $
Gloss	20.00	30.00	30.00

Model No. 2101
CAT - Laughing

Designer:	Albert Hallam
Height:	3", 7.6 cm
Colours:	Grey - gloss
Issued:	1967-1973
Series:	Fun Models

Description	U.K. £	U.S. $	Can. $
Gloss	20.00	30.00	30.00

Note: A white model is known to exist.

Model No. 2139
SIAMESE CAT - Seated, head up

Designer:	Mr. Garbet
Height:	13 ¾", 34.9 cm
Issued:	1. Copper lustre - 1971 (export only)
	2. Seal point, gloss - 1967-1989
Series:	Fireside Models

Colourway	U.K. £	U.S. $	Can. $
1. Copper lustre	55.00	85.00	85.00
2. Seal point, gloss	55.00	85.00	85.00

Model No. 2233
CAT AND DOG WALL PLAQUE
Cat left, dog right

Designer:	Graham Tongue
Height:	9" x 6 ¼", 23 x 15.9 cm (Concave)
Colours:	Unknown - gloss
Issued:	1968-Unknown
Series:	Wall Plaques

Description	U.K.£	U.S.$	Can.$
Gloss	50.00	75.00	75.00

Model No. 2236
CAT WALL PLAQUE

Designer:	Graham Tongue
Height:	9" x 6 ¼", 23 x 15.9 cm (Concave)
Colours:	Ginger cat with yellow eyes on dark pewter background - gloss
Issued:	1968-Unknown
Series:	Wall Plaques

Description	U.K.£	U.S.$	Can.$
Gloss	20.00	30.00	30.00

Photograph not available.
Model number 2301 possibly
not put into production.

Model No. 2301
CAT - Climbing

Designer:	Albert Hallam
Height:	4 ½", 11.9 cm
Colours:	Unknown
Issued:	1969-Unknown

Description	U.K. £	U.S. $	Can. $
Cat- Climbing		Possibly not put into production	

Note: Similar to model no. 1677.

Photograph not available.
Model number 2311 possibly
not put into production.

Model No. 2311
SIAMESE CAT

Designer:	Graham Tongue
Length:	1 ½", 3.8 cm
Colours:	Unknown
Issued:	1970-Unknown

Description	U.K. £	U.S. $	Can. $
Siamese Cat		Possibly not put into production	

Note: Similar to model no. 2139.

Model No. 2480
CHESHIRE CAT

Designer:	Graham Tongue
Height:	1 ½", 3.8 cm
Colours:	Tabby - gloss
Issued:	1973-1982
Series:	Alice in Wonderland

Description	U.K. £	U.S. $	Can. $
Gloss	175.00	275.00	275.00

Model No. K194
CAT - Seated

Designer: Martyn Alcock
Height: 3 ¾", 9.5 cm
Colour: Black and white - gloss
Issued: 1999-2002

Description	U.K. £	U.S. $	Can. $
Gloss	15.00	25.00	25.00

Model No. K229
QUIET PLEASE

Designer: Warren Platt
Height: 1 ¾", 4.4 cm
Colour: Grey and white kittens - gloss
Issued: 1999-2002

Description	U.K. £	U.S. $	Can. $
Gloss	15.00	25.00	25.00

Chapter Four

DOGS

Beswick produced mantelpiece dogs of the old Staffordshire type from about 1898. In 1933, when the shape book was created – in which each model was illustrated by a sketch with details such as height, modeller and dates – these dogs, in various sizes, were the initial numbers. During the 1930s dogs of the novelty type were produced with several unrealistic-looking decorations, including blue and green gloss and mottled blue in a satin-type finish. In fact customers could order novelties in any decoration to match the domestic ware being made at the time. Then in 1941, Arthur Gredington, following his success with realistic models of horses, created the first of the champion dogs, the Dalmatian "Arnoldene," shape number 961. Seven other breeds were also produced in 1941, and four more the following year. These figures were all modelled in a show stance from champions of their particular breed, and almost all of them were modelled by Arthur Gredington.

Over the years most of the popular breeds joined the Beswick "kennel," and many were also produced in a smaller size. Action poses were added to the collection, such as the 1507 Spaniel running. This type of model was reintroduced with the Good Companions series in 1987, the same time several more medium- sized dogs were issued. These and the Good Companions, had a short production run with the Beswick backstamp (some for less than a year), as from August 1989 they were issued with Royal Doulton backstamps and given DA numbers. By 1994 all the Beswick medium-sized dogs had been withdrawn, leaving only the small dogs collection with Beswick backstamps. However, in October 1999 Royal Doulton announced that animal sculptures carrying their backstamp (except limited editions) would revert to the Beswick backstamp.

Many of the dogs share with the horses the distinction of being in continual production for four or five decades. During this time there has been a deterioration in the moulds and decorating processes; therefore, the quality of the models is variable. It is well worth looking out for the older figures that exhibit more mould detail and toning and shading in colour.

In 1993 the "Beswick Collectors Circle" commissioned their only canine model. This was the 3062 "Labrador Walking" in a chocolate gloss colourway. With only 93 of these ordered this model has the smallest edition size of the Beswick Collectors Circle animal commissions.

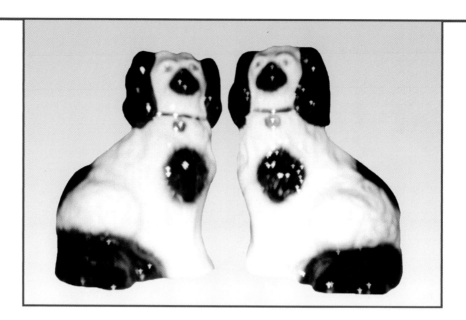

Model Nos. 1 to 6   **OLD STAFFORDSHIRE DOGS**

Designer: Unknown
Colours: Black and white
Issued: 1933-1955
Series: Mantelpiece Dogs

Model No.	1	2	3	4	5	6
Height:	13 ¾", 34.9 cm	11 ½", 29.2 cm	10", 25.4 cm	9", 22.9 cm	7 ½", 19.1 cm	5 ½", 14.0 cm

Price	Model No. 1	Model No. 2	Model No. 3	Model No. 4	Model No. 5	Model No. 6
U.K. £	55.00	50.00	30.00	25.00	25.00	20.00
U.S. $	85.00	75.00	45.00	40.00	40.00	30.00
Can. $	85.00	75.00	45.00	40.00	40.00	30.00

Note: 1. The Old Staffordshire Dogs were available in pairs, left and right facing. The prices above are for single dogs.
        2. A pair of Old Staffordshire Dogs exists in a white with pink lustre colourway.

Model No. 171
DOG - Begging

Designer: Unknown
Height: 4 ¾", 12.1 cm
Colours: White and tan - gloss
Issued: 1934-by 1954

Description	U.K. £	U.S. $	Can. $
Gloss	25.00	40.00	40.00

Model No. 286
DOG - Seated

Designer: Mr. Watkin
Height: 6 ¼", 15.9 cm
Colours: See below
Issued: 1. Blue, gloss – 1934-1967
3. White, gloss – 1934-Unknown
2. White and tan, gloss –1934-by 1954

Colourway	U.K. £	U.S. $	Can. $
1. Blue	30.00	45.00	45.00
2. White	30.00	45.00	45.00
3. White/tan	20.00	30.00	30.00

Model No. 301
SEALYHAM PLAQUE - Bow on right

Designer: Unknown
Height: 7 ½", 19.1 cm
Colours: Cream; blue bow - satin finish
Issued: 1936-1940
Series: Wall Plaques

Description	U.K. £	U.S. $	Can. $
Satin finish	70.00	110.00	110.00

Model No. 302
SEALYHAM - Standing

Designer: Mr. Watkin
Height: 6", 15.0 cm
Colours: 1. Blue - gloss
2. White with dark ears - gloss
Issued: 1. 1936-1967
2. 1936-by 1964

Colourway	U.K. £	U.S. $	Can. $
1. Blue	55.00	85.00	85.00
2. White/dark ears	60.00	90.00	90.00

Model No. 307
SEALYHAM PLAQUE

Designer: Mr. Watkin
Height: 7", 17.8 cm
Colours: Cream - satin finish
Issued: 1935-1940
Series: Wall Plaques

Description	U.K. £	U.S. $	Can. $
Satin finish	70.00	110.00	110.00

Model No. 308
PUPPY - Seated

Designer: Mr. Watkin
Height: 6 ¼", 15.9 cm
Colours: 1. Blue - gloss
  2. White with brown ears - gloss
Issued: 1. 1935-1967
  2. 1935-by 1954

Colourway	U.K. £	U.S. $	Can. $
1. Blue	30.00	45.00	45.00
2. White/brown	25.00	40.00	40.00

Note: Also issued as a money-box.

Model No. 324
Character Dog - Begging

Designer: Miss Greaves
Height: 7", 17.8 cm
Colours: 1. Blue - gloss
  2. Cream - gloss
Issued: 1. 1936-by 1954
  2. 1936-by 1954
Series: Fun Models

Colourway	U.K. £	U.S. $	Can. $
1. Blue	55.00	85.00	85.00
2. Cream	30.00	45.00	45.00

Model No. 361
DACHSHUND - Standing

Designer: Mr. Watkin
Height: 5 ½", 14.0 cm
Issued: 1. Black/tan - gloss; 1936-1983
  2. Blue - gloss; 1936-by 1954
  3. Tan - gloss; 1936-1983

Colourway	U.K. £	U.S. $	Can. $
1. Black/tan	20.00	30.00	30.00
2. Blue	55.00	85.00	85.00
3. Tan	20.00	30.00	30.00

Model No. 373
SEALYHAM PLAQUE - Bow on Left
Designer:	Unknown
Height:	7", 17.8 cm
Colours:	White dog with blue bow - satin matt
Issued:	1936-1940
Series:	Wall Plaques

Colourway	U.K. £	U.S. $	Can. $
White dog	160.00	250.00	250.00

Model No. 453
OLD ENGLISH SHEEPDOG - Seated
Designer:	Unknown	
Height:	8 ½", 21.6 cm	
Colours:	1.	Blue - gloss
	2.	Grey and white - gloss
Issued:	1.	1936-by 1954
	2.	1936-1973

Colourway	U.K. £	U.S. $	Can. $
1. Blue	55.00	85.00	85.00
2. Grey/white	30.00	45.00	45.00

Model No. 454
LOLLOPY DOG - Seated Puppy
Designer:	Miss Greaves	
Height:	4 ¼", 10.8 cm	
Issued:	1.	Blue, gloss – 1936-1969
	2.	Various, satin matt – 1936-by 1954
	3.	White, gloss – 1936-1969
	4.	White, matt – 1936-1969

Colourway	U.K. £	U.S. $	Can. $
1. Blue, gloss	15.00	25.00	25.00
2. Various, satin matt	10.00	15.00	15.00
3. White, gloss	10.00	15.00	15.00
4. White, matt	15.00	25.00	25.00

Model No. 668
DOG PLAQUE
Designer:	Mr. Symcox	
Height:	11", 27.9 cm	
Colours:	1.	English Setter - grey, gloss
	2.	Red Setter - deep red brown - gloss
Issued:	1938-1960	
Series:	Wall Plaques	

Description	U.K. £	U.S. $	Can. $
1. English Setter	125.00	200.00	200.00
2. Red Setter	110.00	175.00	175.00

Model No. 761
DOG WITH TOOTHACHE

Designer: Mr. Watkin
Height: 4 ¼", 10.8 cm
Colours: 1. White dog with red kerchief - gloss
2. White dog with green kerchief - gloss
Issued: 1939-1971
Series: Fun Models

Colourway	U.K. £	U.S. $	Can. $
1. Red kerchief	25.00	40.00	40.00
2. Green kerchief	55.00	85.00	85.00

Model No. 804
DOG WITH LADYBIRD ON NOSE

Designer: Mr. Watkin
Height: 4", 10.1 cm
Colours: White with red ladybird - gloss
Issued: 1940-1969
Series: Fun Models

Description	U.K. £	U.S. $	Can. $
Gloss	15.00	25.00	25.00

Model No. 805
DOG WITH LADYBIRD ON TAIL

Designer: Mr. Watkin
Height: 1. Large - 3 ¾", 9.5 cm
2. Small - 2 ½", 6.4 cm
Colours: White dog with red ladybird - gloss
Issued: 1940-1969
Series: Fun Models

Description	U.K. £	U.S. $	Can. $
1. Large	10.00	15.00	15.00
2. Small	10.00	15.00	15.00

Model No. 813
DOG WITH LADYBIRD ON NOSE

Designer: Mr. Watkin
Height: 4", 10.1 cm
Colours: White dog, red ladybird - gloss
Issued: 1940-1970
Series: Fun Models

Description	U.K. £	U.S. $	Can. $
Gloss	20.00	30.00	30.00

Model No. 907
DOG WITH LADYBIRD ON TAIL

Designer:	Mr. Watkin	
Height:	3 ¾", 9.5 cm	
Colours:	White dog, red ladybird - gloss	
Issued:	1941-1971	
Series:	Fun Models	

Description	U.K. £	U.S. $	Can. $
Gloss	15.00	25.00	25.00

Model No. 917
THREE PUPPIES

Designer:	Mr. Watkin	
Height:	2", 5.0 cm	
Colours:	Brown puppies - gloss	
Issued:	1941-1965	

Description	U.K. £	U.S. $	Can. $
Gloss	10.00	15.00	15.00

Note: The three dogs are same as used on model no. 916 Ashtray, see the Charlton Standard Catalogue of Beswick Pottery.

Model No. 941
FOXHOUND
First Version - Thick legs and tail

Designer:	Mr. Watkin	
Height:	2 ¾", 7.0 cm	
Colours:	White, tan and black - gloss	
Issued:	1941-1969	
Varieties:	2262	

Description	U.K. £	U.S. $	Can. $
Gloss	25.00	40.00	40.00

Note: Remodelled in 1969 see also no. 2263.

Model No. 942
FOXHOUND
First Version - Thick legs and tail

Designer:	Mr. Watkin	
Height:	2 ¾", 7.0 cm	
Colours:	White, tan and black - gloss	
Issued:	1941-1969	
Varieties:	2263	

Description	U.K. £	U.S. $	Can. $
Gloss	25.00	40.00	40.00

Note: Remodelled in 1969 see also no. 2262.

Model No. 943
FOXHOUND
First Version - Thick legs and tail
Designer: Mr. Watkin
Height: 2 ¾", 7.0 cm
Colours: White, tan and black - gloss
Issued: 1941-1969
Varieties: 2265

Description	U.K. £	U.S. $	Can. $
Gloss	25.00	40.00	40.00

Note: Remodelled in 1969 see also no. 2265.

Model No. 944
FOXHOUND
First Version - Thick legs and tail
Designer: Mr. Watkin
Height: 2 ¾", 7.0 cm
Colours: White, tan and black - gloss
Issued: 1941-1969
Varieties: 2264

Description	U.K. £	U.S. $	Can. $
Gloss	25.00	40.00	40.00

Note: Remodelled in 1969 see also no. 2264.

Model No. 961
DALMATIAN "ARNOLDENE" - Large
Designer: Arthur Gredington
Height: 5 ¾", 14.6 cm
Colours: White with black spot - gloss; matt
Issued: 1.   Gloss - 1941-1994
             2.   Matt - 1970-1994

Description	U.K. £	U.S. $	Can. $
1. Gloss	20.00	30.00	30.00
2. Matt	20.00	30.00	30.00

Note: For the small size see no. 1763.

Model No. 962
AIREDALE TERRIER "CAST IRON MONARCH"
Designer: Arthur Gredington
Height: 5 ½", 14.0 cm
Colours: Black and tan - gloss; matt
Issued: 1.   Gloss - 1941-1989
             2.   Matt - 1987-1989

Description	U.K. £	U.S. $	Can. $
1. Gloss	55.00	85.00	85.00
2. Matt	55.00	85.00	85.00

Model No. 963
WIRED-HAIRED TERRIER
"TALAVERA ROMULUS"

Designer:	Arthur Gredington		
Height:	5 ¾", 14.6 cm		
Colours:	White, light sandy brown and black - gloss		
Issued:	1941-1984		

Description	U.K. £	U.S. $	Can. $
Gloss	35.00	55.00	55.00

Model No. 964
SMOOTH-HAIRED TERRIER
"ENDON BLACK ROD"

Designer:	Arthur Gredington		
Height:	5 ½", 14.0 cm		
Colours:	White with black patches - gloss		
Issued:	1941-1973		

Description	U.K. £	U.S. $	Can. $
Gloss	350.00	525.00	525.00

Model No. 965
BULLDOG "BASFORD BRITISH MASCOT" - Large

Designer:	Arthur Gredington		
Height:	5 ½", 14.0 cm		
Colours:	Brindle, tan and white - gloss; matt		
Issued:	1. Gloss - 1941-1990		
	2. Matt - 1987-1989		

Description	U.K. £	U.S. $	Can. $
1. Gloss	30.00	45.00	45.00
2. Matt	30.00	45.00	45.00

Note: For small size see no. 1731.

Model No. 966
IRISH SETTER "SUGAR OF WENDOVER"

Designer:	Arthur Gredington		
Height:	5 ¾", 14.6 cm		
Colours:	Red brown - gloss; matt		
Issued:	1. Gloss - 1941-1989		
	2. Matt - 1987-1989		

Description	U.K. £	U.S. $	Can. $
1. Gloss	25.00	40.00	40.00
2. Matt	20.00	30.00	30.00

Model No. 967
COCKER SPANIEL "HORSESHOE PRIMULA"
Designer: Arthur Gredington
Height: 5 ¾", 14.6 cm
Issued: 1.   Black, gloss – 1965-1982
             2.   Black and white, gloss – 1970-1928
             3.   Golden brown, gloss – 1941-1929
             3.   Golden brown, gloss – 1941-1994
             4.   Golden brown, matt – 1987-1994
             5.   Liver and white, gloss – 1970-1994
             6.   Liver and white, matt – 1987-1994

Colourway	U.K. £	U.S. $	Can. $
1. Black, gloss	55.00	85.00	85.00
2. Black and white, gloss	30.00	45.00	45.00
3. Golden brown, gloss	20.00	30.00	30.00
4. Golden brown, matt	20.00	30.00	30.00
5. Liver and white, gloss	30.00	45.00	45.00
6. Liver and white, matt	30.00	45.00	45.00

Model No. 968
GREAT DANE "RULER OF OUBOURGH"
Designer: Arthur Gredington
Height: 7", 17.8 cm
Colours: 1.   Light sandy brown - gloss; matt
             2.   Brindle - gloss
Issued: 1a. Gloss - 1941-1994
             1b. Matt - 1987-1994
             2.   Unknown

Description	U.K. £	U.S. $	Can. $
1b.Sandy brown - Gloss	30.00	45.00	45.00
1b.Sandy brown - Matt	25.00	40.00	40.00
2. Brindle - gloss			Rare

Model No. 969
ALSATIAN "ULRICA OF BRITTAS" - Large
Designer: Arthur Gredington
Height: 5 ¾", 14.6 cm
Colours: Black and light brown - gloss; matt
Issued: 1.   1942-1994
             2.   1970-1994

Description	U.K. £	U.S. $	Can. $
1. Gloss	20.00	30.00	30.00
2. Matt	20.00	30.00	30.00

Note: For small size see no. 1762.

Model No. 970
BULL TERRIER "ROMANY RHINESTONE" - Large

Designer:	Arthur Gredington
Height:	6 ½", 16.5 cm
Colours:	1. Brindle and white - gloss
	2. White - gloss; matt
Issued:	1. Gloss - 1942-1975
	2a. Gloss - 1942-1994
	2b. Matt - 1987-1994

Colourway	U.K. £	U.S. $	Can. $
1. Brindle/white	150.00	225.00	225.00
2a. White - gloss	60.00	90.00	90.00
2b. White - matt	50.00	75.00	75.00

Model No. 971
SEALYHAM "FORESTEDGE FOXGLOVE"

Designer:	Arthur Gredington
Height:	4 ¼", 10.8 cm
Colours:	White - gloss
Issued:	1942-1967

Description	U.K. £	U.S. $	Can. $
Gloss	90.00	135.00	135.00

Model No. 972
GREYHOUND "JOVIAL ROGER"

Designer:	Arthur Gredington
Height:	6", 15.0 cm
Colours:	Light sandy brown - gloss; matt
Issued:	1. Gloss - 1942-1990
	2. Matt - 1970-1990

Description	U.K. £	U.S. $	Can. $
1. Gloss	35.00	55.00	55.00
2. Matt	30.00	45.00	45.00

Model No. 973
ENGLISH SETTER "BAYLDONE BARONET"

Designer:	Arthur Gredington
Height:	5 ½", 14.0 cm
Colours:	Speckled grey - gloss; matt
Issued:	1. Gloss - 1942-1989
	2. Matt - 1987-1989

Description	U.K. £	U.S. $	Can. $
1. Gloss	50.00	75.00	75.00
2. Matt	30.00	45.00	45.00

Model No. 1002
PUPPIT DOG

Designer: Arthur Gredington
Height: 4 ¾", 12.1 cm
Colours: White with black markings - gloss
Issued: 1944-1969
Series: Fun Models

Description	U.K. £	U.S. $	Can. $
Gloss	25.00	40.00	40.00

Model No. 1054
SPANIEL HOLDING "MY PLATE"

Designer: Arthur Gredington
Height: 4 ¼", 12.1 cm
Colours: White and brown - gloss
Issued: 1947-1967
Series: Fun Models

Description	U.K. £	U.S. $	Can. $
Gloss	25.00	40.00	40.00

Model No. 1055A
CAIRN TERRIER
First Version - With ball on left or right leg

Designer: Arthur Gredington
Height: 4", 10.1 cm
Colours: Beige with brown "stripes," red ball - gloss
Issued: 1946-1969

Description	U.K. £	U.S. $	Can. $
1. Ball on left leg	60.00	90.00	90.00
2. Ball on right leg	60.00	90.00	90.00

Model No. 1055B
CAIRN TERRIER
Second Version - Without ball

Designer: Arthur Gredington
Height: 4", 10.1 cm
Colours: Beige with brown "stripes" - gloss
Issued: 1946-1969

Description	U.K. £	U.S. $	Can. $
Without ball	50.00	75.00	75.00

Model No. 1057
SPANIEL - Running

Designer: Arthur Gredington
Height: 3 ¾", 9.5 cm
Colours: 1. Blue - gloss
             2. White with golden tan patches - gloss
Issued: 1. 1947-1954
             2. 1946-1967

Description	U.K. £	U.S. $	Can. $
1. Blue		Rare	
2. White/tan	35.00	55.00	55.00

Model No. 1058
DOG WITH COLLAR "SCAMP"

Designer: Arthur Gredington
Height: 4 ½", 11.9 cm
Colours: Tan - gloss
Issued: 1948-1973
Seies: Fun Models

Description	U.K. £	U.S. $	Can. $
Gloss	20.00	30.00	30.00

Model No. 1059
PEKINESE - Begging

Designer: Arthur Gredington
Height: 4 ¼", 10.8 cm
Colours: Golden tan - gloss
Issued: 1946-1967

Description	U.K. £	U.S. $	Can. $
Gloss	25.00	40.00	40.00

Model No. 1060
RED SETTER - Lying

Designer: Arthur Gredington
Height: 3", 7.6 cm
Colours: Deep red brown - gloss
Issued: 1946-1973

Description	U.K. £	U.S. $	Can. $
Gloss	70.00	110.00	110.00

Model No. 1061
TERRIER - Lying

Designer:	Arthur Gredington
Height:	2", 5.0 cm
Colours:	White with light tan patches - gloss
Issued:	1946-1973

Description	U.K. £	U.S. $	Can. $
Gloss	50.00	75.00	75.00

Model No. 1062
TERRIER- Walking

Designer:	Arthur Gredington	
Height:	4", 10.1 cm	
Colours:	1.	Blue - gloss
	2.	White with light tan and black patches - gloss
Issued:	1.	1946-1954
	2.	1946-1973

Description	U.K. £	U.S. $	Can. $
1. Blue		Rare	
2. White/tan	55.00	85.00	85.00

Model No. 1088
COMICAL DACHSHUND

Designer:	Miss Jones
Height:	3 ½", 8.9 cm
Colours:	White and brown - gloss
Issued:	1947-1973
Series:	Fun Models

Description	U.K. £	U.S. $	Can. $
Gloss	20.00	30.00	30.00

Model No. 1202
BOXER "BLUE MOUNTAIN GRETA" - Large

Designer:	Arthur Gredington	
Height:	5 ½", 14.0 cm	
Colours:	1.	Brindle - gloss; matt
	2.	Tan - gloss
Issued:	1a.	Gloss - 1950-1989
	1b.	Matt - 1987-1989
	2.	Gloss - 1973-1975

Colourway	U.K. £	U.S. $	Can. $
1a. Brindle - gloss	55.00	85.00	85.00
1b. Brindle - matt	30.00	45.00	45.00
2. Tan - gloss	55.00	85.00	85.00

Model No. 1220
ENGLISH SETTER
Designer: Arthur Gredington
Height: 8", 20.3 cm
Colours: Speckled grey - gloss
Issued: 1951-1973

Description	U.K. £	U.S. $	Can. $
Gloss	350.00	550.00	550.00

Model No. 1239
DOG WITH RUFF - Begging
Designer: Arthur Gredington
Height: 2 ½", 6.4 cm
Colours: White and light tan - gloss
Issued: 1952-1967

Description	U.K. £	U.S. $	Can. $
Gloss	20.00	30.00	30.00

Note: Originally produced in combination as model no.
        1086 "Clown and Dog." See "Beswick Collectables"
        page 256.

Model No. 1240
DOG - Seated
Designer: Arthur Gredington
Height: 2", 5.0 cm
Colours: White and light tan - gloss
Issued: 1952-1952

Description	U.K. £	U.S. $	Can. $
Gloss	20.00	30.00	30.00

Note: Originally produced in combination as model no.
        1096 "Sportsman." See "Beswick Collectables"
        page 258.

Model No. 1241
DOG - Howling
Designer: Arthur Gredington
Height: 1 ¼", 3.2 cm
Colours: White and light tan - gloss
Issued: 1952-1952

Description	U.K. £	U.S. $	Can. $
Gloss	15.00	25.00	25.00

Note: Originally produced in combination as model no. 909
        "Puppy Love." See "Beswick Collectables" page 253.

Model No. 1242
DOG - Barking

Designer:	Arthur Gredington
Height:	1 ¼", 3.2 cm
Colours:	White and light tan - gloss
Issued:	1952-1952

Description	U.K. £	U.S. $	Can. $
Gloss	20.00	30.00	30.00

Note: Originally produced in combination as model no. 906 "Strolling Along."

Model No. 1294
POODLE "EBONIT AV BARBETT"

Designer:	Arthur Gredington	
Height:	5 ¾", 14.0 cm	
Colours:	1.	Black - gloss; matt
	2.	White - gloss
Issued:	1.	1953-1967
	2.	1953-1967

Colourway	U.K. £	U.S. $	Can. $
1a. Black - gloss	250.00	375.00	375.00
1b. Black - matt	200.00	300.00	300.00
2. White- gloss	250.00	375.00	375.00

Model No. 1299A
CORGI "BLACK PRINCE" - Large

Designer:	Arthur Gredington
Height:	5 ½", 14.0 cm
Colours:	Black, tan and white - gloss
Issued:	1953-1982
Varieties:	1299B

Description	U.K. £	U.S. $	Can. $
Gloss	35.00	55.00	55.00

Note: For small size see no. 1736.

Model No. 1299B
CORGI - Large

Designer:	Arthur Gredington	
Height:	5 ½", 14.0 cm	
Colours:	1.	Golden brown - gloss
	2.	Golden brown - matt
Issued:	1.	1953-1994
	2.	1987-1994
Varieties:	1299A	

Description	U.K. £	U.S. $	Can. $
1. Gloss	20.00	30.00	30.00
2. Matt	20.00	30.00	30.00

Note: For small size see no. 1736.

Model No. 1378/1/2/3/4/5/6/7 and M1378/4/6/7
OLD ENGLISH DOGS - Left and right facing pairs

Designer: Unknown
Colour: See below – gloss
Series: Mantelpiece Dogs

Colourway	Model	Height	Issued	U.K. £	Price U.S. $	Can.
Red/gold	1378/1	13 ¼", 33.6 cm	1955-1973	70.00	110.00	110.00
Red/gold	1378/2	11 ½", 29.2 cm	1955-1972	65.00	100.00	100.00
Red/gold	1378/3	10", 25.4 cm	1955-1973	60.00	90.00	90.00
Red/gold	1378/4	9", 22.9 cm	1955-1973	55.00	85.00	85.00
Red/gold	1378/5	7 ½", 19.1 cm	1955-1973	55.00	85.00	85.00
Red/gold	1378/6	5 ½", 14.0 cm	1955-1973	35.00	55.00	55.00
Red/gold	1378/7	3 ½", 8.9 cm	1955-1973	30.00	45.00	45.00
White/gold	1378/1	13 ¼", 33.6 cm	1955-1976	120.00	185.00	185.00
White/gold	1378/2	11 ½", 29.2 cm	1955-1972	95.00	150.00	150.00
White/gold	1378/3	10", 25.4 cm	1955-1989	70.00	110.00	110.00
White/gold						
a. Original	1378/4	9", 22.9 cm	1955-1989	55.00	85.00	85.00
b. Reissued	M1378/4	9", 22.9 cm	1999-2001	15.00	25.00	25.00
White/gold	1378/5	7 ½", 19.1 cm	1955-1989	30.00	45.00	45.00
White/gold						
a. Original	1378/6	5 ½", 14.0 cm	1955-1989	20.00	30.00	30.00
b. Reissued	M1378/6	5 ½", 14.0 cm	1999-2001	15.00	25.00	25.00
White /gold						
a. Original	1378/7	3 ½", 8.9 cm	1955-1989	15.00	25.00	25.00
b. Reissued	1378/7	3 ½", 8.9 cm	1999-2001	10.00	15.00	15.00

Note: Also seen in Opaque white glaze.

Model No. 1386
POODLE

Designer: Arthur Gredington
Height: 3 ½", 8.9 cm
Issued: 1. Black, gloss – 1955-1990
              2. Black, matt – 1988-1989
              3. Chocolate, gloss – 1953-1973
              4. White, gloss – 1955-1990
              5. White, matt – 1984-1989

Colourway	U.K. £	U.S. $	Can. $
1. Black, gloss	15.00	25.00	25.00
2. Black, matt	15.00	25.00	25.00
3. Chocolate, gloss	40.00	60.00	60.00
4. White, gloss	15.00	25.00	25.00
5. White, matt	15.00	25.00	25.00

Note: A few examples are known in an apricot colourway.

Model No. 1460
DACHSHUND - Seated

Designer: Arthur Gredington
Height: 2 ¾", 7.0 cm
Colours: 1. Black and tan - gloss or matt
              2. Tan - gloss or matt
Issued: 1a. Gloss - 1956-2002
              1b. Matt - 1984-1989
              2a. Gloss - 1956-1990
              2b. Matt - 1984-1990

Colourway	U.K. £	U.S. $	Can. $
1a. Black/tan - gloss	15.00	25.00	25.00
1b. Black/tan - matt	15.00	25.00	25.00
2a. Tan - gloss	15.00	25.00	25.00
2b. Tan - matt	15.00	25.00	25.00

Model No. 1461
DACHSHUND - Begging

Designer: Arthur Gredington
Height: 4", 10.1 cm
Colours: 1. Tan - gloss
              2. Black and tan - gloss
Issued: 1. 1957-1975
              2. 1957-1980

Colourway	U.K. £	U.S. $	Can. $
1. Tan	15.00	25.00	25.00
2. Black and tan	15.00	25.00	25.00

Model No. 1548
LABRADOR "SOLOMON OF WENDOVER"- Large

Designer: Arthur Gredington
Height: 5 ½", 14.0 cm
Issued: 1. Black, gloss – 1958-1994
2. Black, matt – 1987-1994
3. Golden yellow, gloss – 1958-1994
4. Golden yellow, matt – 1970-1994

Colourway	U.K. £	U.S. $	Can. $
1. Black, gloss	20.00	30.00	30.00
2. Black , matt	20.00	30.00	30.00
3. Golden yellow, gloss	25.00	40.00	40.00
4. Golden yellow, matt	20.00	30.00	30.00

Model No. 1731
BULLDOG "BOSUN" - Small

Designer: Unknown
Height: 2 ½", 6.4 cm
Colours: Tan and white - gloss; matt
Issued: 1. Gloss - 1960-1997
2. Matt - 1984-1989

Description	U.K. £	U.S. $	Can. $
1. Gloss	15.00	25.00	25.00
2. Matt	15.00	25.00	25.00

Note: For large size see no. 965.

Model No. 1736
CORGI - Small

Designer: Unknown
Height: 2 ¾", 7.0 cm
Colours: Golden brown - gloss; matt
Issued: 1. Gloss - 1961-1996
2. Matt - 1984-1989

Description	U.K. £	U.S. $	Can. $
1. Gloss	15.00	25.00	25.00
2. Matt	15.00	25.00	25.00

Note: For large size see no. 1299.

Model No. 1738
PUP WITH BONE

Designer: Harry Sales
Height: 3 ¾", 9.5 cm
Colours: White - gloss
Issued: 1961-1967
Series: Fun Models

Description	U.K. £	U.S. $	Can. $
Gloss	25.00	40.00	40.00

Model No. 1753
BULL TERRIER - Small

Designer:	Arthur Gredington
Height:	3 ½", 8.9 cm
Colours:	White with bright tan patches - gloss
Issued:	1961-1971

Description	U.K. £	U.S. $	Can. $
Gloss	125.00	200.00	200.00

Note: For large size see no. 970.

Model No. 1754
COCKER SPANIEL

Designer:	Arthur Gredington
Height:	3", 7.6 cm
Issued:	1. Black and white, gloss – 1961-1996
	2. Black and white, matt – 1984-1989
	3. Liver and white, gloss – 1961-1997
	4. Liver and white, matt – 1984-1989

Colourway	U.K. £	U.S. $	Can. $
1. Black and white, gloss	15.00	25.00	25.00
2. Black and white, matt	15.00	25.00	25.00
3. Liver and white, gloss	10.00	15.00	15.00
4. Liver and white, matt	10.00	15.00	15.00

Model No. 1762A
ALSATIAN - Small
First Version - 'Wolf-like,' tail not fully attached to leg

Designer:	Mr. Garbet
Height:	3 ¼", 8.3 cm
Colours:	Black and cream - gloss
Issued:	1961-1963

Description	U.K. £	U.S. $	Can. $
Gloss	20.00	30.00	30.00

Model No. 1762B
ALSATIAN - Small
Second Version - 'Fine head,' tail attached to leg

Designer:	Arthur Gredington
Height:	3 ¼", 8.3 cm
Colours:	Black and cream - gloss
Issued:	1963-1966

Description	U.K. £	U.S. $	Can. $
Gloss	20.00	30.00	30.00

Note: For large size see no. 969.

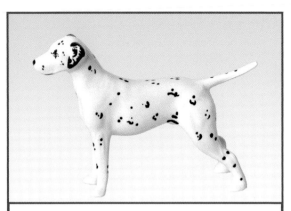

Model No. 1763
DALMATIAN - Small
Designer: Mr. Garbet
Height: 3 ½", 8.9 cm
Colours: White with black spots - gloss; matt
Issued: 1. Gloss - 1961-2002
2. Matt - 1984-1989

Description	U.K. £	U.S. $	Can. $
1. Gloss	20.00	30.00	30.00
2. Matt	20.00	30.00	30.00

Note: For large size see no. 961.

Model No. 1786A
WHIPPET "WINGED FOOT MARKSMAN OF ALLWAYS"
First Version - Tail curls between legs
Designer: Arthur Gredington
Height: 4 ½", 11.9 cm
Colours: Light sandy brown - gloss
Issued: 1961-Unknown

Description	U.K. £	U.S. $	Can. $
Gloss	100.00	150.00	150.00

Model No. 1786B
WHIPPET "WINGED FOOT MARKSMAN OF ALLWAYS"
Second Version - Tail attached to leg
Designer: Arthur Gredington
Height: 4 ½", 11.9 cm
Colours: Light sandy brown - gloss; matt
Issued: 1. Gloss - Unknown-1989
2. Matt - 1987-1989

Description	U.K. £	U.S. $	Can. $
1. Gloss	60.00	90.00	90.00
2. Matt	60.00	90.00	90.00

Model No. 1791
COLLIE "LOCHINVAR OF LADYPARK" - Large
Designer: Arthur Gredington
Height: 5 ¾", 14.6 cm
Colours: Golden brown and white - gloss; matt
Issued: 1. Gloss - 1961-1994
2. Matt - 1970-1994

Description	U.K. £	U.S. $	Can. $
1. Gloss	20.00	30.00	30.00
2. Matt	20.00	30.00	30.00

Note: For small size see no. 1814.

Model No. 1792
SHEEPDOG - Large
Designer: Arthur Gredington
Height: 5 ½", 14.0 cm
Colours: Black and white - gloss; matt
Issued: 1.   Gloss - 1961-1994
              2.   Matt - 1987-1994

Description	U.K. £	U.S. $	Can. $
1. Gloss	20.00	40.00	40.00
2. Matt	15.00	25.00	25.00

Note: For small size see no. 1854.

Model No. 1814
COLLIE - Small
Designer: Arthur Gredington
Height: 3 ¼", 8.3 cm
Colours: Golden brown and white - gloss
Issued: 1962-1975

Description	U.K. £	U.S. $	Can. $
Gloss	20.00	30.00	30.00

Note: For large size see no. 1791.

Model No. 1824
DOG - Singing
Designer: Albert Hallam
Height: 1 ½", 3.8 cm
Colours: Tan - gloss
Issued: 1962-1971
Series: Bedtime Chorus

Description	U.K. £	U.S. $	Can. $
Gloss	20.00	30.00	30.00

Model No. 1852
BOXER - Small
Designer: Arthur Gredington
Height: 3", 7.6 cm
Colours: Tan - gloss
Issued: 1962-1975

Description	U.K. £	U.S. $	Can. $
Gloss	20.00	30.00	30.00

Note: For large size see no. 1202.

Model No. 1854
SHEEPDOG - Small

Designer:	Arthur Gredington
Height:	3", 7.6 cm
Colours:	Black and white - gloss; matt
Issued:	1. Gloss - 1962-2002
	2. Matt - 1987-1989

Description	U.K. £	U.S. $	Can. $
1. Gloss	15.00	25.00	25.00
2. Matt	10.00	15.00	15.00

Note: For large size see no. 1792.

Model No. 1855
RETRIEVER

Designer:	Arthur Gredington
Height:	3 ¼", 8.3 cm
Colours:	1. Black - gloss
	2. Light golden brown - gloss
Issued:	1962-1975

Colourway	U.K. £	U.S. $	Can. $
1. Black	20.00	30.00	30.00
2. Light brown	15.00	25.00	25.00

Model No. 1871
POODLE

Designer:	Arthur Gredington
Height:	4 ¼", 10.8 cm
Colours:	White, red bow - gloss
Issued:	1963-1967

Description	U.K. £	U.S. $	Can. $
Gloss	95.00	150.00	150.00

Note: Used on Model 1869 advertising "Dubonnet", see the Charlton Standard Catalogue of Beswick Pottery.

Model No. 1872
BULLDOG

Designer:	Arthur Gredington
Height:	3 ¾", 9.5 cm
Colours:	White, pale tan ear and around eyes - gloss
Issued:	1963-1967

Description	U.K. £	U.S. $	Can. $
Gloss	25.00	40.00	40.00

Note: Used on Model 1869 advertising "Dubonnet", see the Charlton Standard Catalogue of Beswick Pottery.

Model No. 1933A
BEAGLE "WENDOVER BILLY" - Large

Designer: Arthur Gredington
Height: 5 ½", 14.0 cm
Colours: Black, tan and white - gloss or matt
Issued: 1. 1964-1989
 2. 1987-1989
Varieties: 1933B

Description	U.K. £	U.S. $	Can. $
1. Gloss	25.00	40.00	40.00
2. Matt	20.00	30.00	30.00

Note: For small size see no. 1939.

Model No. 1933B
BEAGLE "WENDOVER BILLY" - on wooden plinth

Designer: Arthur Gredington
Height: 6", 15.0 cm
Colours: Black, tan and white - matt
Issued: 1970-1989
Series: Connoisseur Dogs
Varieties: 1933A

Description	U.K. £	U.S. $	Can. $
Matt	55.00	85.00	85.00

Model No. 1939
BEAGLE "WENDOVER BILLY" - Small

Designer: Arthur Gredington
Height: 3", 7.6 cm
Colours: Black, tan and white - gloss or matt
Issued: 1. Gloss - 1964-2002
 2. Matt - 1984-1989

Description	U.K. £	U.S. $	Can. $
1. Gloss	15.00	25.00	25.00
2. Matt	15.00	25.00	25.00

Note: For large size see no. 1933A.

Model No. 1944
YORKSHIRE TERRIER - Lying

Designer: Arthur Gredington
Height: 3 ½", 8.9 cm
Colours: Grey and tan - gloss
Issued: 1964-1976

Description	U.K. £	U.S. $	Can. $
Gloss	15.00	25.00	25.00

Model No. 1956
LABRADOR - Small

Designer: Arthur Gredington
Height: 3 ¼", 8.3 cm
Issued:
1. Black, gloss – 1964 - 2002
2. Black, matt – 1984 - 1989
3. Golden brown, gloss – 1964- 2002
4. Golden brown, matt – 1984-1989

Colourway	U.K. £	U.S. $	Can. $
1. Black, gloss	10.00	15.00	15.00
2. Black, matt	10.00	15.00	15.00
3. Golden brown, gloss	10.00	15.00	15.00
4. Golden brown, matt	10.00	15.00	15.00

Model No. 1982A
STAFFORDSHIRE BULL TERRIER "BANDITS BRINTIGA"

Designer: Arthur Gredington
Height: 4 ¾", 12.1 cm
Colours: Dark brindle - gloss
Issued: 1964-1969

Description	U.K. £	U.S. $	Can. $
Gloss	250.00	375.00	375.00

Model No. 1982B
STAFFORDSHIRE BULL TERRIER

Designer: Arthur Gredington
Height: 4 ¾", 12.1 cm
Colours: Tan and white - gloss
Issued: 1964-1969

Description	U.K. £	U.S. $	Can. $
Gloss	250.00	375.00	375.00

Model No. 1990
OLD ENGLISH SHEEPDOG

Designer: Mr. Mortimer
Height: 12 ½", 31.7 cm
Colours: Black, grey and white - gloss
Issued: 1964-1970

Description	U.K. £	U.S. $	Can. $
Gloss	325.00	500.00	500.00

Note: "Dulux" advertising ware.

Model No. 1997
PUG "CUTMIL CUTIE" - Large

Designer:	Arthur Gredington
Height:	4 ½", 11.9 cm
Colours:	Light sandy brown - gloss or matt
Issued:	1. Gloss - 1965-1982
	2. Matt - 1970-1982

Description	U.K. £	U.S. $	Can. $
1. Gloss	25.00	40.00	40.00
2. Matt	20.00	30.00	30.00

Model No. 1998
PUG - Small

Designer:	Arthur Gredington
Height:	2 ½", 6.4 cm
Colours:	Light sandy brown - gloss or matt
Issued:	1. Gloss - 1966-1990
	2. Mattt - 1984-1989

Description	U.K. £	U.S. $	Can. $
1. Gloss	15.00	25.00	25.00
2. Matt	15.00	25.00	25.00

Note: This model has also been seen with head forward.

Model No. 2023
JACK RUSSELL TERRIER - Large

Designer:	Arthur Gredington
Height:	5", 12.7 cm
Colours:	White body, tan/black head - gloss or matt
Issued:	1. Gloss - 1965-1994
	2. Matt - 1987-1994

Description	U.K. £	U.S. $	Can. $
1. Gloss	25.00	40.00	40.00
2. Matt	20.00	30.00	30.00

Note: For small size see no. 2109.

Model No. 2037
SCOTTIE

Designer:	Arthur Gredington
Height:	4 ½", 11.9 cm
Colours:	Black - gloss or matt
Issued:	1. Gloss - 1965-1990
	2. Matt - 1987-1989

Description	U.K. £	U.S. $	Can. $
1. Gloss	25.00	40.00	40.00
2. Matt	20.00	30.00	30.00

Model No. 2038
WEST HIGHLAND TERRIER

Designer:	Arthur Gredington
Height:	4 ¾", 12.1 cm
Colours:	White - gloss or matt
Issued:	1. Gloss - 1965-1994
	2. Matt - 1987-1989

Description	U.K. £	U.S. $	Can. $
1. Gloss	30.00	45.00	45.00
2. Matt	25.00	40.00	40.00

Model No. 2045A
BASSET HOUND "FOCHNO TRINKET"

Designer:	Arthur Gredington
Height:	5", 12.7 cm
Colours:	Black, white and tan - gloss or matt
Issued:	1. Gloss - 1965-1994
	2. Matt - 1987-1994

Description	U.K. £	U.S. $	Can. $
1. Gloss	25.00	40.00	40.00
2. Matt	25.00	40.00	40.00

Model No. 2045B
BASSET HOUND "FOCHNO TRINKET"
- on wooden plinth

Designer:	Arthur Gredington
Height:	6", 15.0 cm
Colours:	Black, white and tan - matt
Issued:	1970-1989
Series:	Connoisseur Dogs

Description	U.K. £	U.S. $	Can. $
Matt	55.00	85.00	85.00

Model No. 2102
YORKSHIRE TERRIER LAUGHING

Designer:	Albert Hallam
Height:	3", 7.6 cm
Colours:	Tan - gloss
Issued:	1967-1972
Series:	Fun Models

Description	U.K. £	U.S. $	Can. $
Gloss	10.00	15.00	15.00

Model No. 2107A
KING CHARLES SPANIEL "BLENHEIM"

Designer: Arthur Gredington
Height: 5 ¼", 13.3 cm
Colours: Tan and white - gloss or matt
Issued: 1. Gloss - 1967-1994
2. Matt - 1987-1994

Description	U.K. £	U.S. $	Can. $
1. Gloss	30.00	45.00	45.00
2. Matt	30.00	45.00	45.00

Model No. 2107B
KING CHARLES SPANIEL "JOSEPHINE OF BLAGREAVES"

Designer: Arthur Gredington
Height: 5 ¼", 13.3 cm
Colours: Black, tan and white - gloss or matt
Issued: 1. Gloss - 1967-1994
2. Matt - 1987-1994

Description	U.K. £	U.S. $	Can. $
1. Gloss	30.00	45.00	45.00
2. Matt	30.00	45.00	45.00

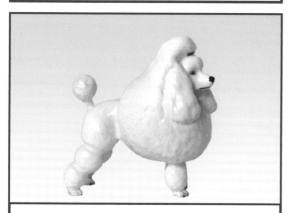

Model No. 2108
POODLE "IVANOLA GOLD DIGGER"

Designer: Arthur Gredington
Height: 5 ¾", 14.6 cm
Colours: White, blue bow - gloss
Issued: 1967-1971

Description	U.K. £	U.S. $	Can. $
Gloss	275.00	425.00	425.00

Model No. 2109
JACK RUSSELL TERRIER - Small

Designer: Arthur Gredington and
Albert Hallam
Height: 2 ½", 6.4 cm
Colours: White with tan head - gloss or matt
Issued: 1. Gloss - 1967 - 2002
2. Matt - 1984-1989

Description	U.K. £	U.S. $	Can. $
1. Gloss	15.00	25.00	25.00
2. Matt	15.00	25.00	25.00

Note: For large size see no. 2023.

Model No. 2112
CAIRN TERRIER

Designer:	Arthur Gredington and Albert Hallam
Height:	2 ¾", 7.0 cm
Colours:	Dark cream - gloss or matt
Issued:	1. Gloss - 1967-1995
	2. Matt - 1984-1989

Description	U.K. £	U.S. $	Can. $
1. Gloss	20.00	30.00	30.00
2. Matt	15.00	25.00	25.00

Model No. 2130
DOG PRAYING

Designer:	Albert Hallam
Height:	3", 7.6 cm
Colours:	Blue - gloss
Issued:	1967-1972
Series:	Fun Models

Description	U.K. £	U.S. $	Can. $
Gloss	15.00	25.00	25.00

Model No. 2221
ST. BERNARD "CORNA GARTH STROLLER"

Designer:	Albert Hallam
Height:	5 ½", 14.0 cm
Colours:	Dark brown, tan and white - gloss or matt
Issued:	1. Gloss - 1968-1989
	2. Matt - 1970-1989

Description	U.K. £	U.S. $	Can. $
1. Gloss	30.00	45.00	45.00
2. Matt	30.00	45.00	45.00

Model No. 2232
OLD ENGLISH SHEEPDOG

Designer:	Albert Hallam
Height:	11 ½", 29.2 cm
Colours:	Grey and white - gloss
Issued:	1968-1989
Series:	Fireside Models

Description	U.K. £	U.S. $	Can. $
Gloss	90.00	150.00	150.00

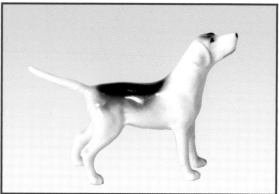

Model No. 2235
BASSETHOUND - Wall Plaque

Designer:	Graham Tongue
Height:	6 ¼" x 4 ½", 15.9 x 11.9 cm (concave)
Colours:	Tan and white head, black satin surround - gloss
Issued:	1968 - Unknown
Series:	Wall Plaques

Description	U.K. £	U.S. $	Can. $
Gloss	55.00	85.00	85.00

Model No. 2262
FOXHOUND
Second Version - Thin legs and tail

Designer:	Graham Tongue
Height:	2 ½", 6.4 cm
Colours:	White, tan and black - gloss or matt
Issued:	1. Gloss - 1969-1997
	2. Matt - 1984-1989
Varieties:	941

Description	U.K. £	U.S. $	Can. $
1. Gloss	20.00	30.00	30.00
2. Matt	20.00	30.00	30.00

Model No. 2263
FOXHOUND
Second Version - Thin legs and tail

Designer:	Graham Tongue
Height:	3", 7.6 cm
Colours:	White, tan and black - gloss or matt
Issued:	1. Gloss - 1969-1997
	2. Matt - 1984-1989
Varieties:	942

Description	U.K. £	U.S. $	Can. $
1. Gloss	20.00	30.00	30.00
2. Matt	20.00	30.00	30.00

Model No. 2264
FOXHOUND
Second Version - Thin legs and tail

Designer:	Graham Tongue
Height:	3", 7.6 cm
Colours:	White, tan and black - gloss or matt
Issued:	1. Gloss - 1969-1997
	2. Matt - 1984-1989
Varieties:	944

Description	U.K. £	U.S. $	Can. $
1. Gloss	20.00	30.00	30.00
2. Matt	20.00	30.00	30.00

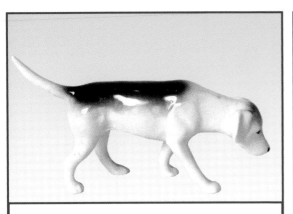

Model No. 2265
FOXHOUND
Second Version - Thin legs and tail
Designer: Graham Tongue
Height: 2 ¾", 7.0 cm
Colours: White, tan and black - gloss or matt
Issued: 1. Gloss - 1969-1997
2. Matt - 1984-1989
Varieties: 943

Description	U.K. £	U.S. $	Can. $
1. Gloss	20.00	30.00	30.00
2. Matt	20.00	30.00	30.00

Model No. 2268
POODLE - Wall Plaque
Designer: Graham Tongue
Height: 6" x 4 ½", 15.9 x 11.9 cm (Concave)
Colours: Unknown - gloss
Issued: 1968-Unknown
Series: Wall Plaques

Description	U.K. £	U.S. $	Can. $
Gloss	150.00	225.00	225.00

Model No. 2271
DALMATIAN
Designer: Graham Tongue
Height: 13 ¾", 34.9 cm
Colours: White with black spots - gloss
Issued: 1969-1989
Series: Fireside Models

Description	U.K. £	U.S. $	Can. $
Gloss	100.00	150.00	150.00

Model No. 2285
AFGHAN HOUND "HAJUBAH OF DAVIEN"
Designer: Graham Tongue
Height: 5 ½", 14.0 cm
Colours: Golden and dark brown - gloss or matt
Issued: 1. Gloss - 1969-1994
2. Matt - 1987-1989

Description	U.K. £	U.S. $	Can. $
1. Gloss	20.00	30.00	30.00
2. Matt	15.00	25.00	25.00

Model No. 2286
DACHSHUND

Designer:	Albert Hallam
Height:	10 ½", 26.7 cm
Colours:	1. Black and tan - gloss
	2. Tan - gloss
Issued:	1. 1969-1981
	2. 1969-1981
Series:	Fireside Models

Colourway	U.K. £	U.S. $	Can. $
1. Black/tan	70.00	110.00	110.00
2. Tan	70.00	110.00	110.00

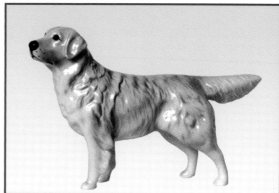

Model No. 2287
GOLDEN RETRIEVER "CABUS CADET"

Designer:	Graham Tongue
Height:	5 ½", 14.0 cm
Colours:	Light golden brown - gloss or matt
Issued:	1. Gloss - 1969-1994
	2. Matt - 1987-1994

Description	U.K. £	U.S. $	Can. $
1. Gloss	30.00	45.00	45.00
2. Matt	30.00	45.00	45.00

Model No. 2299
DOBERMAN PINSCHER "ANNASTOCK LANCE"

Designer:	Graham Tongue
Height:	5 ¾", 14.6 cm
Colours:	Black and tan - gloss or matt
Issued:	1. Gloss - 1970-1994
	2. Matt - 1987-1994

Description	U.K. £	U.S. $	Can. $
1. Gloss	25.00	40.00	40.00
2. Matt	20.00	30.00	30.00

Model No. 2300
BEAGLE

Designer:	Albert Hallam
Height:	12 ¾", 32.4 cm
Colours:	Black, tan and white - gloss
Issued:	1969-1983
Series:	Fireside Models

Description	U.K. £	U.S. $	Can. $
Gloss	95.00	150.00	150.00

Model No. 2314
LABRADOR

Designer:	Graham Tongue
Height:	13 ½", 34.3 cm
Colours:	1. Black - gloss
	2. Golden brown - gloss
Issued:	1970-1989
Series:	Fireside Models

Colourways	U.K. £	U.S. $	Can. $
1. Black	160.00	250.00	250.00
2. Golden brown	90.00	140.00	140.00

Model No. 2339
POODLE

Designer:	Graham Tongue
Height:	5 ¾", 14.6 cm
Colours:	1. Black - gloss
	2. White - gloss
Issued:	1971-1983

Colourway	U.K. £	U.S. $	Can. $
1. Black	20.00	30.00	30.00
2. White	20.00	30.00	30.00

Model No. 2377
YORKSHIRE TERRIER

Designer:	Graham Tongue
Height:	10 ¼", 26.0 cm
Colours:	Grey and tan - gloss
Issued:	1971-1989
Series:	Fireside Models

Description	U.K. £	U.S. $	Can. $
Gloss	70.00	110.00	110.00

Model No. 2410
ALSATIAN

Designer:	Graham Tongue
Height:	14", 35.5 cm
Colours:	Dark and sandy brown - gloss
Issued:	1972-1989
Series:	Fireside Models

Description	U.K. £	U.S. $	Can. $
Gloss	125.00	200.00	200.00

Model No. 2448
LAKELAND TERRIER

Designer:	Albert Hallam
Height:	3 ¼", 8.3 cm
Colours:	Pale tan and black - gloss or matt
Issued:	1. Gloss - 1973-1998
	2. Matt - 1984-1989

Description	U.K. £	U.S. $	Can. $
1. Gloss	20.00	30.00	30.00
2. Matt	15.00	25.00	25.00

Model No. 2454
CHIHUAHUA - Lying on cushion

Designer:	Albert Hallam
Height:	2 ¾", 7.0 cm
Colours:	Cream dog, maroon cushion - gloss or matt
Issued:	1. Gloss - 1973-1996
	2. Matt - 1984-1989

Description	U.K. £	U.S. $	Can. $
1. Gloss	20.00	30.00	30.00
2. Matt	20.00	30.00	30.00

Model No. 2581
COLLIE - on wooden plinth

Designer:	Graham Tongue
Height:	8", 20.3 cm
Colours:	Golden brown and white - matt
Issued:	1979-1989
Series:	Connoisseur Dogs

Description	U.K. £	U.S. $	Can. $
Matt	30.00	45.00	45.00

Model No. 2587
ALSATIAN - on wooden plinth

Designer:	Graham Tongue
Height:	9", 22.9 cm
Colours:	Dark and sandy brown - matt
Issued:	1979-1989
Series:	Connoisseur Dogs

Description	U.K. £	U.S. $	Can. $
Matt	30.00	45.00	45.00

Model No. 2929
COLLIE - Wall Plaque

Designer:	Graham Tongue
Height:	Unknown
Colours:	Golden brown and white - matt
Issued:	1986-1989
Series:	Best of Breed

Description	U.K. £	U.S. $	Can. $
Matt	25.00	40.00	40.00

Note: Head from model no. 2581 mounted on wood.

Model No. 2932
ALSATIAN - Wall Plaque

Designer:	Graham Tongue
Height:	Unknown
Colours:	Black and cream - matt
Issued:	1986-1989
Series:	Best of Breed

Description	U.K. £	U.S. $	Can. $
Matt	25.00	40.00	40.00

Note: Head from model no. 2587 mounted on wood.

Model No. 2946
MEAL TIME

Designer:	Unknown
Height:	3 ½", 8.9 cm
Colours:	White and tan - gloss
Issued:	1986-1989
Series:	Playful Puppies

Description	U.K. £	U.S. $	Can. $
Gloss	20.00	30.00	30.00

Note: Taken from Royal Doulton HN 1158.
Makes a set of six with model numbers 2947, 2948, 2949, 2950 and 2951.

Model No. 2947
GNAWING

Designer:	Unknown
Height:	4 ¼", 10.8 cm
Colours:	White and tan - gloss
Issued:	1986-1989
Series:	Playful Puppies

Description	U.K. £	U.S. $	Can. $
Gloss	20.00	30.00	30.00

Note: Taken from Royal Doulton HN 1159.
Makes a set of six with model numbers 2946, 2948, 2949, 2950 and 2951.

Model No. 2948
PLAY TIME

Designer:　　Unknown
Height:　　　3 ¾", 9.5 cm
Colours:　　White and tan - gloss
Issued:　　　1986-1989
Series:　　　Playful Puppies

Description	U.K. £	U.S. $	Can. $
Gloss	20.00	30.00	30.00

Note:　Taken from Royal Doulton HN 2654.
Makes a set of six with model numbers 2946, 2947, 2949, 2950 and 2951.

Model No. 2949
JUGGLING

Designer:　　Unknown
Height:　　　3", 7.6 cm
Colours:　　White and tan - gloss
Issued:　　　1986-1989
Series:　　　Playful Puppies

Description	U.K. £	U.S. $	Can. $
Gloss	20.00	30.00	30.00

Note:　Taken from Royal Doulton HN 1103.
Makes a set of six with model numbers 1946, 2947, 2948, 2950 and 2951.

Model No. 2950
NAP TIME

Designer:　　Unknown
Height:　　　4 ½", 11.9 cm
Colours:　　White and tan - gloss
Issued:　　　1986-1989
Series:　　　Playful Puppies

Description	U.K. £	U.S. $	Can. $
Gloss	20.00	30.00	30.00

Note:　Taken from Royal Doulton HN 1099.
Makes a set of six with model numbers 2946, 2947, 2948, 2949 and 2951.

Model No. 2951
CAUGHT IT

Designer:　　Unknown
Height:　　　2 ¾", 7.0 cm
Colours:　　White and tan - gloss
Issued:　　　1986-1989
Series:　　　Playful Puppies

Description	U.K. £	U.S. $	Can. $
Gloss	20.00	30.00	30.00

Note:　Taken from Royal Doulton HN 1097.
Makes a set of six with model numbers 2946, 2947, 2948, 2949 and 2950.

Model No. 2980
SPANIEL - on ceramic plinth
Designer: Alan Maslankowski
Height: 8 ¼", 21.0 cm
Colours: 1. Black - matt
              2. Black and white - matt
              3. Golden - matt
              4. Liver and white - matt
              5. White - matt
Issued: See below
Series: Spirited Dogs

Colourway	Issued	U.K. £	U.S. $	Can. $
1. Black	1987-1989	35.00	55.00	55.00
2. Black/white	1987-1989	35.00	55.00	55.00
3. Golden	1987-1989	35.00	55.00	55.00
4. Liver/white	1987-1989	30.00	45.00	45.00
5. White	1987-1989	30.00	45.00	45.00

Model No. 2982
PEKINESE - Begging
Designer: Alan Maslankowski
Height: 5 ½", 14.0 cm
Colours: Cream - gloss or matt
Issued: 1987-1989
Series: Good Companions

Description	U.K. £	U.S. $	Can. $
1. Gloss	25.00	40.00	40.00
2. Matt	25.00	40.00	40.00

Model No. 2984
NORFOLK TERRIER
Designer: Alan Maslankowski
Height: 4", 10.1 cm
Colours: Brown - gloss or matt
Issued: 1987-1989
Series: Good Companions

Description	U.K. £	U.S. $	Can. $
1. Gloss	65.00	100.00	100.00
2. Matt	65.00	100.00	100.00

Model No. 2985
POODLE - on cushion

Designer:	Alan Maslankowski
Height:	5 ½", 14.0 cm
Colours:	White poodle, turquoise cushion - gloss or matt
Issued:	1987-1989
Series:	Good Companions

Description	U.K. £	U.S. $	Can. $
1. Gloss	55.00	85.00	85.00
2. Matt	45.00	70.00	70.00

Note: One example is known of an apricot poodle on green cushion, gloss.

Model No. 2986
SETTER - on ceramic base

Designer:	Graham Tongue
Height:	8 ½", 21.6 cm
Colours:	1. Black, matt
	2. Bronze finish
	3. English Setter – Liver/white, matt
	4. Gordon Setter – Black/tan, matt
	5. Red Setter – Deep red brown, matt
	6. White, matt
Issued:	See below
Series:	See below

Colourway	Issued	Series	U.K. £	U.S. $	Can. $
1. Black, matt	1987-1989	Spirited Dogs	65.00	100.00	100.00
2. Bronze	1989-1993	Britannia	65.00	100.00	100.00
3. English Setter	1987-1989	Spirited Dogs	65.00	100.00	100.00
4. Gordon Setter	1988-1989	Spirited Dogs	70.00	110.00	110.00
5. Red Setter	1987-1989	Spirited Dogs	70.00	110.00	110.00
6. White	1987-1989	Spirited Dogs	65.00	100.00	100.00

Model No. 3011
POINTER - on ceramic plinth

Designer:	Graham Tongue
Height:	8 ½", 21.6 cm
Colour:	See below
Issued:	See below
Series:	See below

Colourway	Issued	Series	U.K. £	U.S. $	Can. $
1. Black, matt	1987-1989	Spirited Dogs	70.00	110.00	110.00
2. Bronze finish	1989-1993	Britannia	60.00	95.00	95.00
3. White, matt	1987-1989	Spirited Dogs	60.00	95.00	95.00
4. White/brown, matt	1987-1989	Spirited Dogs	70.00	110.00	110.00

Model No. 3013
DACHSHUND - Standing

Designer:	Alan Maslankowski
Height:	4 ¼", 10.8 cm
Colours:	1. Black and tan - gloss or matt
	2. Tan - gloss or matt
Issued:	1987-1989
Series:	Good Companions

Description	U.K. £	U.S. $	Can. $
1. Gloss	20.00	30.00	30.00
2. Matt	15.00	25.00	25.00

Model No. 3055
ROTTWEILER

Designer:	Alan Maslankowski
Height:	5 ¼", 13.3 cm
Colours:	Black and tan - gloss or matt
Issued:	1988-1989

Description	U.K. £	U.S. $	Can. $
1. Gloss	20.00	30.00	30.00
2. Matt	20.00	30.00	30.00

Model No. 3058 / D3058
OLD ENGLISH SHEEP DOG - Walking

Designer:	Warren Platt
Height:	5 ½", 14.0 cm
Colours:	Grey and white - gloss or matt

Description	U.K. £	U.S. $	Can. $
1. Gloss			
Model 3058 1988-89	30.00	45.00	45.00
Model D3058 1999-2002	30.00	45.00	45.00
2. Matt			
Model 3058 1988-1989	30.00	45.00	45.00

Model No. 3060
STAFFORDSHIRE BULL TERRIER

Designer:	Alan Maslankowski
Height:	4", 10.1 cm
Colours:	1. White and tan - gloss or matt
	2. Brindle - gloss or matt
Issued:	See below

Colourway	Issued	U.K. £	U.S. $	Can. $
1a. White/tan - gloss	1988-1989	100.00	150.00	150.00
1b. White/tan - matt	1988-1989	100.00	150.00	150.00
2a. Brindle - gloss	1988-1989	100.00	150.00	150.00
2b. Brindle - matt	1988-1989	100.00	150.00	150.00

Model No. 3062A
LABRADOR - on ceramic plinth

Designer:	Alan Maslankowski		
Height:	6 ½", 16.5 cm		
Colours:	1. Black - matt		
	2. Golden - matt		
Issued:	1988-1989		
Series:	Spirited Dogs		
Varieties:	3062B		

Colourways	U.K. £	U.S. $	Can. $
1. Black	60.00	90.00	90.00
2. Golden	50.00	75.00	75.00

Model No. 3062B
LABRADOR - Walking

Designer:	Alan Maslankowski		
Height:	5", 12.7 cm		
Colours:	Chocolate brown - gloss		
Issued:	1993 in a limited edition of 93		
Varieties:	3062A		

Description	U.K. £	U.S. $	Can. $
Gloss	500.00	750.00	750.00

Note: Produced for the Beswick Collectors Circle with a special BCC backstamp. One example is known in golden gloss.

Model No. 3066
RETRIEVER - on ceramic base

Designer:	Graham Tongue		
Height:	7 ½", 19.1 cm		
Colours:	See below		
Issued:	1. Golden, matt – 1988-1989		
	2. Bronze – 1989-1989		
Series:	1. Spirited Dogs		
	2. Britannia		

Colourway	U.K. £	U.S. $	Can. $
1. Golden	55.00	85.00	85.00
2. Bronze	30.00	45.00	85.00

Note: Shown here on a Royal Doulton plinth.

Model No. 3070
AFGHAN HOUND - Running

Designer:	Alan Maslankowski		
Height:	5 ½", 14.0 cm		
Colours:	Light brown and cream - gloss or matt		
Issued:	1988-1989		

Description	U.K. £	U.S. $	Can. $
1. Gloss	75.00	115.00	115.00
2. Matt	55.00	85.00	85.00

Model No. 3073 / D3073
ALSATIAN - Standing

Designer:	Alan Maslankowski
Height:	5 ¾", 14.6 cm
Colours:	Black and light brown - gloss or matt
Issued:	See below

Description	U.K. £	U.S. $	Can. $
Model 3073			
1. Gloss – 1988-1989	25.00	40.00	40.00
2. Matt – 1988-1989	25.00	40.00	40.00
Model D3073			
1. Gloss – 1999-2002	25.00	40.00	40.00

Model No. 3080
SHETLAND SHEEPDOG - Seated

Designer:	Alan Maslankowski
Height:	5 ½", 14.0 cm
Colours:	Golden brown and white - gloss or matt
Issued:	1988-1989
Series:	Good Companions

Description	U.K. £	U.S. $	Can. $
1. Gloss	90.00	140.00	140.00
2. Matt	60.00	90.00	90.00

Model No. 3081 / D3081
BOXER - Standing

Designer:	Alan Maslankowski
Height:	5 ½", 14.0 cm
Colours:	Golden brown and white - gloss or matt
Issued:	See below

Description	U.K. £	U.S. $	Can. $
Model 3081			
1. Gloss - 1988-89	20.00	30.00	30.00
2. Matt - 1988-89	20.00	30.00	30.00
Model D3081			
1. Gloss - 1999-2001	20.00	30.00	30.00

Model No. 3082
CAIRN TERRIER - Standing

Designer:	Warren Platt
Height:	4 ¾", 12.1 cm
Colours:	Light brown - gloss or matt
Issued:	1988-1989
Series:	Good Companions

Description	U.K. £	U.S. $	Can. $
1. Gloss	20.00	30.00	30.00
2. Matt	20.00	30.00	30.00

Model No. 3083
YORKSHIRE TERRIER - Seated

Designer:	Warren Platt		
Height:	5 ½", 14.0 cm		
Colours:	Grey and light brown - gloss and matt		
Issued:	1988-1989		
Series:	Good Companions		

Description	U.K. £	U.S. $	Can. $
1. Gloss	20.00	30.00	30.00
2. Matt	20.00	30.00	30.00

Model No. 3121
DOBERMAN

Designer:	Alan Maslankowski		
Height:	5 ¼", 13.3 cm		
Colours:	Black and tan - gloss or matt		
Issued:	1988-1989		

Description	U.K. £	U.S. $	Can. $
1. Gloss	25.00	40.00	40.00
2. Matt	20.00	30.00	30.00

Model No. 3129
ROUGH COLLIE

Designer:	Warren Platt		
Height:	5 ½", 14.0 cm		
Colours:	Golden brown and white - gloss or matt		
Issued:	1988-1989		

Description	U.K. £	U.S. $	Can. $
1. Gloss	55.00	85.00	85.00
2. Matt	95.00	150.00	150.00

Model No. 3135/D3135
SPRINGER SPANIEL

Designer:	Amanda Hughes-Lubeck		
Height:	5", 12.7 cm		
Colours:	Dark brown and white - gloss or matt		
Issued:	See below		

Description	U.K. £	U.S. $	Can. $
Model 3135			
1. Gloss, 1988-89	25.00	40.00	40.00
2. Matt, 1988-89	20.00	30.00	30.00
Model D3135			
1. Gloss, 1999-2002	25.00	40.00	40.00

Model No. 3149
WEST HIGHLAND TERRIER - Seated

Designer:	Martyn Alcock		
Height:	5", 12.7 cm		
Colours:	White - gloss or matt		
Issued:	1989-1989		
Series:	Good Companions		

Description	U.K. £	U.S. $	Can. $
1. Gloss	25.00	40.00	40.00
2. Matt	20.00	30.00	30.00

Model No. 3155
CAVALIER KING CHARLES SPANIEL - Standing

Designer:	Warren Platt		
Height:	5 ½", 14.0 cm		
Colours:	1. Black/tan/white - gloss or matt		
	2. Tan/white - gloss or matt		
Issued:	1989-1989		
Series:	Good Companions		

Description	U.K. £	U.S. $	Can. $
1a. Black/tan/white - gloss	70.00	110.00	110.00
1b. Black/tan/white - matt	70.00	110.00	110.00
2a. Tan/white - gloss	70.00	110.00	110.00
2b. Tan/white - matt	70.00	110.00	110.00

Model No. 3258
ALSATIAN - Standing

Designer:	Unknown		
Height:	3 ¼", 8.3 cm		
Colours:	Black and cream - gloss		
Issued:	1991-1997		

Description	U.K. £	U.S. $	Can. $
Gloss	15.00	25.00	25.00

Model No. 3260
ROTTWEILER - Standing

Designer:	Unknown		
Height:	3 ½", 8.9 cm		
Colours:	Black and tan - gloss		
Issued:	1991-1998		

Description	U.K. £	U.S. $	Can. $
Gloss	15.00	25.00	25.00

Model No. 3262
YORKSHIRE TERRIER - Standing

Designer:	Unknown	
Height:	3 ½", 8.9 cm	
Colours:	Grey and sandy brown - gloss	
Issued:	1991-1997	

Description	U.K. £	U.S. $	Can. $
Gloss	15.00	25.00	25.00

Model No. 3270
GOLDEN RETRIEVER - Standing

Designer:	Unknown	
Height:	2 ¾", 7.0 cm	
Colours:	Pale golden brown - gloss	
Issued:	1991-2002	

Description	U.K. £	U.S. $	Can. $
Gloss	15.00	25.00	25.00

Model No. 3351/D222
BULLDOG

Designer:	Warren Platt	
Height:	5", 12.7 cm	
Colours:	White with tan patches - gloss	
Issued:	1999-2002	

Description	U.K. £	U.S. $	Can. $
Gloss	15.00	25.00	25.00

Note: Used on Commissioned models "Solid Friendship" and "That's My Boy"

Model No. 3375
HOUNDS - Seated

Designer:	Martyn Alcock	
Height:	2 ¼", 5.7 cm	
Colours:	Black, tan and white - gloss	
Issued:	1993-1997	

Description	U.K. £	U.S. $	Can. $
Gloss	15.00	25.00	25.00

Model No. 3376
GOLDEN RETRIEVERS - Seated
Designer: Martyn Alcock
Height: 2", 5.0 cm
Colours: Golden brown - gloss
Issued: 1993-1997

Description	U.K. £	U.S. $	Can. $
Gloss	15.00	25.00	25.00

Model No. 3377
COCKER SPANIEL - Standing
Designer: Amanda Hughes-Lubeck
Height: 3", 7.6 cm
Colours: Golden brown - gloss
Issued: 1993-1997

Description	U.K. £	U.S. $	Can. $
Gloss	15.00	25.00	25.00

Model No. 3378
ALSATIAN - Lying
Designer: Amanda Hughes-Lubeck
Height: 2 ½", 6.4 cm
Colours: Black and cream - gloss
Issued: 1993-2002

Description	U.K. £	U.S. $	Can. $
Gloss	15.00	25.00	25.00

Model No. 3379
BULLDOG - Seated
Designer: Warren Platt
Height: 2 ½", 6.4 cm
Colours: White with pale tan patch - gloss
Issued: 1993-2002

Description	U.K. £	U.S. $	Can. $
Gloss	15.00	25.00	25.00

Note: Used on Commissioned model "That's My Boy"

Model No. 3380
JACK RUSSELL TERRIER - Standing

Designer:	Warren Platt		
Height:	2 ½", 6.4 cm		
Colours:	White with pale brown ears and patches on head - gloss		
Issued:	1993-1997		

Description	U.K. £	U.S. $	Can. $
Gloss	30.00	45.00	45.00

Model No. 3381
RETRIEVER - Walking

Designer:	Warren Platt		
Height:	2", 5.0 cm		
Colours:	Golden brown - gloss		
Issued:	1993-1997		

Description	U.K. £	U.S. $	Can. $
Gloss	15.00	25.00	25.00

Model No. 3382
SCOTTISH TERRIER - Standing

Designer:	Martyn Alcock		
Height:	3", 7.6 cm		
Colours:	Black - gloss		
Issued:	1993-2002		

Description	U.K. £	U.S. $	Can. $
Gloss	15.00	25.00	25.00

Model No. 3383
COCKER SPANIELS - Seated

Designer:	Martyn Alcock		
Height:	2", 5.0 cm		
Colours:	Golden brown - gloss		
Issued:	1993-1997		

Description	U.K. £	U.S. $	Can. $
Gloss	15.00	25.00	25.00

Model No. 3384
BULLDOGS - Seated
Designer: Martyn Alcock
Height: 2 ¼", 5.7 cm
Colours: White with pale tan patches - gloss
Issued: 1994-2002

Description	U.K. £	U.S. $	Can. $
Gloss	15.00	25.00	25.00

Model No. 3385
DALMATIAN - Standing
Designer: Amanda Hughes-Lubeck
Height: 3", 7.6 cm
Colours: White with black spots - gloss
Issued: 1994-1997

Description	U.K. £	U.S. $	Can. $
Gloss	15.00	25.00	25.00

Model No. 3436
CAVALIER KING CHARLES SPANIEL - Seated
Designer: Amanda Hughes-Lubeck
Height: 2 ½", 6.4 cm
Colours: White with golden brown patches - gloss
Issued: 1994-2002

Description	U.K. £	U.S. $	Can. $
Gloss	15.00	25.00	25.00

Model No. 3467
WEST HIGHLAND WHITE TERRIERS - Seated
Designer: Amanda Hughes-Lubeck
Height: 2", 5.0 cm
Colours: White - gloss
Issued: 1994-2002

Description	U.K. £	U.S. $	Can. $
Gloss	20.00	30.00	30.00

Model No. 3468
OLD ENGLISH SHEEPDOGS - Seated
Designer: Warren Platt
Height: 2", 5.0 cm
Colours: Grey and white - gloss
Issued: 1995-2002

Description	U.K. £	U.S. $	Can. $
Gloss	15.00	25.00	25.00

Model No. 3475
BOXERS - One seated, one lying
Designer: Amanda Hughes-Lubeck
Height: 2 ¼", 5.7 cm
Colours: Tan - gloss
Issued: 1995-1998

Description	U.K. £	U.S. $	Can. $
Gloss	15.00	25.00	25.00

Model No. 3490
ROTTWEILERS - One seated, one lying
Designer: Warren Platt
Height: 2", 5.0 cm
Colours: Black and tan - gloss
Issued: 1995-1997

Description	U.K. £	U.S. $	Can. $
Gloss	20.00	30.00	30.00

Model No. D142
GOLDEN RETRIEVER
Designer: Amanda Hughes-Lubeck
Height: 5", 12.7 cm
Colours: Golden brown - gloss
Issued: 1999-2002

Description	U.K. £	U.S. $	Can. $
Gloss	35.00	55.00	55.00

Model No. D145
LABRADOR - standing

Designer:	Warren Platt
Height:	5", 12.7 cm
Colours:	1. Black - gloss
	2. Golden - gloss
Issued:	1999-2002

Colourway	U.K. £	U.S. $	Can. $
1. Black	35.00	55.00	55.00
2. Golden	35.00	55.00	55.00

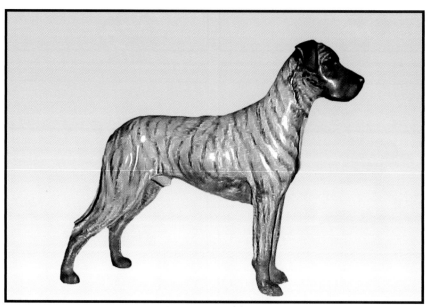

Great Dane, Model 968
Brindle Colourway

Chapter Five

FARM ANIMALS - CATTLE

As the number of Beswick collectors grows dramatically, this particular section of Beswick animals has become more popular. This is mainly due to the accurate reproduction of champion-stock animals, where meticulous attention to detail by the designers and modellers at the Beswick factory, and then Beswick Studio of Royal Doulton, produced some superb models over the years.

This is very noticeable with the Hereford Cattle, since as the breed standard has changed, the models have been updated. Just compare the models of the early Herefords with the ones that followed; they are very different in shape.

It is also interesting to note that when the calves were discontinued in the mid 1970s, with the exception of the Friesian, public pressure brought about their reintroduction ten years later. Although the later models were altered from the originals, they can all live together as one happy family. Thus, for example, Aberdeen Angus Cattle becomes a set of four rather than just three.

As with all models that have had long production periods the cattle will be found, on the lighter coloured models, with various degrees of shading. It may be attributed to changes in glazing application and/or composition. Earlier models are more sought after due to better colouring and definition.

The models of the best-known breeds have survived to the present, but the lesser-known breeds, such as the Galloways, sadly had a short production run and now, as a result, are highly sought after by collectors.

The Connoisseur Range of cattle on polished wooden bases is truly impressive. With a satin matt finish, more detail can generally be achieved than on the gloss models—this, of course, was reflected in the retail price.

In 1992 the Beswick Collectors' Circle commissioned a set of the Friesian Cattle (shape numbers 1439, 1362 and 2690) in a red and white colourway. Known as the "Red Friesian's" the bull, cow and calf were issued in very small numbers of only 129, 130 and 132 respectively. The Beswick Collectors' Circle calf, was the only gloss version of this particular model since it was only produced in a matt finish as part of the Connoisseur series. This set of cattle has continued to increase quite spectacularly in value. A further cattle family was commissioned by the Beswick Collectors' Club in 1998. These were the Limousin bull (shape 2463) cow (3065) and calf (1827) which were issued in edition sizes of 653, 656 and 711). The Beswick Collectors' Club's final commission in 2002 was that of the Rare Breeds series Black Galloway Cow in an edition of 505.

In 2001 Beswick introduced the Rare Breeds Series, which included three new cattle models.

INDEX BY MODEL NUMBER

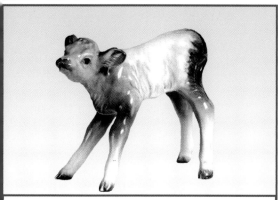

Model No. 854
HEREFORD CALF

Designer: Arthur Gredington
Height: 4 ½", 11.9 cm
Colour: 1. Brown and white - gloss
2. Roan - gloss
3. Blue
Issued: 1940-c.1957

Colourway	U.K. £	U.S. $	Can. $
1. Brown/white	100.00	150.00	150.00
2. Roan	1,000.00	1,500.00	1,500.00
3. Blue	200.00	300.00	300.00

Note: Examples known in grey roan and cream satin.

Model No. 899
HEREFORD COW
First Version - Horns are upright

Designer: Arthur Gredington
Height: 5", 12.7 cm
Colour: Brown and white - gloss
Issued: 1941-1941
Varieties: 948 (Horns point forward)

Colourway	U.K. £	U.S. $	Can. $
Brown/white	500.00	750.00	750.00

Note: Model no. 899 was remodelled in 1941 and became model no. 948.

Model No. 901A
HEREFORD CALF
First Version - Mouth open

Designer: Arthur Gredington
Height: 4", 10.1 cm
Colour: 1. Roan and white - gloss
2. Tan and white - gloss
Issued: 1940-Unknown
Varieties: 901B (mouth closed)

Colourway	U.K. £	U.S. $	Can. $
1. Roan/white	1,000.00	1,500.00	1,500.00
2. Tan/white	400.00	600.00	600.00

Model No. 901B
HEREFORD CALF
Second Version - Mouth closed

Designer: Arthur Gredington
Height: 3 ¾", 9.5 cm
Colour: See below - gloss
Issued: Unknown-c.1957
Varieties: 901A (mouth open)

Colourway	U.K. £	U.S. $	Can. $
1. Brown/white	90.00	150.00	150.00
2. Roan/white	750.00	1,150.00	1,150.00
3. White		Rare	

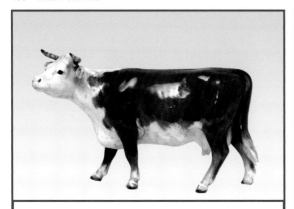

Model No. 948
HEREFORD COW
Second Version - Horns point forward

Designer: Arthur Gredington
Height: 5", 12.7 cm
Colour: 1.   Brown and white - gloss
             2.   Roan and white - gloss
Issued: 1941-c.1957
Varieties: 899 (horns are upright)

Colourway	U.K. £	U.S. $	Can. $
1. Brown/white	350.00	550.00	550.00
2. Roan/white	2,500.00	3,750.00	3,750.00

Model No. 949
HEREFORD BULL

Designer: Arthur Gredington
Height: 5 ¾", 14.6 cm
Colour: Brown and white - gloss
Issued: 1941-c.1957

Colourway	U.K. £	U.S. $	Can. $
Brown/white	200.00	300.00	300.00

Note: Colourways exists in roan and red.

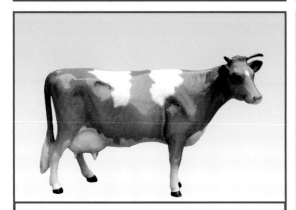

Model No. 1248A
GUERNSEY COW
First Version - Horns and ears separate

Designer: Arthur Gredington
Height: 4 ¼", 10.8 cm
Colour: Golden brown and white - gloss
Issued: 1952-1953
Varieties: 1248B (Horns and ears moulded together)

Colourway	U.K. £	U.S. $	Can. $
Golden Brown	175.00	275.00	275.00

Note: Modelled from the Standard of the Guernsey Cattle
Society.

Model No. 1248B
GUERNSEY COW
Second Version - Horns and ears are moulded together

Designer: Arthur Gredington
Height: 4 ¼", 10.8 cm
Colour: Golden brown and white - gloss or matt
Issued: 1.   Gloss - 1953-1989
             2.   Matt - 1985-1989
Varieties: 1248A (Horns and ears separate)

Description	U.K. £	U.S. $	Can. $
1. Gloss	125.00	200.00	200.00
2. Matt	250.00	375.00	375.00

Model No. 1248B/1249A
GUERNSEY COW AND CALF - on wooden plinth

Designer:	Arthur Gredington
Height:	4 ¼", 10.8 cm
Colour:	Golden brown and white - matt
Issued:	c.1988

Description	U.K. £	U.S. $	Can. $
Matt	400.00	600.00	600.00

Note: Cow is no. 1248B; Calf is no. 1249A. Issued as a special commission for the Guernsey Cattle Society c.1988

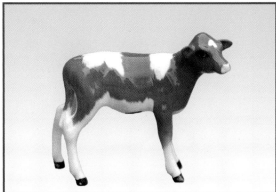

Model No. 1249A
GUERNSEY CALF

Designer:	Arthur Gredington
Height:	2 ¾", 7.0 cm
Colour:	Golden brown and white - gloss or matt
Issued:	1. Gloss - 1952-1975
	2. Matt - 1987-1989
Reissued:	3. Gloss - 1985-1989

Description	U.K. £	U.S. $	Can. $
1. Gloss	95.00	150.00	150.00
2. Matt	275.00	425.00	425.00
3. Gloss reissued	60.00	90.00	90.00

Model No. 1249B
AYRSHIRE CALF

Designer:	Arthur Gredington
Height:	2 ¾", 7.0 cm
Colour:	Brown and white - gloss or matt
Modelled:	1952
Issued:	1. Gloss - 1956-1975
	2. Matt - 1987-1989
Reissued:	3. Gloss - 1985-1990

Description	U.K. £	U.S. $	Can. $
1. Gloss	100.00	150.00	150.00
2. Matt	300.00	450.00	450.00
3. Gloss reissued	75.00	115.00	115.00

Model No. 1249C
FRIESIAN CALF

Designer:	Arthur Gredington
Height:	2 ¾", 7.0 cm
Colour:	Black and white - gloss or matt
Modelled:	1952
Issued:	1. Gloss - 1956-1997
	2. Matt - 1987-1989

Description	U.K. £	U.S. $	Can. $
1. Gloss	60.00	90.00	90.00
2. Matt	400.00	600.00	600.00

Note: This model was produced in red and white matt in 1992 for a Netherlands wholesaler.

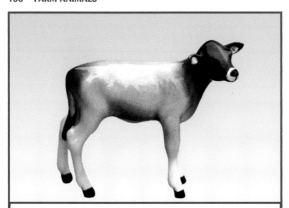

Model No. 1249D
JERSEY CALF

Designer: Arthur Gredington
Height: 2 ¾", 6.4 cm
Colour: Light brown with shading darker
             around the head - gloss or matt
Issued: 1. 1956-1975
             2. 1987-1989
Reissued: 3. 1985-1997

Description	U.K. £	U.S. $	Can. $
1. Gloss	60.00	90.00	90.00
2 Matt	225.00	350.00	350.00
3. Gloss reissued	60.00	90.00	90.00

Model No. 1249E
HEREFORD CALF

Designer: Arthur Gredington
Height: 2 ¾", 7.0 cm
Colour: Brown and white - gloss
Modelled: 1952
Issued: This model was especially commissioned,
             sometime between 1975 and 1985, when
             the only calf in production was the
             Friesian.

Description	U.K. £	U.S. $	Can. $
Brown/white	250.00	375.00	375.00

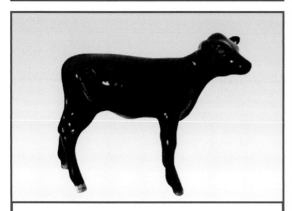

Model No. 1249F
ABERDEEN ANGUS CALF

Designer: Arthur Gredington
Height: 2 ¾", 7.0 cm
Colour: Black - gloss
Modelled: 1952
Issued: Unknown

Description	U.K. £	U.S. $	Can. $
Black	700.00	1,050.00	1,050.00

Model No. 1345
JERSEY COW CH. "NEWTON TINKLE"

Designer: Arthur Gredington
Height: 4 ¼", 10.8 cm
Colour: Light brown with shading darker
             around the head - gloss or matt
Issued: 1.   Gloss - 1954-1997
             2.   Matt - 1985-1989

Description	U.K. £	U.S. $	Can. $
1. Gloss	100.00	150.00	150.00
2. Matt	250.00	375.00	375.00

Model No. 1345/1249D
JERSEY COW AND CALF - on wooden plinth

Designer:	Arthur Gredington	
Height:	5 ¼", 13.3 cm	
Colour:	Light brown with shading especially around the head - gloss	
Issued:	1993-1996	
Series:	Plinthed Animals	

Description	U.K. £	U.S. $	Can. $
Light Brown	175.00	275.00	275.00

Note: Cow is no. 1345; Calf is no. 1249D.

Model No. 1350
AYRSHIRE COW CH. "ICKHAM BESSIE"

Designer:	Arthur Gredington	
Height:	5", 12.7 cm	
Colour:	Brown and white - gloss or matt	
Issued:	1. Gloss - 1954-1990	
	2. Matt - 1985-1989	

Description	U.K. £	U.S. $	Can. $
1. Gloss	150.00	225.00	225.00
2. Matt	300.00	450.00	450.00

Model No. 1360
HEREFORD COW

Designer:	Arthur Gredington	
Height:	4 ¼", 10.8 cm	
Colour:	Brown and white - gloss or matt	
Issued:	1. Gloss - 1954-1997	
	2. Matt - 1985-1989	

Description	U.K. £	U.S. $	Can. $
1. Gloss	100.00	150.00	150.00
2. Matt	175.00	275.00	275.00

Note: Modelled from the standard of the Hereford Cattle Society. Polled Hereford cows could have been supplied between 1965 and 1970.

Model No. 1360/1827C
HEREFORD COW AND CALF - on wooden plinth

Designer:	Graham Tongue	
Height:	7", 17.8 cm	
Colour:	Brown and white - gloss	
Issued:	1993-1996	
Series:	Plinthed Animals	

Description	U.K. £	U.S. $	Can. $
Gloss	175.00	275.00	275.00

Note: Cow is no. 1360; Calf is no. 1827C.

Model No. 1362A
FRIESIAN COW CH. "CLAYBURY LEEGWATER"

Designer:	Arthur Gredington
Height:	4 ½", 11.9 cm
Colour:	Black and white - gloss or matt
Issued:	1. Gloss - 1954-1997
	2. Matt - 1985-1989
Varieties:	1362B

Description	U.K. £	U.S. $	Can. $
1. Gloss	85.00	125.00	125.00
2. Matt	225.00	350.00	350.00

Note: This model was produced in red and white matt in 1992 for a Netherlands wholesaler.

Model No. 1362B
RED FRIESIAN COW

Designer:	Arthur Gredington
Height:	4 ½", 11.9 cm
Colour:	Red and white - gloss or matt
Modelled:	1954
Issued:	1992 in an edition of 130
Varieties:	1362A

Colourway	U.K. £	U.S. $	Can. $
1. Gloss	750.00	1,150.00	1,150.00
2. Matt	950.00	1,475.00	1,475.00

Note: Gloss produced for the Beswick Collectors Circle with special B.C.C. and Beswick backstamps.

Model No. 1362/1249C
FRIESIAN COW AND CALF - on wooden plinth

Designer:	Graham Tongue
Height:	5 ½", 14.0 cm
Colour:	Black and white - gloss
Issued:	1993-1996
Series:	Plinthed Animals

Colourway	U.K. £	U.S. $	Can. $
Black/white	225.00	350.00	350.00

Note: Cow is no. 1362; Calf is no. 1249C.

Model No. 1363A
HEREFORD BULL
First Version - Horns protrude from ears

Designer:	Arthur Gredington
Height:	4 ½", 10.8 cm
Colour:	Brown and white - gloss or matt
Issued:	1. Gloss - 1955-unknown
	2. Matt - 1985-unknown

Description	U.K. £	U.S. $	Can. $
1. Gloss	125.00	200.00	200.00
2. Matt	275.00	425.00	425.00

Note: Polled Hereford cows could have been supplied between 1965 and 1970. A red colourway exists.

Model No. 1363B
HEREFORD BULL
Second Version - Horns flush to ears

Designer:	Arthur Gredington
Height:	4 ½", 10.8 cm
Colour:	Brown and white - gloss or matt
Issued:	1. Gloss - Unknown-1997
	2. Matt - 1985-1989

Description	U.K. £	U.S. $	Can. $
1. Gloss	75.00	115.00	115.00
2. Matt	200.00	300.00	300.00

Note: Modelled from the standard of the Hereford Cattle Society. This model has also appeared as a money-box.

Model No. 1363C
HEREFORD BULL - on wooden plinth

Designer:	Arthur Gredington
Height:	5 ½", 14.0 cm
Colour:	Brown and white - satin matt
Modelled:	1955
Issued:	1968-1975
Series:	Connoisseur

Description	U.K. £	U.S. $	Can. $
Satin Matt	160.00	250.00	250.00

Note: Issued on a teak stand. The base was changed to polished wood in 1974. Polled Hereford bulls could have been supplied between 1965 and 1971.

Model No. 1406A
ABERDEEN ANGUS CALF

Designer:	Arthur Gredington
Height:	3", 7.6 cm
Colour:	Black - gloss
Issued:	1956-1975

Colourway	U.K. £	U.S. $	Can. $
Black	275.00	425.00	425.00

Note: Examples of model 1406 are known painted as a Belted Galloway Calf.

Model No. 1406B
HEREFORD CALF

Designer:	Arthur Gredington
Height:	3", 7.6 cm
Colour:	Brown and white - gloss
Issued:	1956-1975

Colourway	U.K. £	U.S. $	Can. $
Brown/white	95.00	150.00	150.00

Model No. 1406C
DAIRY SHORTHORN CALF
Designer: Arthur Gredington
Height: 3", 7.6 cm
Colour: Brown and white with shading - gloss
Issued: 1956-1973

Colourway	U.K. £	U.S. $	Can. $
Brown/white	425.00	650.00	650.00

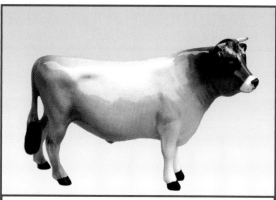

Model No. 1422
JERSEY BULL CH. "DUNSLEY COY BOY"
Designer: Arthur Gredington
Height: 4 ½", 11.9 cm
Colour: Light brown with shading and
              darker head - gloss or matt
Issued   1.   Gloss - 1956-1997
              2.   Matt - 1985-1989

Description	U.K. £	U.S. $	Can. $
1. Gloss	125.00	200.00	200.00
2. Matt	225.00	350.00	350.00

Model No. 1439A
FRIESIAN BULL CH. "CODDINGTON HILT BAR"
Designer: Arthur Gredington
Height: 4 ¾", 12.1 cm
Colour: Black and white - gloss or matt
Issued: 1.   Gloss - 1956-1997
              2.   Matt - 1985-1989

Description	U.K. £	U.S. $	Can. $
1. Gloss	80.00	125.00	125.00
2. Matt	175.00	275.00	275.00

Note: This model was produced in red and white matt in
        1992 for a Netherlands wholesaler, (£1500.00).

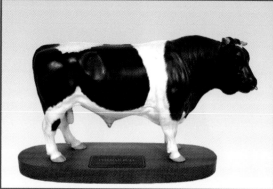

Model No. 1439B
FRIESIAN BULL - on teak plinth
Designer: Arthur Gredington
Height: 5 ½", 14.0 cm
Colour: Black and white - satin matt
Modelled: 1956
Issued: 1968-1973
Varieties: 1439A
Series: Connoisseur Cattle

Description	U.K. £	U.S. $	Can. $
Satin matt	125.00	200.00	200.00

Model No. 1439C
RED FRIESIAN BULL

Designer:	Arthur Gredington
Height:	4 ¾", 12.1 cm
Colour:	Red and white - gloss
Modelled:	1956
Issued:	1992 in an edition of 129

Description	U.K. £	U.S. $	Can. $
Gloss	1,000.00	1,500.00	1,500.00

Note: Produced for the Beswick Collectors Circle with special B.C.C. and Beswick backstamps.

Model No. 1451
GUERNSEY BULL
CH. "SABRINA'S SIR RICHMOND 14th"

Designer:	Colin Melbourne
Height:	4 ¾", 11.9 cm
Colour:	Tan/brown and white - gloss or matt
Issued:	1. Gloss - 1956-1989
	2. Matt - 1985-1989

Description	U.K. £	U.S. $	Can. $
1. Gloss	150.00	225.00	225.00
2. Matt	275.00	425.00	425.00

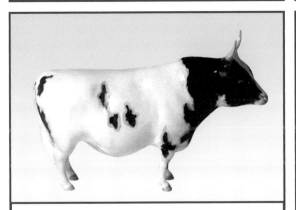

Model No. 1454A
AYRSHIRE BULL CH. "WHITEHILL MANDATE"
First Version - Thin legs, narrow tail

Designer:	Colin Melbourne
Height:	5 ¼", 13.3 cm
Colour:	Brown and white with shading - gloss
Issued:	1956-1957

Colourway	U.K. £	U.S. $	Can. $
Brown/white	1,200.00	1,850.00	1,850.00

Note: The First Version was modelled with noticeably thinner legs and a narrow tail.

Model No. 1454B
AYRSHIRE BULL CH. "WHITEHILL MANDATE"
Second Version - Thick legs and tail

Designer:	Colin Melbourne
Height:	5 ¼", 13.3 cm
Colour:	Brown, white and shaded - gloss or matt
Issued:	1. Gloss - 1957-1990
	2. Matt - 1985-1989

Description	U.K. £	U.S. $	Can. $
1. Gloss	200.00	300.00	300.00
2. Matt	200.00	300.00	300.00

Model No. 1504
DAIRY SHORTHORN BULL
CH. "GWERSYLT LORD OXFORD 74th"

Designer:	Arthur Gredington
Height:	5", 12.7 cm
Colour:	Brown and white with shading - gloss
Issued:	1957-1973

Colourway	U.K. £	U.S. $	Can. $
Brown/white	550.00	850.00	850.00

Model No. 1510
DAIRY SHORTHORN COW
CH. "EATON WILD EYES 91 ST"

Designer:	Arthur Gredington
Height:	4 ¾", 12.1 cm
Colour:	Brown and white with shading - gloss
Issued:	1957-1973

Description	U.K. £	U.S. $	Can. $
Gloss	750.00	1,150.00	1,150.00

Model No. 1562
ABERDEEN ANGUS BULL

Designer:	Arthur Gredington
Height:	4 ½", 11.9 cm
Colour:	Black - gloss or matt
Issued:	1. Gloss - 1958-1989
	2. Matt - 1985-1989

Description	U.K. £	U.S. $	Can. $
1. Gloss	100.00	150.00	150.00
2. Matt	225.00	350.00	350.00

Note: This model was approved by the Breed Society.

Model No. 1563
ABERDEEN ANGUS COW

Designer:	Arthur Gredington
Height:	4 ¼", 10.8 cm
Colour:	Black - gloss or matt
Issued:	1. Gloss - 1959-1989
	2. Matt - 1985-1989

Description	U.K. £	U.S. $	Can. $
1. Gloss	150.00	225.00	225.00
2. Matt	250.00	375.00	375.00

Note: This model was approved by the Breed Society.

Model No. 1740
HIGHLAND COW

Designer: Arthur Gredington
Height: 5 ¼", 3.3 cm
Colour: Tan and brown - gloss or matt
Issued: 1.   Gloss - 1961-1990
            2.   Matt - 1985-1989

Description	U.K. £	U.S. $	Can. $
1. Gloss	150.00	225.00	225.00
2. Matt	375.00	575.00	575.00

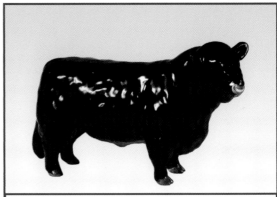

Model No. 1746A
GALLOWAY BULL

Designer: Arthur Gredington
Height: 4 ½", 11.9 cm
Colour: Black - gloss
Modelled: 1961
Issued: 1962-1969
Varieties: 1746B, 1746C

Colourway	U.K. £	U.S. $	Can. $
Black	1,800.00	2,750.00	2,750.00

Model No. 1746B
GALLOWAY BULL - BELTED

Designer: Arthur Gredington
Height: 4 ½", 11.9 cm
Colour: Black and white - gloss
Modelled: 1961
Issued: 1963-1969
Varieties: 1746A, 1746C

Colourway	U.K. £	U.S. $	Can. $
Black/white	2,000.00	3,000.00	3,000.00

Model No. 1746C
GALLOWAY BULL - SILVER DUNN

Designer: Arthur Gredington
Height: 4 ½", 11.9 cm
Colour: Fawn and brown - gloss
Modelled: 1961
Issued: 1962-1969
Varieties: 1746A, 1746B

Colourway	U.K. £	U.S. $	Can. $
Fawn/brown	1,500.00	2,250.00	2,250.00

Model No. 1827A
ABERDEEN ANGUS CALF

Designer: Arthur Gredington
Height: 3", 7.6 cm
Colour: Black - gloss or matt
Issued: 1.   Gloss - 1985-1989
             2.   Matt - 1987-1989

Description	U.K. £	U.S. $	Can. $
1. Gloss	200.00	300.00	300.00
2. Matt	200.00	300.00	300.00

Model No. 1827B
CHAROLAIS CALF

Designer: Arthur Gredington
Height: 3", 7.6 cm
Colour: Cream - gloss or matt
Issued: 1.   Gloss - 1985-1997
             2.   Matt - 1987-1989

Description	U.K. £	U.S. $	Can. $
1. Gloss	85.00	130.00	130.00
2. Matt	200.00	300.00	300.00

Model No. 1827C
HEREFORD CALF

Designer: Arthur Gredington
Height: 3", 7.6 cm
Colour: Brown and white - gloss or matt
Issued: 1.   Gloss - 1985-1997
             2.   Matt - 1987-1989

Description	U.K. £	U.S. $	Can. $
1. Gloss	70.00	100.00	100.00
2. Matt	250.00	375.00	375.00

Model No. 1827D
HIGHLAND CALF

Designer: Arthur Gredington
Height: 3", 7.6 cm
Colour: Tan and brown - gloss or matt
Issued: 1.   Gloss - 1962-1990
             2.   Matt - 1987-1989

Description	U.K. £	U.S. $	Can. $
1. Gloss	50.00	75.00	75.00
2. Matt	200.00	300.00	300.00

Model No. 1827E
LIMOUSIN CALF

Designer: Arthur Gredington
Height: 3", 7.6 cm
Colour: Brown and white - gloss
Issued: 1998 in a limited edition of 711

Description	U.K. £	U.S. $	Can. $
Gloss	250.00	375.00	375.00

Note: Special colourway produced for The Beswick
       Collectors Club. The B.C.C. backstamp appears
       in addition to the normal Beswick backstamp.

Model No. 2008
HIGHLAND BULL

Designer: Arthur Gredington
Height: 5", 12.7 cm
Colour: Tan/brown - gloss or matt
Issued: 1. Gloss - 1965-1990
           2. Matt - 1985-1989

Description	U.K. £	U.S. $	Can. $
1. Gloss	150.00	225.00	225.00
2. Matt	200.00	300.00	300.00

Model No. 2463A
CHAROLAIS BULL

Designer: Alan Maslankowski
Height: 5", 12.7 cm
Colour: Cream - gloss or matt
Modelled: 1973
Issued: 1. Gloss - 1979-1997
           2. Matt - 1985-1989

Description	U.K. £	U.S. $	Can. $
1. Gloss	130.00	200.00	200.00
2. Matt	275.00	425.00	425.00

Model No. 2463B
LIMOUSIN BULL

Designer: Alan Maslankowski
Height: 5", 12.7 cm
Colour: Brown and white - gloss
Issued: 1998 in a limited edition of 653

Description	U.K. £	U.S. $	Can. $
Gloss	275.00	425.00	425.00

Note: Special colourway produced for The Beswick
       Collectors Club. The B.C.C. backstamp appears
       in addition to the normal Beswick backstamp.

Model No. A2463A
CHAROLAIS BULL - on wooden plinth

Designer: Alan Maslankowski
Height: 5 ½", 14.0 cm
Colour: Cream - satin matt
Modelled: 1973
Issued: 1975-1979
Series: Connoisseur Cattle

Description	U.K. £	U.S. $	Can. $
Satin matt	130.00	200.00	200.00

Model No. A2542A
HEREFORD BULL - on wooden plinth

Designer: Graham Tongue
Height: 7 ½", 19.1 cm
Colour: Brown and white - satin matt
Modelled: 1975
Issued: 1976-1989
Series: Connoisseur

Description	U.K. £	U.S. $	Can. $
Satin matt	150.00	225.00	225.00

Model No. A2542B
HEREFORD BULL - on ceramic plinth

Designer: Graham Tongue
Height: 7 ½", 19.1 cm
Colour: Bronze, black shading - satin
Modelled: 1975
Issued: 1989-1992
Series: Britannia Collection

Description	U.K.£	U.S.$	Can.$
Satin	225.00	325.00	325.00

Model No. 2549A
POLLED HEREFORD BULL

Designer: Graham Tongue
Height: 5", 12.7 cm
Colour: Brown, white ringed nose - gloss or matt
Modelled: 1975
Issued: 1. Gloss – 1977-1997
         2. Matt – 1985-1989

Description	U.K. £	U.S. $	Can. $
1. Gloss	125.00	190.00	190.00
2. Matt	275.00	425.00	425.00

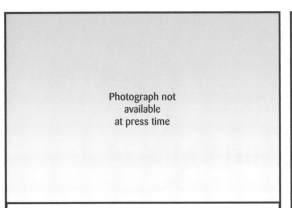

Photograph not
available
at press time

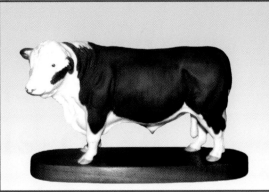

Model 2549B
POLLED HEREFORD BULL- on ceramic base

Designer:	Graham Tongue
Height:	5", 12.7 cm
Colour:	Bronze, black shading - satin
Modelled:	1975
Issued:	1989-1992
Series:	Britannia Collection

Colourway	U.K.£	U.S.$	Can.$
Bronze/black	250.00	375.00	375.00

Model No. A2574
POLLED HEREFORD BULL - on wooden plinth

Designer:	Graham Tongue
Height:	7 ½", 19.1 cm
Colour:	Brown and white - satin matt
Modelled:	1976
Issued:	1977-1989
Series:	Connoisseur

Description	U.K. £	U.S. $	Can. $
Satin matt	150.00	225.00	225.00

Model No. A2580
FRIESIAN BULL - on wooden plinth

Designer:	Graham Tongue
Height:	7 ½", 19.1 cm
Colour:	Black and white - satin matt
Modelled:	1976
Issued:	1978-1989
Series:	Connoisseur Cattle

Description	U.K. £	U.S. $	Can. $
Satin matt	175.00	275.00	275.00

Model No. A2600
CHAROLAIS BULL - on wooden plinth

Designer:	Graham Tongue
Height:	7 ½", 19.1 cm
Colour:	Cream - satin matt
Issued:	1971-1979
Series:	Connoisseur

Description	U.K. £	U.S. $	Can. $
Satin matt	175.00	275.00	275.00

Model No. A2607
FRIESIAN COW - on wooden plinth

Designer:	Graham Tongue
Height:	7 ½", 19.1 cm
Colour:	Black and white - satin matt
Modelled:	1977
Issued:	1979-1989
Series:	Connoisseur

Description	U.K. £	U.S. $	Can. $
Satin matt	175.00	275.00	275.00

Model No. A2607/2690
FRIESIAN COW AND CALF - on wooden plinth

Designer:	Graham Tongue
Height:	6 ½", 16.5 cm
Colour:	Black and white - satin matt
Modelled:	Cow - 1977; Calf - 1982
Issued:	1982-1989
Series:	Connoisseur

Description	U.K. £	U.S. $	Can. $
Satin matt	300.00	450.00	450.00

Note: Cow is no. A2607; Calf is no. 2690.

Model No. A2648/2652
CHAROLAIS COW AND CALF - on wooden plinth

Designer:	Graham Tongue
Height:	7 ¼", 18.4 cm
Colour:	Cream - satin matt
Modelled:	1979
Issued:	1981-1989
Series:	Connoisseur

Description	U.K. £	U.S. $	Can. $
Satin matt	225.00	350.00	350.00

Note: Cow is no. A2648; Calf is no. 2652 which was never issued individually.

Model No. A2667/2669
HEREFORD COW AND CALF - on wooden plinth

Designer:	Graham Tongue
Height:	7", 17.8 cm
Colour:	Brown and white - satin matt
Modelled:	1980
Issued:	1981-1989
Series:	Connoisseur

Description	U.K. £	U.S. $	Can. $
Satin matt	225.00	350.00	350.00

Note: Cow is no. A2667; Calf is no. 2669, which was never issued individually.

Model No. 2690
RED FRIESIAN CALF

Designer: Graham Tongue
Height: 2 ¼", 5.7 cm
Colour: Red and white - gloss
Modelled: 1980
Issued: 1992 in a special edition of 132

Description	U.K. £	U.S. $	Can. $
Gloss	600.00	900.00	900.00

Note: Produced as a free standing model, in this special
colourway for The Beswick Collectors Circle. The
B.C.C. backstamp appears in addition to the normal
Beswick Backstamp.

Model No. 3075A
CHAROLAIS COW

Designer: Unknown
Height: 5", 12.7 cm
Colour: Cream - gloss or matt
Modelled: 1987
Issued: 1.   Gloss - 1988-1997
             2.   Matt - 1988-1989

Description	U.K. £	U.S. $	Can. $
1. Gloss	200.00	300.00	300.00
2. Matt	300.00	450.00	450.00

Model No. 3075B
LIMOUSIN COW

Designer: Unknown
Height: 5", 12.7 cm
Colour: Brown and white - gloss
Issued: 1998 in a limited edition of 656

Description	U.K. £	U.S. $	Can. $
Gloss	275.00	425.00	425.00

Note: Special colourway produced for The Beswick
Collectors Club.The B.C.C. backstamp appears in
addition to the normal Beswick backstamp.

Model No. 3075A/1827B
CHAROLAIS COW AND CALF - on wooden plinth

Designer: 3075 - Unknown
             1827B - Arthur Gredington
Height: 6", 15.0 cm
Colour: Cream - gloss
Issued: 1993-1996

Description	U.K. £	U.S. $	Can. $
Gloss	175.00	275.00	275.00

Note: Cow is no. 3075A; Calf is no. 1827B.

Model No. 4111
RED POLL COW

Designer:	Robert Donaldson
Length:	6 ¼", 15.9 cm
Colour:	Red - gloss
Issued:	2001-2002
Series:	Rare Breeds

Description	U.K. £	U.S. $	Can. $
Gloss	80.00	120.00	120.00

Model No. 4112
SHETLAND COW

Designer:	Robert Donaldson
Length:	5 ¼", 13.3 cm
Colour:	Black and white - gloss
Issued:	2001-2002
Series:	Rare Breeds

Description	U.K. £	U.S. $	Can. $
Gloss	100.00	150.00	150.00

Model No. 4113A
BELTED GALLOWAY COW

Designer:	Robert Donaldson
Length:	5 ¼", 13.3 cm
Colour:	Black and white - gloss
Issued:	2001-2002
Series:	Rare Breeds

Description	U.K. £	U.S. $	Can. $
Gloss	100.00	150.00	150.00

Model No. 4113B
BLACK GALLOWAY COW

Designer:	Robert Donaldson
Length:	5 ¼", 13.3 cm
Colour:	Black - gloss
Issued:	2002 only
Series:	Rare Breeds

Description	U.K. £	U.S. $	Can. $
Gloss	300.00	450.00	450.00

Note: Produced for the Beswick Collectors Club in 2002 in a limited edition of 505.

FARM ANIMALS

OTHERS

With the exception of the earlier models, the majority of the animals in this group are realistically portrayed. Examples of this are the goat and kid, which make a delightful pair, and the donkeys, as popular now as they ever were.

In 2001, Beswick finally introduced a Rare Breeds Series for other animals usually found on a farm besides cattle. Seven new models were introduced.

A rather interesting if somewhat strange version of the donkey (shape number 2267) model has been found. This is known as the "worst footballer" donkey. Apparently two factory managers, who both managed local football teams were given permission for this model to be specially decorated wearing a footballer's strip and fixed to a base together with a football. This was presented to the "worst" player in each team! However the recipients are probably having the last laugh as these donkeys are very rare with no more than 14 produced in total. They were produced annually, one model for each of the two teams, for about six years during the late 1990s. To date two variations have been found – one in a black and white striped shirt and black shorts and one in a yellow with green patches shirt with green shorts.

INDEX BY MODEL NUMBER

Model No. 323
LAMB ON BASE

Designer:	Miss Greaves
Height:	7 ½", 19.1 cm
Colour:	1. Blue - gloss
	2. Cream - satin matt
	3. Natural - satin matt
Issued:	c.1935-by 1954

Colourway	U.K. £	U.S. $	Can. $
1. Blue	45.00	70.00	70.00
2. Cream	40.00	60.00	60.00
3. Natural	65.00	100.00	100.00

Note: Modelled in Deco style.

Model No. 369
DONKEY

Designer:	Miss Greaves
Height:	8", 20.3 cm
Colour:	1. Blue - gloss
	2. Cream - satin matt
	3. Natural - satin matt
Issued:	1936-by 1954

Colourway	U.K. £	U.S. $	Can. $
1. Blue	45.00	70.00	70.00
2. Cream	40.00	60.00	60.00
3. Natural	65.00	100.00	100.00

Note: Modelled in Deco style.

Model No. 398
GOAT

Designer:	Mr. Owen
Height:	4 ½", 11.9 cm
Colour:	See below
Issued:	1936-by 1954

Colourway	U.K. £	U.S. $	Can. $
1. Blue - gloss	20.00	30.00	30.00
2. Green - satin matt	20.00	30.00	30.00
3. Natural - satin matt	20.00	30.00	30.00
4. White - satin matt	15.00	25.00	25.00

Model No. 832
PIG

Designer:	Arthur Gredington
Height:	3 ¾", 9.5 cm
Colour:	White and pink with grey patches - gloss
Issued:	1940-1971
Set:	833, 834

Colourway	U.K. £	U.S. $	Can. $
White	20.00	30.00	30.00

Note: Also exists as a money box.

Model No. 833
PIGLET - Running

Designer:	Arthur Gredington	
Height:	1 ¾", 4.5 cm	
Colour:	White and pink with grey patches - gloss	
Issued:	1940-1971	
Set:	832, 834	

Colourway	U.K. £	U.S. $	Can. $
White	15.00	25.00	25.00

Model No. 834
PIGLET - Trotting

Designer:	Arthur Gredington	
Height:	1 ½", 3.8 cm	
Colour:	White and pink with grey patches - gloss	
Issued:	1940-1971	
Set:	832, 833	

Colourway	U.K. £	U.S. $	Can. $
White	15.00	25.00	25.00

Photograph not available.
Model number 897 possibly
not put into production.

Model No. 897
DONKEY FOAL

Designer:	Arthur Gredington	
Height:	Unknown	
Colour:	Natural - gloss	
Issued:	1941-Unknown	

Description	U.K. £	U.S. $	Can. $
Gloss		Probably not put into production	

Note: Similar to model no. 950.

Model No. 935
SHEEP

Designer:	Arthur Gredington	
Height:	3 ½", 8.9 cm	
Colour:	White - gloss	
Issued:	1941-1971	
Set:	936, 937, 938	

Colourway	U.K. £	U.S. $	Can. $
White	30.00	45.00	45.00

Model No. 936
LAMB

Designer:	Arthur Gredington		
Height:	3 ¼", 8.3 cm		
Colour:	White - gloss		
Issued:	1941-1971		
Set:	935, 937, 938		

Colourway	U.K. £	U.S. $	Can. $
White	20.00	30.00	30.00

Model No. 937
LAMB

Designer:	Arthur Gredington		
Height:	2", 5.0 cm		
Colour:	White - gloss		
Issued:	1941-1971		
Set:	935, 936, 938		

Colourway	U.K. £	U.S. $	Can. $
White	20.00	30.00	30.00

Model No. 938
LAMB

Designer:	Arthur Gredington		
Height:	2", 5.0 cm		
Colour:	White - gloss		
Issued:	1941-1971		
Set:	935, 936, 937		

Colourway	U.K. £	U.S. $	Can. $
White	20.00	30.00	30.00

Model No. 950
DONKEY FOAL

Designer:	Arthur Gredington		
Height:	5", 12.7 cm		
Colour:	Grey-brown - gloss		
Issued:	1941-1962		

Colourway	U.K. £	U.S. $	Can. $
Grey-brown	100.00	150.00	150.00

Model No. 1035
GOAT

Designer:	Arthur Gredington		
Height:	5 ½", 14.0 cm		
Colour:	Tan - gloss		
Issued:	1945-1971		
Set:	1036		

Colourway	U.K. £	U.S. $	Can. $
Tan	95.00	150.00	150.00

Model No. 1036
KID

Designer:	Arthur Gredington		
Height:	2 ½", 6.4 cm		
Colour:	Tan - gloss		
Issued:	1945-1971		
Set:	1035		

Colourway	U.K. £	U.S. $	Can. $
Tan	55.00	85.00	85.00

Model No. 1364A
DONKEY
First Version - Tail free from hind leg

Designer:	Mr. Orwell
Height:	4 ½", 11.9 cm
Colour:	Natural brown - gloss
Issued:	Jan. 1955- Oct. 1955

Colourway	U.K. £	U.S. $	Can. $
Brown	Probably not put into production.		

Model No. 1364B
DONKEY
Second Version - Tail attached to hind leg

Designer:	Mr. Orwell	
Height:	4 ½", 11.9 cm	
Colour:	Natural - gloss or matt	
Issued:	1. Gloss - Oct. 1955-2002	
	2. Matt - 1987-1989	

Description	U.K. £	U.S. $	Can. $
1. Gloss	25.00	40.00	40.00
2. Matt	25.00	40.00	40.00

Model No. 1452A
SOW Ch. "WALL QUEEN 40th"
Designer:	Arthur Gredington
Height:	2 ¾", 7.0 cm
Colour:	White - gloss or matt
Issued:	1. Gloss - 1956-1998
	2. Matt - 1987-1989

Description	U.K. £	U.S. $	Can. $
1. Gloss	25.00	40.00	40.00
2. Matt	30.00	45.00	45.00

Model No. 1452B
SOW - on wooden plinth
Designer:	Arthur Gredington
Height:	3 ¾", 9.5 cm
Colour:	White - gloss
Issued:	1993-1995

Colourway	U.K. £	U.S. $	Can. $
White	55.00	85.00	85.00

Model No. 1453A
BOAR Ch. "WALL CHAMPION BOY 53rd"
Designer:	Arthur Gredington
Height:	2 ¾", 7.0 cm
Colour:	White - gloss or matt
Issued:	1. Gloss - 1956-1998
	2. Matt - 1987-1989

Description	U.K. £	U.S. $	Can. $
1. Gloss	30.00	45.00	45.00
2. Matt	35.00	50.00	50.00

Model No. 1453B
BOAR - on wooden plinth
Designer:	Arthur Gredington
Height:	3 ¾", 9.5 cm
Colour:	White - gloss
Issued:	1993 -1995

Colourway	U.K. £	U.S. $	Can. $
White	55.00	85.00	85.00

Model No. 1511
WESSEX SADDLEBACK SOW "MERRYWOOD SILVER WINGS 56th"

Designer:	Colin Melbourne
Height:	2 ¾", 7.0 cm
Colour:	Black and white - gloss
Issued:	1957-1969
Set:	1512

Colourway	U.K. £	U.S. $	Can. $
Black/white	425.00	650.00	650.00

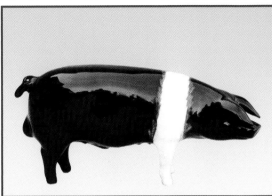

Model No. 1512
WESSEX SADDLEBACK BOAR "FARACRE VISCOUNT 3rd"

Designer:	Colin Melbourne
Height:	2 ¾", 7.0 cm
Colour:	Black and white - gloss
Issued:	1957-1969
Set:	1511

Colourway	U.K. £	U.S. $	Can. $
Black/white	425.00	650.00	650.00

Model No. 1765
BLACK-FACED SHEEP

Designer:	Mr. Garbet
Height:	3 ¼", 8.3 cm
Colour:	Black and white - gloss or matt
Modelled:	1961
Issued:	1. Gloss - 1963-2002
	2. Matt - 1987-1989
Set:	1828

Description	U.K. £	U.S. $	Can. $
1. Gloss	20.00	30.00	30.00
2. Matt	25.00	40.00	40.00

Model No. 1765/1828
BLACK-FACED SHEEP AND LAMB
- on wooden plinth

Designer:	Mr. Garbet and Arthur Gredington
Height:	3 ¾", 9.5 cm
Colour:	Black and white - gloss
Issued:	1993-1996

Colourway	U.K. £	U.S. $	Can. $
Black/white	40.00	60.00	60.00

Note: Sheep is no. 1765; Lamb is no. 1828.

Model No. 1828
BLACK-FACED LAMB

Designer:	Arthur Gredington
Height:	2 ½", 6.4 cm
Colour:	Black and white - gloss or matt
Modelled:	1962
Issued:	1. Gloss - 1963-2002
	2. Matt - 1987-1989
Set:	1765

Description	U.K. £	U.S. $	Can. $
1. Gloss	15.00	25.00	25.00
2. Matt	15.00	25.00	25.00

Model No. 1917
MERINO RAM

Designer:	Arthur Gredington
Height:	4 ¼", 10.8 cm
Colour:	Grey with white face - gloss
Modelled:	1963
Issued:	1964-1967

Colourway	U.K. £	U.S. $	Can. $
Grey	2,500.00	3,875.00	3,875.00

Model No. 2103
LAUGHING PIGS

Designer:	Albert Hallam
Height:	2¾", 7.0 cm
Colour:	White and pink - gloss
Modelled:	1967
Issued:	1968-1971
Series:	Fun Models

Colourway	U.K. £	U.S. $	Can. $
White/pink	25.00	40.00	40.00

Model No. 2110
DONKEY FOAL

Designer:	Graham Tongue
Height:	4 ½", 11.9 cm
Colour:	Grey-brown - gloss or matt
Modelled:	1967
Issued:	1. Gloss - 1968-2002
	2. Matt - 1987-1989

Description	U.K. £	U.S. $	Can. $
1. Gloss	25.00	40.00	40.00
2. Matt	25.00	40.00	40.00

Model No. 2267A
DONKEY

Designer:	Albert Hallam and Graham Tongue
Height:	5 ½", 14.0 cm
Colour:	Grey-brown - gloss or matt
Modelled:	1969
Issued:	1. Gloss - 1970-2002
	2. Matt - 1987-1989

Description	U.K. £	U.S. $	Can. $
1. Gloss	25.00	40.00	40.00
2. Matt	30.00	45.00	45.00

Model No. 2267B
DONKEY

Designer:	Albert Hallam and Graham Tongue
Height:	5 ½" 14.0 cm
Colour:	See note below
Modelled:	1969
Issued:	c1994-1998

Description	U.K. £	U.S. $	Can. $
2267B	300.00	450.00	450.00

Note: Approximately 14 presentation donkeys were produced on a base and with a football. The donkeys were painted wearing various coloured striped football shirts (Football Model No. 3366).

Model No. 2746
PIG AND PIGLET "Piggy Back"

Designer:	Graham Tongue
Length:	6 ½", 16.5 cm
Colour:	Pink and white - gloss
Modelled:	1981
Issued:	1983-1994
Series:	Fun Models

Colourway	U.K. £	U.S. $	Can. $
Pink/white	25.00	40.00	40.00

Note: One example known with spots.

Model No. 3071
BLACK-FACED RAM

Designer:	Mr. Chawner
Height:	3 ¼", 8.3 cm
Colour:	Black and white - gloss or matt
Modelled:	1987
Issued:	1. Gloss - 1988-2002
	2. Matt - 1988-1989

Description	U.K. £	U.S. $	Can. $
1. Gloss	25.00	40.00	40.00
2. Matt	25.00	40.00	40.00

Model No. 4114
TAMWORTH SOW

Designer:	Robert Donaldson
Size:	3 ¼" x 6 ¾", 8.2 x 17.1 cm
Colour:	Tan - gloss
Issued:	2001-2002
Series:	Rare Breeds

Colourway	U.K. £	U.S. $	Can. $
Tan	60.00	90.00	90.00

Model No. 4116
GLOUCESTERSHIRE OLD SPOT

Designer:	Robert Donaldson
Size:	3 ¼" x 7", 8.2 x 17.8 cm
Colour:	White with black markings - gloss
Issued:	2001-2002
Series:	Rare Breeds

Colourway	U.K. £	U.S. $	Can. $
White/black	175.00	275.00	275.00

Model No. 4117
MIDDLEWHITE BOAR

Designer:	Robert Donaldson
Length:	4", 10.1 cm
Colour:	White - gloss
Issued:	2001-2002
Series:	Rare Breeds

Colourway	U.K. £	U.S. $	Can. $
White	40.00	60.00	60.00

Model No. 4118
BERKSHIRE BOAR

Designer:	Robert Donaldson
Length:	3 ¼", 8.2 cm
Colour:	Black and grey - gloss
Issued:	2001-2002
Series:	Rare Breeds

Colourway	U.K. £	U.S. $	Can. $
Black/grey	40.00	60.00	60.00

Model No. 4122
COTSWOLD SHEEP

Designer:	Robert Donaldson	
Size:	4 ½" x 6", 11.4 x 15.2 cm	
Colour:	White - gloss	
Issued:	2001-2002	
Series:	Rare Breeds	

Colourway	U.K. £	U.S. $	Can. $
White	150.00	225.00	225.00

Model No. 4123
WENSLEYDALE SHEEP

Designer:	Robert Donaldson	
Size:	4 ¼" x 6", 10.8 x 15.2 cm	
Colout:	White with black markings - gloss	
Issued:	2001-2002	
Series:	Rare Breeds	

Colourway	U.K. £	U.S. $	Can. $
White/black	45.00	70.00	70.00

Model No. 4124
BORERAY SHEEP

Designer:	Robert Donaldson	
Size:	4 ½" x 5 ½", 11.4 x 14.0 cm	
Colout:	White with black markings - gloss	
Issued:	2001-2002	
Series:	Rare Breeds	

Colourway	U.K. £	U.S. $	Can. $
White /black	115.00	175.00	175.00

Model No. G189
VIETNAMESE POT-BELLIED PIG

Designer:	Amanda Hughes-Lubeck	
Size:	3" x 6", 7.6 x 15.2 cm	
Colour:	Dark brown - gloss	
Issued:	1999-2002	

Description	U.K. £	U.S. $	Can. $
Gloss	45.00	70.00	70.00

Model No. G213
VIETNAMESE POT-BELLIED PIGLET
Designer: Warren Platt
Size: 1 ½" x 3", 3.8 x 7.6 cm
Colour: Grey - gloss
Issued: 1999-2002

Description	U.K. £	U.S. $	Can. $
Gloss	25.00	40.00	40.00

Model G215
TAMWORTH PIG
Designer: Amanda Hughes-Lubeck
Size: 3" x 6", 7.6 x 15.2 cm
Colour: Brownish pink - gloss
Issued: 1999-2002

Description	U.K. £	U.S. $	Can. $
Gloss	45.00	70.00	70.00

Model No. G223
NIGERIAN POT-BELLIED PYGMY GOAT
Designer: Amanda Hughes-Lubeck
Height: 5 ¼", 14.0 cm
Colour: White with black markings - gloss
Issued: 1999-2002

Description	U.K. £	U.S. $	Can. $
Gloss	30.00	45.00	45.00

Model No. G230
GLOUCESTER OLD SPOT PIG
Designer: Amanda Hughes-Lubeck
Size: 3" x 5 ½", 7.6 x 14.0 cm
Colour: Pale pink with black markings - gloss
Issued: 1999-2002

Description	U.K. £	U.S. $	Can. $
Gloss	80.00	125.00	125.00

Chapter Six
FISH

All but one of these fish models are realistically portrayed. The detail on many of them is amazing, for example the Golden Trout. So many colours were used, and the result is simply stunning.

The only stylized version of a fish is one from the Moda series. All the rest are supported on bases, although their fins are still vulnerable to damage. Very few, therefore, have survived intact to the present, and as a result they are particularly hard to find in mint condition, although restored ones do appear.

INDEX BY MODEL NUMBER

Model No. 1032
TROUT

Designer:	Arthur Gredington
Height:	6 ¼", 15.9 cm
Colour:	Brown and dark green - gloss
Issued:	1945-1975

Description	U.K. £	U.S. $	Can. $
Gloss	70.00	100.00	100.00

Model No. 1047
ANGEL FISH

Designer:	Arthur Gredington
Height:	7 ¼", 18.4 cm
Colour:	Silver, red and green-brown - gloss
Issued:	1946-1967

Description	U.K. £	U.S. $	Can. $
Gloss	300.00	450.00	450.00

Model No. 1232
OCEANIC BONITO

Designer:	Arthur Gredington
Height:	7 ¼", 18.4 cm
Colour:	Blue, silver and green - gloss
Issued:	1952-1968

Description	U.K. £	U.S. $	Can. $
Gloss	400.00	600.00	600.00

Model No. 1233
ATLANTIC SALMON

Designer:	Arthur Gredington
Height:	6 ½", 16.5 cm
Colour:	Blue, silver and green - gloss
Issued:	1952-1970

Description	U.K. £	U.S. $	Can. $
Gloss	250.00	375.00	375.00

Model No. 1235
BARRACUDA

Designer: Arthur Gredington
Height: 4 ¾", 12.1 cm
Colour: Blue and silver
Issued: 1952-1968

Description	U.K. £	U.S. $	Can. $
Gloss	325.00	475.00	475.00

Model No. 1243
MARLIN

Designer: Arthur Gredington
Height: 5 ½", 14.0 cm
Colour: Blue, grey and green
Issued: 1952-1970

Description	U.K. £	U.S. $	Can. $
Gloss	700.00	1,050.00	1,050.00

Model No. 1246
GOLDEN TROUT

Designer: Arthur Gredington
Height: 6", 15.0 cm
Colour: Blue, yellow and green
Issued: 1952-1970

Description	U.K. £	U.S. $	Can. $
Gloss	125.00	200.00	200.00

Model No. 1266
LARGE-MOUTHED BLACK BASS

Designer: Arthur Gredington
Height: 5", 12.7 cm
Colour: Yellow, black, beige and blue
Issued: 1952-1968

Description	U.K. £	U.S. $	Can. $
Gloss	400.00	600.00	600.00

Model No. 1390
TROUT

Designer:	Arthur Gredington		
Colour:	Brown and dark green - gloss		
Height:	4", 10.1 cm		
Issued:	1955-1975		

Description.	U.K. £	U.S. $	Can. $
Gloss	60.00	90.00	90.00

Model No. 1485
BLACK BASS

Designer:	Colin Melbourne		
Height:	6", 15.0 cm		
Colour:	Brown and dark green - gloss		
Issued:	1957-1968		

Description	U.K. £	U.S. $	Can. $
Gloss	500.00	775.00	775.00

Model No. 1874
ROACH

Designer:	Arthur Gredington		
Height:	6 ¼", 15.9 cm		
Colour:	Turquoise and browns		
Issued:	1963-1971		

Description	U.K. £	U.S. $	Can. $
Gloss	550.00	850.00	850.00

Model No. 1875
PERCH

Designer:	Arthur Gredington		
Height:	6 ¼", 15.9 cm		
Colour:	Greens and browns		
Issued:	1963-1971		

Description	U.K. £	U.S. $	Can. $
Gloss	550.00	850.00	850.00

Model No. 2066
SALMON

Designer:	Graham Tongue
Height:	8", 20.3 cm
Colour:	Browns and silver - gloss
Issued:	1966-1975

Description	U.K. £	U.S. $	Can. $
Gloss	225.00	325.00	325.00

Model No. 2087
TROUT

Designer:	Graham Tongue
Height:	6", 15.0 cm
Colour:	Brown with red-brown spots - gloss
Issued:	1967-1975

Description	U.K. £	U.S. $	Can. $
Gloss	225.00	325.00	325.00

Model No 2254
FISH (Stylized Model)

Designer:	Harry Sales
Height:	4 ½", 11.9 cm
Colour:	1. Black with brown tail, fins and stripes – satin
	2. Dark and light blue – gloss
Issued:	1968-1971
Series:	Moda

Colourways	U.K. £	U.S. $	Can. $
1. Black	125.00	200.00	200.00
2. Blue	125.00	200.00	200.00

Chapter Seven

HORSES

Beswick is most readily associated with the production of accurately modelled horses. Indeed horses form the largest section by far of all the Beswick range. From 1939 to 1989, Beswick produced over 150 different horse models, the vast majority available in several colourways and in gloss or matt finishes. Although each model had a shape number, many were only listed in price lists and catalogues as horse, mare or foal, which left less knowledgeable collectors and dealers with a considerable identification problem! Some horses do have their names incorporated into their backstamp (for example, the Mountain and Moorland ponies) or numbers imprinted into their base (such as the lying down foal, 915), and of course those with riders are easy to sort out. But those that remain need careful examination to determine exactly which models they are.

A further consideration is colour. Initially Beswick produced horses in dark chestnut, light brown, dark brown, rocking horse grey and even in blue gloss. Later brown, painted white, opaque, palomino, chestnut and light grey glosses were added to the range, and most of the initial colourways were dropped. Special colours were also used for specific models, such as on the 2282 Fjord. From 1970 onwards, matt finishes were introduced in various colours: brown, grey, palomino, white and black. Within each colour there can be considerable variations, from a light tone with shading to an all-over, solid, one-tone version of the same colour. Avid collectors will value the former, which usually indicates an earlier example, painted when more attention was paid to details like well-painted eyes and pink mouths.

The Beswick stable comprises the full spectrum of the equine world, from children's ponies, specific breeds, famous racehorses, to the giant Shires, whilst the Colin Melbourne series added a contemporary touch to the collection.

Arthur Gredington modelled Beswick's first realistic horse in 1939 when he produced the first version of the 1938 Derby winner, Bois Roussel. Although a handful of other modellers made contributions to the horse models it was Arthur Gredington who was responsible for the vast majority until he retired in 1968. Graham Tongue then took over, adding many more horses to the range, including a new bronze finish for the Britannia Series. In August 1989 all except three Beswick horses became Doulton Animals and so from that date, although they continued to be produced in the Beswick factory, they were backstamped with the name of the parent company, Royal Doulton. In 1994 to mark the Beswick Centenary it was a horse model that was chosen as a special piece to represent Beswick. This was the large rearing model of Downland Cancara. Graham Tongue modelled this magnificent horse. In 1995 Cancara was issued with a Royal Doulton backstamp and the three remaining Beswick horses were completely withdrawn.

1996 saw the revival of the Beswick backstamp on horses when the 1642 Dartmoor pony stallion was commissioned by Doug Middleweek in bright bay gloss as "Warlord." Warlord was followed at the end of 1997 with a brand new model of a Dartmoor Mare "Another Bunch." The set was completed in 1998 with the "birth" of their foal Another Star. Doug was planning to continue the Native ponies theme but unfortunately this has not been possible.

At the time of writing there is still ONE horse shape, known to have been in general production, which has not come to light. This is the action foal 766. Why this remains elusive is something of a mystery. It was illustrated in the 1940 Overseas brochure/price list which stated it as being available on or off a ceramic base in Dark Chestnut and Light Brown colourways. The model was priced at 14 shillings per dozen in "Dark Chestnut" and 13 shillings per dozen in "Light Brown off stand"! Surely out of these "dozens" some have survived?!

There remain a handful of horse models which reached various stages of production and it is a possibility that there are the odd examples somewhere! These include 2451, a mounted piece given the title of "The Outlaw" which was to be part of a "Riders of the World" collection. Unfortunately this was not pursued further than a prototype. "The Outlaw" was modelled by Graham Tongue in March 1973.

At least three other horse models are recorded in the shape book which did not get as far as being generally released by Beswick. All were designed during the late 1970s. They are 2468 Icelandic Pony and 2626 Haflinger Pony both by Graham Tongue; 2577 Racehorse by David Littleton. The 2548 Small Shire, also referred to as the "Whitbread" Shire as it was intended as a souvenir for visitors to the Whitbread Shire Horse Farm in Kent to purchase, does exist as there were a small number actually produced. Examples, in grey gloss and matt, are now in the hands of a few extremely lucky collectors and are illustrated in this book. Although no examples of the Haflinger have come to my attention I do know that they exist as I saw them in Graham Tongue's studio several years ago. This was at least ten years following the Haflinger's original modelling and suggest that Doulton were perhaps reconsidering issuing it. They were obviously trial pieces, being in various colourways and were attractive action models. It is a great pity that once more the model was rejected. There could be an Icelandic Pony model in existence but the racehorse was not illustrated in the shape book and so probably did not get to the stage where models could exist.

The Beswick Collectors Circle commissioned their first Beswick model in 1990. This was the 818 Shire in black gloss which was back stamped with a large circular BESWICK ENGLAND in gold. There were only around 135 of these produced making them valuable and highly sought after today. In 1995 the Circle commissioned the then Royal Doulton back stamped model of a Shetland Pony to represent the skewbald mare "Hollydell Dixie". Five hundred and fifty three of these formed the edition size and carried the Beswick Collectors Circle as well as Beswick backstamps.

When the Beswick Collectors Circle co-ordinators retired, the Beswick Collectors Club was founded and they continued to commission models commencing in 1996 with the 975 Cantering Shire in gloss in a limited edition of 735. The following year the 976 mare and 947 foal were commissioned in a cream dun colourway. Black 710 mares were issued and 730 foals. In 1990 and 2000 the Club specials were the Champion Welsh Pony. This was first issued in black gloss (edition size 580) and then a year later in white gloss (edition size of 505). Both of these were free standing (whereas the normal range version was mounted on a wooden plinth) and wore a "Beswick" green rug with yellow binding. The Club was negotiating to commission the grazing New Forest pony in bay gloss to represent "Pepper" (the Redwings Horse Sanctuary pony adopted by them) when they received the news that the Beswick factory was to close.

The seven equine specials commissioned by the Beswick Collectors Circle/Club form a nice little group when displayed together and having been produced in such small quantities are certain to continue to increase in value.

Following the return to the Beswick backstamp as from October 1999 the range of Beswick horses was extended during 2000 and 2001 by several new models in the Connoisseur and Spirit series. All these newer models were in matt finish and mounted on either a wooden or slate effect base.

Prices for many of the equine pieces have continued to "level off" and in some cases have fallen. Rarer shapes and colourways, particularly concerning Shires and mounted pieces, obviously still command premium prices. However some models and colourways which were considered "rare" in the past have now been located in sufficient numbers to satisfy the more ardent collectors. Hence although there have been some spectacular auction prices realised recently they are for very rarely found items. Perhaps the emphasis for some collectors now is to try and "improve" their collections by looking for better examples of models – those with shading in their overall colour, good detail in the eye/nose area, and muscle detail within the mould – all indicating an "older" example. The internet auction site eBay always has a number of Beswick horses, mainly relatively common, but also some rarities, available amongst the thousand or so pieces of Beswick continually listed. However there has also been an increase in equine items listed as "Beswick" which have never come out of the Beswick factory. Included have been models of rocking horses and Thelwell type ponies (the latter actually manufactured by "Cheval" a South African ceramic company) mounted on authentic Beswick ceramic bases. The general rule must be to beware of anything offered as "Beswick" if it is not between the pages of this book!

The 818 Shire continues to be the most commonly seen Beswick equine at Collectors Fairs, invariably in brown gloss. The 818 has the distinction of not only being Beswick's longest produced unaltered horse shape but also the one found in the most range of production colours. Fifteen colourways have now been located, including blue gloss (and there could be a few more!)

Sadly the Beswick factory closed in December 2002, but the many equine products made there go on and hopefully will be treasured by many for many years to come.

In 2005 UKI Ceramics commissioned the last "Beswick" horse produced by Nile Street – The Black Hunter (H260) in a limited edition of 500 pieces.

Over the past year on-line auctions have listed several "Ponies painted in Pinto" with Beswick backstamps. We believe these figures are not correct.

INDEX BY MODEL NUMBER

Model No. 701 / H701

BOIS ROUSSEL
RACEHORSE

There are two varieties of Bois Roussell. The first version was introduced in 1939 and is rarely backstamped.

FIRST VERSION :   The tail is attached to the hind legs all the way down and the legs are long and thick.

Designer: Arthur Gredington
Height: 8", 20.3 cm

Colourway	Finish	Intro.	Disc.	U.K. £	U.S. $	Can. $
Blue	Gloss	1939	1947		Extremely Rare	
Light brown	Gloss	1940	1947	175.00	275.00	275.00
Dark brown	Gloss	1940	1947	175.00	275.00	275.00
Dark chestnut	Gloss	1939	1947	275.00	425.00	425.00
Rocking horse grey	Gloss	c.1940	1947	475.00	725.00	725.00

SECOND VERSION: In 1947 Bois Roussel was remodelled with only the tail-end attached to the leg.

Colourway	Finish	Model	Intro.	Disc.	U.K. £	U.S. $	Can. $
Brown							
a. Original issue	Gloss	701	1947	1989	30.00	45.00	45.00
b. Reissued	Gloss	H701	1999	2002	30.00	45.00	45.00
Brown							
a. Original issue	Matt	701	1979	1989	45.00	70.00	70.00
b. Reissued	Matt	H701	1999	2002	45.00	70.00	70.00
Chestnut	Gloss	701	1958	1967	300.00	450.00	450.00
Grey	Gloss	701	1960	1989	60.00	90.00	90.00
Grey	Matt	701	1970	1989	40.00	60.00	60.00
Opaque	Gloss	701	1960	1967	200.00	300.00	300.00
Painted white	Gloss	701	1952	1967	375.00	575.00	575.00
Palomino	Gloss	701	1960	1989	60.00	90.00	90.00
Palomino	Matt	701	1970	1983	45.00	70.00	70.00
Piebald	Gloss	701	Unknown	Unknown	475.00	725.00	725.00
Rocking horse grey	Gloss	701	1947	1962	450.00	700.00	700.00
White	Matt	701	1970	1982	60.00	90.00	90.00

SERIES: On ceramic stand or wooden plinths

The stand was shape no. 1809, modelled by Albert Hallam in 1963.

Colourway/stand/finish	Intro.	Disc.	U.K. £	U.S. $	Can. $
Brown/brown ceramic/gloss	c.1963	Unknown	100.00	150.00	150.00
Brown/copper lustre ceramic/gloss	c.1963	Unknown	75.00	115.00	115.00
Chestnut/ceramic/gloss	c.1963	Unknown	375.00	575.00	575.00
Brown/wooden plinth/matt	c.1989	c.1989	45.00	70.00	70.00

Model No. 728

FOAL
(Comical Type)

Designer: Arthur Gredington
Height: 5", 12.7 cm

Colourway	Finish	Intro.	Disc.	U.K. £	U.S. $	Can. $
Black	Satin	Unknown	Unknown	450.00	700.00	700.00
Blue	Gloss	1939	1954	525.00	800.00	800.00
Brown	Gloss	1940	1971	25.00	40.00	40.00
Chestnut	Gloss	1958	1966	175.00	275.00	275.00
Dark chestnut	Gloss	1939	1954	275.00	425.00	425.00
Grey	Gloss	1961	1971	65.00	100.00	100.00
Opaque	Gloss	1961	1971	150.00	230.00	230.00
Painted white	Gloss	1961	1966	200.00	300.00	300.00
Palomino	Gloss	1961	1971	65.00	100.00	100.00
Rocking horse grey	Gloss	c.1940	1962	250.00	375.00	375.00
Stone/ivory	Satin	Unknown	1954	95.00	150.00	150.00
White	Matt	1970	1970	50.00	75.00	75.00

Model No. 763/1421

FOAL
(Small, Stretched, Upright)

First Version: Long ears

Second Version: Short ears

Designer: Arthur Gredington
Height: 3 ½", 8.9 cm

FIRST VERSION: Long ears, thick legs. Outline of mane more wavy.
When viewed from the back legs almost touch.

Colourway	Finish	Intro.	Disc.	U.K. £	U.S. $	Can. $
Blue	Gloss	1940	Unknown	500.00	750.00	750.00
Brown	Gloss	1940	Unknown	30.00	45.00	45.00
Rocking horse grey	Gloss	c.1940	Unknown	280.00	425.00	425.00

SECOND VERSION: Short ears, thick legs. Outline of mane less wavy.

Colourway	Finish	Intro.	Disc.	U.K. £	U.S. $	Can. $
Blue	Gloss	Unknown	1956	500.00	750.00	750.00
Brown	Gloss	Unknown	1956	30.00	45.00	45.00
Painted white	Gloss	Unknown	1956	175.00	275.00	275.00
Rocking horse grey	Gloss	Unknown	1956	280.00	425.00	425.00

THIRD VERSION: Very thin legs with off hind stretched out well behind the near hind. Tail is slightly bent.

In 1956 model no. 763 was completely remodelled by Arthur Gredington, but the model no. 763 was retained.

Colourway	Finish	Intro.	Disc.	U.K. £	U.S. $	Can. $
Brown	Gloss	1956	1976	20.00	30.00	30.00
Chestnut	Gloss	1958	1967	150.00	225.00	225.00
Grey	Gloss	1961	1976	45.00	70.00	70.00
Opaque	Gloss	1961	1973	95.00	150.00	150.00
Painted white	Gloss	1962	1967	150.00	225.00	225.00
Palomino	Gloss	1956	1976	35.00	55.00	55.00
Rocking horse grey	Gloss	1956	1961	200.00	300.00	300.00
White	Matt	1970	1976	35.00	55.00	55.00

Model No. 766

FOAL - TROTTING
(With Or Without Base)

Designer: Arthur Gredington
Height: 3 ¾", 9.5 cm

VARIATION No. 1.   Free standing

Colourway	Finish	Intro.	Disc.	U.K. £	U.S. $	Can. $
Blue	Gloss	1940	By 1954			
Light brown	Gloss	1940	By 1954			
Dark brown	Gloss	1940	By 1954	All colourways are extremely rare		
Dark chestnut	Gloss	1940	By 1954			
Rocking horse grey	Gloss	1940	By 1954			

VARIATION No. 2.   On ceramic base

Colourway	Finish	Intro.	Disc.	U.K. £	U.S. $	Can. $
Blue	Gloss	1940	By 1954			
Light brown	Gloss	1940	By 1954	All colourways are extremely rare		
Dark brown	Gloss	1940	By 1954			
Dark chestnut	Gloss	1940	By 1954			

Model No. 815 / F815

FOAL
(Small, Stretched, Facing Right)

Designer: Arthur Gredington
Height: 3 ¼", 8.3 cm

Colourway	Finsh	Model	Intro.	Disc.	U.K. £	U.S. $	Can. $
Blue	Gloss	815	1940	1954	475.00	750.00	750.00
Brown							
a. Original issue	Gloss	815	1940	1989	15.00	25.00	25.00
b. Reissued	Gloss	F815	1999	1999	15.00	25.00	25.00
Brown	Matt	815	1979	1989	20.00	30.00	30.00
Chestnut	Gloss	815	1958	1967	175.00	275.00	275.00
Dark chestnut	Gloss	815	1940	1954	175.00	275.00	275.00
Grey	Gloss	815	1961	1989	30.00	45.00	45.00
Opaque	Gloss	815	1961	1973	100.00	150.00	150.00
Painted white	Gloss	815	1962	1967	150.00	225.00	225.00
Palomino	Gloss	815	1961	1989	20.00	30.00	30.00
Pink	Gloss	815	1940	1954		Extremely Rare	
Rocking horse grey	Gloss	815	c.1940	1962	200.00	300.00	300.00
White	Matt	815	1970	1982	35.00	55.00	55.00

Model No. 818 / H818   **SHIRE MARE**

In recognition of 50 years of production of model number 818 a black gloss shire mare was commissioned by the Beswick Collectors Circle in 1990. Approximately 135 of these were issued with a gold backstamp for Circle Members.

An example in an Iron Grey colourway exists.

Designer: Arthur Gredington
Height: 8 ½", 21.6 cm

FIRST VERSION: Without Harness

Colourway	Finish	Model	Intro.	Disc.	U.K. £	U.S. $	Can. $
Black	Gloss	818	Unknown	Unknown	550.00	850.00	850.00
Black (BCC90)	Gloss	818	1990	1990	625.00	975.00	975.00
Blue	Gloss	818	c.1940	1954		Extremely Rare	
Brown							
a. Original issue	Gloss	818	1940	1989	25.00	40.00	40.00
b. Reissued	Gloss	H818	1999	1999	25.00	40.00	40.00
Brown	Matt	818	1979	1989	50.00	75.00	75.00
Chestnut	Gloss	818	1958	1967	1,200.00	1,800.00	1,800.00
Grey	Gloss	818	1961	1989	60.00	90.00	90.00
Iron Grey	Gloss	818	1952	Unknown		Very Rare	
Opaque	Gloss	818	1961	1973	425.00	650.00	650.00
Painted white	Gloss	818	1961	1970	925.00	1,425.00	1,425.00
Palomino	Gloss	818	1961	1973	1,500.00	2,300.00	2,300.00
Piebald	Gloss	818	Unknown	Unknown	1,250.00	1,950.00	1,950.00
Pink	Gloss	818	1952	Unknown		Very Rare	
Rocking horse grey	Gloss	818	c.1940	1962	425.00	650.00	650.00
Skewbald	Gloss	818	Unknown	Unknown	1,850.00	2,800.00	2,800.00
White	Matt	818	1970	1982	120.00	180.00	180.00

Note: Other than the Beswick Collectors Circle Special which has a blue and yellow ribbon, all models of No.818 have yellow ribbons.

SECOND VERSION: Dressed; Series – Harnessed Horses

Colourway	Finish	Intro.	Disc.	U.K. £	U.S. $	Can. $
Brown	Gloss	1974	1982	80.00	125.00	125.00
Grey	Gloss	1974	1982	115.00	175.00	175.00

Model No. 836

FOAL
(Large, Stretched)

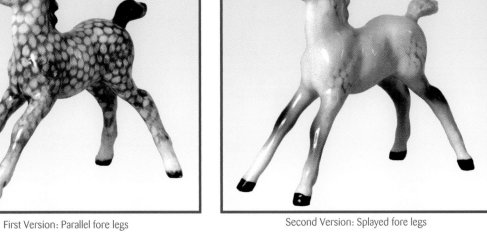

First Version: Parallel fore legs

Second Version: Splayed fore legs

Designer: Arthur Gredington
Height: 5", 12.7 cm

FIRST VERSION: Parallel fore legs.

Colourway	Finish	Intro.	Disc.	U.K. £	U.S. $	Can. $
Blue	Gloss	Unknown	Unknown	475.00	725.00	725.00
Brown	Gloss	1940	Unknown	20.00	30.00	30.00
Light Brown	Gloss	c.1940-50	Unknown	25.00	40.00	40.00
Brown	Matt	1979	Unknown	25.00	40.00	40.00
Chestnut	Gloss	1961	Unknown	200.00	300.00	300.00
Grey	Gloss	1961	Unknown	45.00	70.00	70.00
Opaque	Gloss	1961	Unknown	100.00	150.00	150.00
Painted white	Gloss	1961	Unknown	200.00	300.00	300.00
Palomino	Gloss	1961	Unknown	30.00	45.00	45.00
Pink	Gloss	Unknown	Unknown		Extremely Rare	
Rocking horse grey	Gloss	1961	Unknown	450.00	700.00	700.00
White	Matt	1970	Unknown	35.00	55.00	55.00

SECOND VERSION: Splayed fore legs.

Colourway	Finish	Intro.	Disc.	U.K. £	U.S. $	Can. $
Brown	Gloss	Unknown	1984	20.00	30.00	30.00
Brown	Matt	Unknown	1984	20.00	30.00	30.00
Chestnut	Gloss	Unknown	1967	200.00	300.00	300.00
Grey	Gloss	Unknown	1983	40.00	60.00	60.00
Opaque	Gloss	Unknown	1973	100.00	150.00	150.00
Painted white	Gloss	Unknown	1967	200.00	300.00	300.00
Palomino	Gloss	Unknown	1984	40.00	60.00	60.00
White	Matt	Unknown	1982	25.00	40.00	40.00

Model No. 855/1090/H855   **STOCKY JOGGING MARE**

FIRST VERSION: Modelled September 1940. Near fore leg is raised off the ground, near hind leg is under the body. Tail attached to the leg all the way down. Legs rather crudely modelled.

Designer: Arthur Gredington
Height: 6", 5.0 cm

Colourway	Finish	Intro.	Disc.	U.K. £	U.S. $	Can. $
Blue	Gloss	1940	1941			
Dark brown	Gloss	1940	1941		All colourways are	
Light brown	Gloss	1940	1941		extremely rare	
Dark chestnut	Gloss	1940	1941			
Rocking horse grey	Gloss	1940	1941			

Note: This model is rarely found with a backstamp.

SECOND VERSION: Modelled September 1941. Near fore leg is raised off the ground, near hind leg is under the body. Tail arched away from the leg. More shape to the joints of the legs.

Colourway	Finish	Intro.	Disc.	U.K. £	U.S. $	Can. $
Blue	Gloss	1941	1947	1,000.00	1,500.00	1,500.00
Brown	Gloss	1941	1947	250.00	375.00	375.00
Dark chestnut	Gloss	1941	1947	375.00	575.00	575.00
Rocking horse grey	Gloss	1941	1947	550.00	825.00	825.00
White	Matt	Unknown	Unknown		Rare	

Note: 1. This model is rarely found with a backstamp.
           2. A white matt colourway is known to exist.

THIRD VERSION: Shape no. 1090 was modelled in 1947 but retained the number 855.
Off fore leg raised from the ground, off hind leg under the body.
Tail more arched from the body. Head lowered. A chunkier model.

Colourway	Finish	Model	Intro.	Disc.	U.K. £	U.S. $	Can. $
Black (BCC 2005)	Gloss	855	2005	2005	150.00	225.00	225.00
Blue	Gloss	855	1947	Unknown		Extremely Rare	
Brown							
a. Original issue	Gloss	855/1090	1947	1989	30.00	45.00	45.00
b. Reissued	Gloss	H855	1999	2002	30.00	45.00	45.00
Chestnut	Gloss	855	1958	1967	300.00	450.00	450.00
Grey	Gloss	855	1961	1989	50.00	75.00	75.00
Opaque	Gloss	855	1961	1973	200.00	300.00	300.00
Painted white	Gloss	855	1961	1967	275.00	425.00	425.00
Palomino	Gloss	855	1961	1989	60.00	90.00	90.00
Rocking horse grey	Gloss	855	c.1947	1962	475.00	725.00	725.00
White	Matt	855	1970	1982	60.00	90.00	90.00

Note: This model was produced in black gloss on a ceramic base for the Index Catalogue.

Model No. 868

HUNTSMAN (On Rearing Horse)

Designer: Arthur Gredington   Height: 10", 25.4 cm

Style One, First Version   Style One, Second Version

STYLE ONE: On rearing horse

FIRST VERSION: Huntsman is sitting straight up and his lower legs are vertical.
His coat is cut away at the waist. He is riding a common headed horse.

COLOURWAY No. 1. Orangey red coat, cream breeches.

Colourway	Finish	Intro.	Disc.	U.K. £	U.S. $	Can. $
Brown	Gloss	1940	1952	300.00	450.00	450.00
Dark chestnut	Gloss	1940	1952	600.00	900.00	900.00
Rocking horse grey	Gloss	c.1940	1952	1,200.00	1,800.00	1,800.00

COLOURWAY No. 2. Scarlet coat and white breeches.

Colourway	Finish	Intro.	Disc.	U.K. £	U.S. $	Can. $
Brown	Gloss	1940	1952	175.00	275.00	275.00
Rocking horse grey	Gloss	c.1948	1952	1,000.00	1,500.00	1,500.00

SECOND VERSION: Huntsman is leaning back slightly. His coat is not cut away at the waist.
The horse's head has an Arab appearance (dished profile).

Colourway	Finish	Intro.	Disc.	U.K. £	U.S. $	Can. $
Brown	Gloss	1952	1995	175.00	275.00	275.00
Chestnut	Gloss	1958	1967	575.00	900.00	900.00
Grey	Gloss	1962	1972	350.00	535.00	535.00
Opaque	Gloss	1971	1973	450.00	675.00	675.00
Painted white	Gloss	1965	1971	900.00	1,350.00	1,350.00
Palomino	Gloss	1961	1972	900.00	1,350.00	1,350.00
Rocking horse grey	Gloss	1952	1962	1,000.00	1,500.00	1,500.00
White	Matt	1971	1981	450.00	675.00	675.00

SERIES: Britannia Collection

Colourway	Finish	Intro.	Disc.	U.K. £	U.S. $	Can. $
Bronze	Satin	1989	1993	160.00	250.00	250.00

Note: An example of Colourway No. 1 is known to exist in grey gloss.

Model No. 915 / F915   FOAL (Lying)

Designer: Arthur Gredington
Height: 3 ¼", 8.3 cm

Colourway	Finish	Model	Intro.	Disc.	U.K. £	U.S. $	Can. $
Brown							
a. Original issue	Gloss	915	1941	1989	20.00	30.00	30.00
b. Reissued	Gloss	F915	1999	2002	20.00	30.00	30.00
Brown	Matt	915	1979	1989	20.00	30.00	30.00
Chestnut	Gloss	915	1958	1967	200.00	300.00	300.00
Grey	Gloss	915	1961	1989	45.00	70.00	70.00
Opaque	Gloss	915	1961	1973	100.00	150.00	150.00
Painted white	Gloss	915	1962	1967	200.00	300.00	300.00
Palomino	Gloss	915	1961	1989	35.00	55.00	55.00
Rocking horse grey	Gloss	915	c.1942	1962	275.00	400.00	400.00
White	Matt	915	1970	1982	30.00	45.00	45.00

Note: An example in a black colourway exists.

Model No. 939   GIRL ON JUMPING HORSE

The horse used for model 939 is also that used for model 982 "Huntswoman."

Designer: Arthur Gredington
Height: 9 ¾", 24.7 cm
Colour: Brown - gloss
Issued: 1941-1965

Colourway	U.K. £	U.S. $	Can. $
Brown	300.00	450.00	450.00

Model No. 946 / F946   **FOAL**
                                      (Grazing)

First Version: Off-side hooves almost touch   Second Version: Legs well separated

Designer: Arthur Gredington
Height: 3 ¼", 8.3 cm

FIRST VERSION: Has common head and the off-side hooves almost touch.

Colourway	Finish	Model	Intro.	Disc.	U.K. £	U.S. $	Can. $
Brown	Gloss	946	1941	1955	40.00	60.00	60.00
Dark Chestnut	Gloss	946	Unknown	Unknown	200.00	300.00	300.00
Rocking horse grey	Gloss	946	1941	1955	400.00	600.00	600.00

SECOND VERSION: Much finer head with the legs being well separated.

Colourway	Finish	Model	Intro.	Disc.	U.K. £	U.S. $	Can. $
Brown							
a. Original issue	Gloss	946	1955	1989	30.00	45.00	45.00
b. Reissued	Gloss	F946	1999	2002	30.00	45.00	45.00
Brown	Matt	946	1979	1989	20.00	30.00	30.00
Chestnut	Gloss	946	1958	1967	200.00	300.00	300.00
Grey	Gloss	946	1961	1989	45.00	70.00	70.00
Opaque	Gloss	946	1961	1967	100.00	150.00	150.00
Painted white	Gloss	946	1961	1967	200.00	300.00	300.00
Palomino	Gloss	946	1961	1989	45.00	70.00	70.00
Rocking horse grey	Gloss	946	1955	1962	300.00	450.00	450.00
White	Matt	946	1970	1982	35.00	55.00	55.00

Model No. 947 / F947

FOAL
(Large, Head Down)

This model in the dun colourway, along with the Mare (976), was the 1997 Beswick Collectors Club Special. They show both the "Beswick" and BCC97 backstamps. The Foal (in the dun colourway) was issued in a limited edition of 730.

Designer: Arthur Gredington
Height: 4 ½", 11.9 cm

Colourway	Finish	Model	Intro.	Disc.	U.K. £	U.S. $	Can. $
Brown							
a. Original issue	Gloss	947	1941	1989	20.00	30.00	30.00
b. Reissued	Gloss	F947	1999	2002	20.00	30.00	30.00
Brown	Matt	947	1979	1989	25.00	40.00	40.00
Chestnut	Gloss	947	1958	1967	175.00	275.00	275.00
Dun (BCC97)	Gloss	947	1997	1997	125.00	200.00	200.00
Grey	Gloss	947	1961	1983	55.00	85.00	85.00
Opaque	Gloss	947	1961	1973	80.00	120.00	120.00
Painted white	Gloss	947	1962	1967	200.00	300.00	300.00
Palomino	Gloss	947	1961	1983	30.00	45.00	45.00
Rocking horse grey	Gloss	947	c.1942	1962	600.00	900.00	900.00
White	Matt	947	1970	1982	30.00	45.00	45.00

Model No. 951

SHIRE FOAL
(Large)

Designer: Arthur Gredington
Height: 6 ¼", 15.9 cm

Colourway	Finish	Intro.	Disc.	U.K. £	U.S. $	Can. $
Blue	Gloss	1941	Unknown	575.00	900.00	900.00
Brown	Gloss	1941	1971	30.00	45.00	45.00
Chestnut	Gloss	1958	1967	275.00	425.00	425.00
Grey	Gloss	1961	1971	100.00	150.00	150.00
Opaque	Gloss	1961	1971	120.00	180.00	180.00
Painted white	Gloss	1962	1967	300.00	450.00	450.00
Palomino	Gloss	1961	1971	160.00	250.00	250.00
Rocking horse grey	Gloss	1941	1962	325.00	500.00	500.00
White	Matt	1970	1970	80.00	120.00	120.00

Model No. 953   **MARE AND FOAL ON BASE**

The mare is a modern 976 with the foal and the base varying.

FIRST VERSION: The foal has its tail and near fore leg slightly raised.
                                   The base is rectangular.

Designer: Arthur Gredington
Height: 7 ¾", 19.7 cm

Colourway	Finish	Intro.	Disc.	U.K. £	U.S. $	Can. $
Brown	Gloss	1941	1949	500.00	750.00	750.00
Rocking horse grey	Gloss	1941	1949	1,300.00	2,000.00	2,000.00

Model 953, Second Version   Model 953, Third Version

SECOND VERSION: Foal has all four legs attached to an irregularly shaped base and the tail hangs straight down.

Colourway	Finish	Intro.	Disc.	U.K. £	U.S. $	Can. $
Brown mare / orangey bay foal	Gloss	1949	1983	90.00	140.00	140.00
Chestnut	Gloss	1958	1967	975.00	1,500.00	1,500.00
Grey	Gloss	1958	1972	375.00	575.00	575.00
Opaque	Gloss	1971	1973	300.00	450.00	450.00
Painted white mare / brown foal	Gloss	1962	1967	300.00	450.00	450.00
Painted white mare / painted white foal	Gloss	1962	1967	350.00	550.00	550.00
Palomino	Gloss	1958	1972	475.00	725.00	725.00
Rocking horse grey	Gloss	1950	1962	650.00	1,000.00	1,000.00
White	Matt	1971	1981	125.00	200.00	200.00

THIRD VERSION: Foal is model no. 1813, second version, on an irregularly shaped base.

Colourway	Finish	Intro.	Disc.	U.K. £	U.S. $	Can. $
Brown mare with an orangey bay foal	Gloss	1981	1983	80.00	125.00	125.00
Brown mare and foal, green matt base	Matt	1981	1983	80.00	125.00	125.00
White	Matt	1981	1983	80.00	125.00	125.00

Model No. 975 / H975   **CANTERING SHIRE**

This model in the black gloss colourway was the 1996 Beswick Collectors Club Special in a limited edition of 735.

Designer: Arthur Gredington
Height: 8 ¾", 22.2 cm

Colourway	Finish	Intro.	Disc.	U.K. £	U.S. $	Can. $
Black (BCC96)	Gloss	1996	1996	175.00	275.00	275.00
Brown	Gloss	1943	1989	35.00	50.00	50.00
Brown	Matt	1980	1989	35.00	50.00	50.00
Chestnut	Gloss	1958	1967	800.00	1,250.00	1,250.00
Grey	Gloss	1961	1989	85.00	130.00	130.00
Opaque	Gloss	1966	1967	300.00	450.00	450.00
Painted white	Gloss	1962	1967	400.00	600.00	600.00
Palomino	Gloss	1961	1970	1,250.00	1,900.00	1,900.00
Rocking horse grey	Gloss	c.1944	1962	500.00	750.00	750.00
White	Matt	1971	1982	80.00	120.00	120.00

Note: Examples are known in flambé and piebald gloss.

Model No. 976

MARE
(Facing Left)

This model and the foal (947) in dun gloss were the 1997 Beswick Collectors Club Special. They have both the "Beswick" and BCC97 backstamps. The Mare (in the dun colourway) was issued in a limited edition of 710.

Designer: Arthur Gredington
Height: 6 ¾", 17.2 cm

Colourway	Finish	Intro.	Disc.	U.K. £	U.S. $	Can. $
Brown	Gloss	1941	1989	35.00	50.00	50.00
Brown	Matt	1979	1989	35.00	50.00	50.00
Chestnut	Gloss	1958	1967	450.00	700.00	700.00
Dun (BCC97)	Gloss	1997	1997	175.00	275.00	275.00
Grey	Gloss	1962	1989	55.00	85.00	85.00
Opaque	Gloss	1961	1973	160.00	250.00	250.00
Painted white	Gloss	1961	1967	325.00	500.00	500.00
Palomino	Gloss	1961	1983	55.00	85.00	85.00
Rocking horse grey	Gloss	c.1942	1962	650.00	1,000.00	1,000.00
White	Matt	1970	1982	45.00	70.00	70.00

Model No. 982

HUNTSWOMAN

The horse used for model 982 is the same as that used for model 939 "Girl on Jumping Horse."

STYLE ONE: Rider and Horse Jumping

Designer:	Arthur Gredington
Height:	10", 25.4 cm

Colourway	Finish	Intro.	Disc.	U.K. £	U.S. $	Can. $
Brown	Gloss	1942	1967	325.00	500.00	500.00

Model No. 996

FOAL
(Small, Gambolling left)

Designer:	Arthur Gredington
Height:	3 ¼", 8.3 cm

Colourway	Finish	Intro.	Disc.	U.K. £	U.S. $	Can. $
Brown	Gloss	1943	1976	20.00	30.00	30.00
Blue	Gloss	1941	Unknown	350.00	550.00	550.00
Chestnut	Gloss	1958	1967	175.00	275.00	275.00
Grey	Gloss	1961	1976	20.00	30.00	30.00
Opaque	Gloss	1961	1973	60.00	90.00	90.00
Painted white	Gloss	1961	1967	175.00	275.00	275.00
Palomino	Gloss	1961	1976	30.00	45.00	45.00
Rocking horse grey	Gloss	c.1944	1962	350.00	525.00	525.00
White	Matt	1970	1976	30.00	45.00	45.00

Model No. 997 / F997

FOAL
(Small, Stretched, Facing Left)

Designer: Arthur Gredington
Height: 3 ¼", 8.3 cm

Colourway	Finish	Model	Intro.	Disc.	U.K. £	U.S. $	Can. $
Brown							
a. Original issue	Gloss	997	1943	1989	15.00	25.00	25.00
b. Reissued	Gloss	F997	1999	2002	15.00	25.00	25.00
Brown	Matt	997	1979	1989	15.00	25.00	25.00
Chestnut	Gloss	997	1958	1967	175.00	275.00	275.00
Grey	Gloss	997	1961	1989	35.00	50.00	50.00
Opaque	Gloss	997	1961	1973	65.00	100.00	100.00
Painted white	Gloss	997	1961	1967	160.00	250.00	250.00
Palomino	Gloss	997	1961	1989	25.00	40.00	40.00
Rocking horse grey	Gloss	997	c.1944	1962	275.00	450.00	450.00
White	Matt	997	1970	1982	25.00	40.00	40.00

Model No. 1014

WELSH COB
(Rearing)

Designer: Arthur Gredington   Height: 10 ¼", 26.0 cm

First Version: Tail attached to base   Second Version: Tail hangs loose

FIRST VERSION: The tail is attached to the ceramic base.

Colourway	Finish	Intro.	Disc.	U.K. £	U.S. $	Can. $
Black	Gloss	Unknown	Unknown	200.00	300.00	300.00
Brown	Gloss	1944	Unknown	90.00	135.00	135.00
Chestnut	Gloss	1958	Unknown	400.00	600.00	600.00
Grey	Gloss	1961	Unknown	300.00	450.00	450.00
Opaque	Gloss	1961	Unknown	225.00	350.00	350.00
Painted white	Gloss	1962	Unknown	350.00	550.00	550.00
Palomino	Gloss	1961	Unknown	325.00	500.00	500.00
Piebald	Gloss	Unknown	Unknown		Extremely Rare	
Rocking horse grey	Gloss	c.1945	Unknown	800.00	1,200.00	1,200.00
White	Matt	1970	Unknown	115.00	175.00	175.00

SECOND VERSION: Tail hangs loose.

Colourway	Finish	Intro.	Disc.	U.K. £	U.S. $	Can. $
Black	Gloss	c.1990	c.1990	200.00	300.00	300.00
Brown	Gloss	Unknown	1989	75.00	115.00	115.00
Chestnut	Gloss	Unknown	1967	400.00	600.00	600.00
Grey	Gloss	Unknown	1973	300.00	450.00	450.00
Grey	Matt	Unknown	1983	130.00	200.00	200.00
Opaque	Gloss	Unknown	1973	200.00	300.00	300.00
Painted white	Gloss	Unknown	1967	350.00	550.00	550.00
Palomino	Gloss	Unknown	1973	200.00	300.00	300.00
White	Matt	Unknown	1983	75.00	115.00	115.00

Note: An example is known in a black satin matt colourway.

Model No. 1033 / H1033
SHETLAND PONY
(Woolly Shetland Mare)

Designer: Arthur Gredington
Height: 5 ¾", 14.6 cm

Colourway	Finish	Model	Intro.	Disc.	U.K. £	U.S. $	Can. $
Brown							
a. Original issue	Gloss	1033	1945	1989	25.00	40.00	40.00
b. Reissued	Gloss	H1033	1999	2002	25.00	40.00	40.00
Brown	Matt	1033	Unknown	Unknown	35.00	55.00	55.00
Chestnut	Gloss	1033	Unknown	Unknown	450.00	700.00	700.00
Dapple grey	Gloss	1033	Unknown	Unknown	450.00	700.00	700.00
Palomino	Gloss	1033	Unknown	Unknown	450.00	700.00	700.00
White	Matt	1033	1973	1982	20.00	30.00	30.00

Note: Examples are known in bay matt and treacle and white gloss.

Model No. 1034 / F1034
SHETLAND FOAL
Designer: Arthur Gredington
Height: 3 ¾", 9.5 cm

Colourway	Finish	Model	Intro.	Disc.	U.K. £	U.S. $	Can. $
Brown							
a. Original issue	Gloss	1034	1945	1989	20.00	30.00	30.00
b. Reissued	Gloss	F1034	1999	2002	20.00	30.00	30.00
Brown	Matt	1034	1979	1989	20.00	30.00	30.00
White	Matt	1034	1973	1982	30.00	45.00	45.00

Model No. 1037

RACEHORSE AND JOCKEY
(Walking Racehorse)

The jockey's silks, for an extra payment, could be decorated as the purchaser wished. A great many colourways and number cloths could exist.

Colourway No. 1 - Stripes on saddlecloth

Colourway No. 2 - Number on saddlecloth

Designer: Arthur Gredington
Height: 8 ½", 21.6 cm

STYLE ONE: Walking Racehorse

Colourway No. 1.   Stripes on saddlecloth

Colourway	Finish	Intro.	Disc.	U.K. £	U.S. $	Can. $
Brown	Gloss	1945	Unknown	250.00	375.00	375.00

Colourway No. 2.   Number on saddlecloth

Colourway	Finish	Intro.	Disc.	U.K. £	U.S. $	Can. $
Brown	Gloss	Unknown	1976	250.00	375.00	375.00
Chestnut	Gloss	Unknown	Unknown	525.00	800.00	800.00

Model No. 1050
GRAZING SHIRE
Designer: Arthur Gredington
Height: 5 ½", 14.0 cm

Colourway	Finish	Intro.	Disc.	U.K. £	U.S. $	Can. $
Brown	Gloss	1946	1970	55.00	85.00	85.00
Chestnut	Gloss	1958	1967	775.00	1,200.00	1,200.00
Grey	Gloss	1962	1970	350.00	525.00	525.00
Opaque	Gloss	1961	1970	775.00	1,200.00	1,200.00
Painted white	Gloss	1962	1967	775.00	1,200.00	1,200.00
Palomino	Gloss	1961	1970	775.00	1,200.00	1,200.00
Rocking horse grey	Gloss	c.1947	1962	775.00	1,200.00	1,200.00

Note: A copper lustre model is known to exist.

Model No. 1053
SHIRE FOAL
(Small)
Designer: Arthur Gredington
Height: 5", 12.7 cm

Colourway	Finish	Intro.	Disc.	U.K. £	U.S. $	Can. $
Blue	Gloss	Unknown	Unknown	450.00	700.00	700.00
Brown	Gloss	1946	1984	25.00	40.00	40.00
Brown	Matt	1979	1984	25.00	40.00	40.00
Chestnut	Gloss	1958	1967	400.00	600.00	600.00
Grey	Gloss	1961	1973	100.00	150.00	150.00
Opaque	Gloss	1961	1973	125.00	200.00	200.00
Painted white	Gloss	1962	1967	275.00	425.00	425.00
Palomino	Gloss	1961	1973	125.00	200.00	200.00
Rocking horse grey	Gloss	c.1947	1962	400.00	600.00	600.00
White	Matt	1970	1982	50.00	75.00	75.00

Model No. 1084
FOAL
(Medium, Almost Stood Square)
Designer: Arthur Gredington
Height: 4 ½", 11.9 cm

Colourway	Finish	Intro.	Disc.	U.K. £	U.S. $	Can. $
Brown	Gloss	1947	1984	20.00	30.00	30.00
Brown	Matt	1979	1983	20.00	30.00	30.00
Chestnut	Gloss	1958	1967	225.00	350.00	350.00
Grey	Gloss	1961	1973	50.00	75.00	75.00
Opaque	Gloss	1961	1973	100.00	150.00	150.00
Painted white	Gloss	1961	1967	225.00	350.00	350.00
Palomino	Gloss	1961	1973	60.00	90.00	90.00
Rocking horse grey	Gloss	c.1948	1962	400.00	600.00	600.00
White	Matt	1970	1982	35.00	55.00	55.00

Model No. 1085
FOAL
(Medium, Head Down)
Designer: Arthur Gredington
Height: 3 ½", 8.9 cm

Colourway	Finish	Intro.	Disc.	U.K. £	U.S. $	Can. $
Brown	Gloss	1947	1971	25.00	40.00	40.00
Chestnut	Gloss	1958	1967	225.00	350.00	350.00
Grey	Gloss	1961	1971	90.00	140.00	140.00
Opaque	Gloss	1961	1971	125.00	200.00	200.00
Painted white	Gloss	1961	1967	200.00	300.00	300.00
Palomino	Gloss	1961	1971	55.00	85.00	85.00
Rocking horse grey	Gloss	c.1948	1962	300.00	450.00	450.00
White	Matt	1970	1970	60.00	90.00	90.00

Model No. 1145

KNIGHT IN ARMOUR
(The Earl of Warwick)

Designer: Arthur Gredington
Height: 10 ¾", 27.8 cm

Colourway	Finish	Intro.	Disc.	U.K. £	U.S. $	Can. $
Grey	Gloss	1949	1973	875.00	1,350.00	1,350.00

Model No. 1182

SWISH TAIL HORSE

Designer: Arthur Gredington
Height: 8 ¾", 22.2 cm

First Version: The tail is attached to the quarter almost parallel to the ground

Second Version: The tail is slightly lower down and only to the edge of the quarter

FIRST VERSION: The tail is attached to the quarters almost parallel to the ground.

Colourway	Finish	Intro.	Disc.	U.K. £	U.S. $	Can. $
Brown	Gloss	1950	c.1982	40.00	60.00	60.00
Brown	Matt	1970	c.1982	40.00	60.00	60.00
Chestnut	Gloss	1958	1967	250.00	375.00	375.00
Grey	Gloss	1961	c.1982	110.00	175.00	175.00
Grey	Matt	1970	c.1982	60.00	90.00	90.00
Opaque	Gloss	1961	1973	225.00	350.00	350.00
Painted white	Gloss	1961	1967	250.00	375.00	375.00
Palomino	Gloss	1961	c.1982	75.00	110.00	110.00
Palomino	Matt	1970	c.1982	60.00	90.00	90.00
Rocking horse grey	Gloss	c.1951	1962	600.00	900.00	900.00
White	Matt	1970	c.1982	60.00	90.00	90.00

SECOND VERSION: The tail is attached slightly lower down and only to the edge of the quarters.

Colourway	Finish	Intro.	Disc.	U.K. £	U.S. $	Can. $
Brown	Gloss	c.1982	1989	30.00	45.00	45.00
Brown	Matt	c.1982	1989	30.00	45.00	45.00
Grey	Gloss	c.1982	1989	80.00	120.00	120.00
Grey	Matt	c.1982	1989	50.00	75.00	75.00
Palomino	Gloss	c.1982	1983	60.00	90.00	90.00
Palomino	Matt	c.1982	1983	50.00	75.00	75.00
White	Matt	c.1982	1982	50.00	75.00	75.00

Model No. 1197

PONY
(Head Up)

Designer: Arthur Gredington
Height: 5 ½", 14.0 cm

Colourway	Finish	Intro.	Disc.	U.K. £	U.S. $	Can. $
Brown	Gloss	1950	1975	50.00	75.00	75.00
Chestnut	Gloss	1958	1967	425.00	650.00	650.00
Grey	Gloss	1962	1975	100.00	150.00	150.00
Opaque	Gloss	1961	1973	200.00	300.00	300.00
Painted white	Gloss	1961	1967	300.00	450.00	450.00
Palomino	Gloss	1961	1975	80.00	120.00	120.00
Piebald	Gloss	Unknown	Unknown		Extremely Rare	
Rocking horse grey	Gloss	c.1951	1962	450.00	700.00	700.00
White	Matt	1970	1975	80.00	120.00	120.00

Model No. 1261 / H1261

PALOMINO
(Prancing Arab Type)

Designer: Arthur Gredington
Height: 6 ¾", 17.2 cm

Model No. 1261 First Version

First Version - Thicker tail

Second Version - Thinner tail

FIRST VERSION: Thicker tail with more definition.

Colourway	Finish	Model No.	Intro.	Disc.	U.K. £	U.S. $	Can. $
Brown	Gloss	1261	1961	Unknown	30.00	45.00	45.00
Brown	Matt	1261	1970	Unknown	30.00	45.00	45.00
Chestnut	Gloss	1261	1958	1967	450.00	700.00	700.00
Grey	Gloss	1261	1961	Unknown	50.00	75.00	75.00
Grey	Matt	1261	1970	Unknown	55.00	85.00	85.00
Opaque	Gloss	1261	1961	1973	175.00	275.00	275.00
Painted white	Gloss	1261	1961	1967	225.00	350.00	350.00
Palomino	Gloss	1261	1952	Unknown	45.00	70.00	70.00
Palomino	Matt	1261	1970	Unknown	45.00	70.00	70.00
Rocking horse grey	Gloss	1261	c.1956	1962	450.00	700.00	700.00
White	Matt	1261	1970	Unknown	65.00	100.00	100.00

SECOND VERSION: Thinner tail with little definition.

Colourway	Finish	Model	Intro.	Disc.	U.K. £	U.S. $	Can. $
Brown							
a. Original issue	Gloss	1261	Unknown	1989	30.00	45.00	45.00
b. Reissued	Gloss	H1261	1999	2002	30.00	45.00	45.00
Brown	Matt	1261	Unknown	1989	30.00	45.00	45.00
Grey							
a. Original issue	Gloss	1261	Unknown	1989	30.00	45.00	45.00
b. Reissued	Gloss	H1261	1999	2002	30.00	45.00	45.00
Grey	Matt	1261	Unknown	1989	30.00	45.00	45.00
Palomino							
a. Original issue	Gloss	1261	Unknown	1989	30.00	45.00	45.00
b. Reissued	Gloss	H1261	1999	2002	30.00	45.00	45.00
Palomino	Matt	1261	Unknown	1989	30.00	45.00	45.00
White	Matt	1261	Unknown	1982	30.00	45.00	45.00

Model No. 1265   ARAB "XAYAL"

The charcoal grey colourway with four white socks is the authentic colouring for " Xayal. " The charcoal grey colourway varies from black to charcoal grey.

Arab " Xayal "

Arab " Xayal " Connoisseur Horse

Designer: Arthur Gredington
Height: 6 ¼", 15.9 cm

Colourway	Finish	Intro.	Disc.	U.K. £	U.S. $	Can. $
Black	Gloss	Unknown	Unknown	300.00	450.00	450.00
Brown	Gloss	1952	1989	30.00	45.00	45.00
Dark	Gloss	Unknown	Unknown	30.00	45.00	45.00
Charcoal grey	Gloss	1952	1984	300.00	450.00	450.00
Chestnut	Gloss	1958	1967	300.00	450.00	450.00
Grey	Gloss	1961	1989	50.00	75.00	75.00
Opaque	Gloss	1961	1973	160.00	250.00	250.00
Painted white	Gloss	1961	1967	250.00	375.00	375.00
Palomino	Gloss	1961	1989	50.00	75.00	75.00
Rocking horse grey	Gloss	c.1953	1962	475.00	725.00	725.00
White	Matt	1961	1984	50.00	75.00	75.00

SERIES: Connoisseur Horses

Height: 7 ¼", 18.4 cm

Colourway	Finish	Intro.	Disc.	U.K. £	U.S. $	Can. $
Dark brown	Matt	1970	1989	85.00	130.00	130.00

Model No. 1359

SUFFOLK PUNCH
CHAMPION "HASSE DAINTY"

Designer: Mr. Orwell
Height: 8", 20.3 cm

Colourway	Finish	Intro.	Disc.	U.K. £	U.S. $	Can. $
Light chestnut	Gloss	1954	Unknown	200.00	300.00	300.00
Dark chestnut	Gloss	Unknown	1971	275.00	425.00	425.00
Grey	Gloss	1965	1965	1,200.00	1,800.00	1,800.00
Palomino	Gloss	Unknown	Unknown	1,000.00	1,500.00	1,500.00

COLOURWAY DESCRIPTIONS

Light Chestnut: Light chestnut horse with much lighter chestnut hooves. Blended thin stripe down the front of the head. Mane and tail are cream with yellow ribbon braided through the mane ending with cream and maroon. Two maroon bows on the tail.

Dark Chestnut: Much darker chestnut horse with dark chestnust mane and tail. Definite white blaze extending over muzzle, and four short white socks. The mane ribbon is lemon with pink at the end and the tail bows are lemon and pink and indistinct.

Model No. 1361   **HACKNEY**

The black colourway is the authentic colouring of "Black Magic of Nork" and has white patches on the flanks.

Designer: Mr. Orwell
Height: 7 ¾", 19.7 cm

Colourway	Finish	Intro.	Disc.	U.K. £	U.S. $	Can. $
Black	Gloss	1955	1983	90.00	150.00	150.00
Black	Matt	1980	1983	75.00	115.00	115.00
Brown	Gloss	1955	1982	100.00	150.00	150.00
Chestnut	Gloss	1958	1967	450.00	675.00	675.00
Grey	Gloss	1961	1975	325.00	500.00	500.00
Opaque	Gloss	1961	1973	250.00	375.00	375.00
Painted white	Gloss	1961	1967	375.00	575.00	575.00
Palomino	Gloss	1961	1970	325.00	500.00	500.00
Rocking horse grey	Gloss	c.1956	1962	450.00	675.00	675.00
White	Matt	1970	1982	60.00	90.00	90.00

Model No. 1373   **PINTO PONY**

First Version: Tail attached to hind leg from hock down   Second Version: Tail hangs loose

Designer: Arthur Gredington
Height: 6 ½", 16.5 cm

FIRST VERSION: Tail is attached to the hind leg from the hock down.

Colourway	Finish	Intro.	Disc.	U.K. £	U.S. $	Can. $
Chestnut	Gloss	1958	1967	650.00	1,000.00	1,000.00
Grey	Gloss	1962	1970	350.00	550.00	550.00
Palomino	Gloss	1961	1970	700.00	1,100.00	1,100.00
Piebald (black and white)	Gloss	1972	Unknown	115.00	175.00	175.00
Skewbald (brown and white)	Gloss	1955	Unknown	115.00	175.00	175.00

SECOND VERSION: Tail hangs loose.

Colourway	Finish	Intro.	Disc.	U.K. £	U.S. $	Can. $
Piebald (black/white)	Gloss	Unknown	1989	115.00	175.00	175.00
Piebald (black/white)	Matt	Unknown	1989	115.00	175.00	175.00
Skewbald (brown/white)	Gloss	Unknown	1989	115.00	175.00	175.00
Skewbald (brown/white)	Matt	Unknown	1989	115.00	175.00	175.00

Model No. 1374

GALLOPING HORSE

Model no. 1374 was the horse used for no. 1377 Canadian Mounted Cowboy. However no. 1374 has only three hooves attached to the base compared to four hooves attached in the ridden variety.

Designer: Mr. Orwell
Height: 7 ½", 19.1 cm

Colourway	Finish	Intro.	Disc.	U.K. £	U.S. $	Can. $
Brown	Gloss	1955	1975	115.00	175.00	175.00
Chestnut	Gloss	1958	1967	350.00	550.00	550.00
Grey	Gloss	1962	1973	200.00	300.00	300.00
Palomino	Gloss	1961	1973	150.00	225.00	225.00

Model No. 1375

CANADIAN MOUNTIE

Designer: Arthur Gredington
Height: 8 ¼", 21.0 cm

Colourway	Finish	Intro.	Disc.	U.K. £	U.S. $	Can. $
Black horse	Gloss	1955	1976	500.00	750.00	750.00
Brown horse	Gloss	Unknown	Unknown	700.00	1,075.00	1,075.00

Model No. 1377

CANADIAN MOUNTED COWBOY

The horse used for model 1377 was also that used for model 1374.

Designer: Mr. Orwell
Height: 8 ¾", 22.2 cm

Colourway	Finish	Intro.	Disc.	U.K. £	U.S. $	Can. $
Palomino	Gloss	1955	1973	1,200.00	1,800.00	1,800.00

Model No. 1391

MOUNTED INDIAN

Designer: Mr. Orwell
Height: 8 ½", 21.6 cm

Colourway	Finish	Intro.	Disc.	U.K. £	U.S. $	Can. $
Skewbald	Gloss	1955	1990	350.00	550.00	550.00

Model No. 1407 / F1407 ARAB FOAL

Designer: Arthur Gredington
Height: 4 ½", 11.9 cm

Colourway	Finish	Model	Intro.	Disc.	U.K. £	U.S. $	Can. $
Brown							
a. Original issue	Gloss	1407	1956	1989	20.00	30.00	30.00
b. Reissued	Gloss	F1407	1999	2002	20.00	30.00	30.00
Brown	Matt	1407	1979	1989	20.00	30.00	30.00
Chestnut	Gloss	1407	1958	1967	275.00	425.00	425.00
Grey	Gloss	1407	1961	1989	40.00	60.00	60.00
Opaque	Gloss	1407	1961	1973	100.00	150.00	150.00
Painted white	Gloss	1407	1961	1967	225.00	350.00	350.00
Palomino	Gloss	1407	1961	1989	40.00	60.00	60.00
Rocking horse grey	Gloss	1407	c.1957	1962	300.00	450.00	450.00
White	Matt	1407	1970	1982	30.00	45.00	45.00

Model No. 1480

PONY
(Boy's Pony)

Designer: Arthur Gredington
Height: 3 ¾", 9.5 cm
Issued: Brown gloss, 1957-1967
             Chestnut gloss, 1958-1967
             Grey gloss, 1957-1967
             Opaque, 1957-1967
             Painted white, 1957-1957
             Palomino gloss, 1957-1967
             Rocking horse grey, 1957-1962

Colourway	U.K. £	U.S. $	Can. $
Brown	75.00	115.00	115.00
Chestnut	700.00	1,075.00	1,075.00
Grey	325.00	500.00	500.00
Opaque	160.00	250.00	250.00
Painted white	425.00	650.00	650.00
Palomino	150.00	225.00	225.00
Rocking horse grey	525.00	825.00	825.00

Model No. 1483

PONY
(Girl's Pony)

Designer: Arthur Gredington
Height: 5", 12.7 cm
Issued: 1.   Brown, gloss – 1957-1967
             2.   Chestnut, gloss, –1958-1967
             3.   Grey, gloss – 1957-1967
             4.   Opaque, gloss – 1957-1967
             5.   Painted white, gloss – 1957-1967
             6.   Piebald, gloss - unknown
             7.   Rocking horse grey – 1957-1962
             8.   Skewbald, gloss – 1957-1967
                  (brown/white)

Colourway	U.K. £	U.S. $	Can. $
Brown	75.00	115.00	115.00
Chestnut	700.00	1,075.00	1,075.00
Grey	325.00	500.00	500.00
Opaque	160.00	250.00	250.00
Painted white	350.00	550.00	550.00
Palomino	275.00	425.00	425.00
Piebald	325.00	500.00	500.00
Rocking horse grey	325.00	500.00	500.00
Skewbald	150.00	225.00	225.00

Model No. 1484

HUNTSMAN'S HORSE

This model was used as the horse in model no. 1501 "The Huntsman." Examples are known in liver chestnut gloss and black gloss.

Designer:	Arthur Gredington
Height:	6 ¾", 17.2 cm
Issued:	1. Brown, gloss – 1957-1982
	2. Chestnut, gloss – 1958-1967
	3. Grey, gloss – 1957-1982
	4. Opaque, gloss – 1957-1973
	5. Painted white, gloss – 1957-1967
	6. Palomino, gloss – 1957-1982
	7. Rocking horse grey, gloss – 1957-1962
	8. White, matt – 1970-1982

Colourway	U.K. £	U.S. $	Can. $
Brown	60.00	90.00	90.00
Chestnut	325.00	500.00	500.00
Grey	75.00	115.00	115.00
Opaque	175.00	275.00	275.00
Painted white	425.00	650.00	650.00
Palomino	85.00	130.00	130.00
Rocking horse grey	525.00	800.00	800.00
White	50.00	75.00	75.00

Model No. 1499

GIRL ON PONY

The pony used for model no. 1499 was also available separately as model no. 1483 "Girl's Pony." The Girl on Pony is available in two variations, one with the girl looking straight ahead and the other has the girl looking down at the pony's neck. There is no price difference between the two variations. Examples have been found with a red jacket.

| Designer: | Arthur Gredington |
| Height: | 5 ½", 14.0 cm |

Colourway	Finish	Intro.	Disc.	U.K. £	U.S. $	Can. $
Brown	Gloss	1957	1965	1,750.00	2,750.00	2,750.00
Light dapple grey	Gloss	c.1961	1965	2,000.00	3,000.00	3,000.00
Palomino	Gloss	c.1957	1965	1,750.00	2,750.00	2,750.00
Piebald	Gloss	c.1957	Unk.	2,500.00	3,750.00	3,750.00
Rocking horse grey	Gloss	c.1961	1962	1,500.00	2,325.00	2,325.00
Skewbald	Gloss	1957	1965	250.00	375.00	375.00

Model No. 1500   **BOY ON PONY**

The pony used for model number 1500 was also available separately as model number 1480 "Boy's Pony." The Boy on Pony is available in two variations, one with the boy looking straight ahead and the other has the boy looking down at the pony's neck. There is no price difference between the two variations. Examples have been found with the boy wearing a red jacket.

Designer: Arthur Gredington
Height: 5 ½", 14.0 cm
Issued: Brown, gloss – c.1961-1976
            Chestnut, gloss – c.1961-1967
            Light dapple grey, gloss –c.1961-1976
            Palomino, gloss – 1957-1976
            Rocking horse grey, gloss – c.1961-1962
            Skewbald, gloss – Unknown

Colourway	U.K. £	U.S. $	Can. $
Brown	600.00	900.00	900.00
Chestnut	1,250.00	1,950.00	1,950.00
Light dapple grey	1,250.00	1,950.00	1,950.00
Palomino	250.00	400.00	400.00
Rocking horse grey	1,250.00	1,950.00	1,950.00
Skewbald	1,100.00	1,700.00	1,700.00

Note: An example in grey gloss is known to exist.

Model No. 1501   **HUNTSMAN**

STYLE TWO: Standing

The horse used for model 1501 was also available separately as model number 1484 "Huntsman's Horse."

Designer: Arthur Gredington
Height: 8 ¼", 21.0 cm
Issued: Brown, gloss – 1957-1995
            Chestnut, gloss – 1965-1967
            Grey, gloss – 1962-1975
            Opaque, gloss – 1971-1973
            Painted white, gloss – 1958-1971
            Palomino, gloss – 1965-1971
            Rocking horse grey, gloss – c.1958-1962
            White, matt – 1971-1981

Colourway	U.K. £	U.S. $	Can. $
Brown	200.00	300.00	300.00
Chestnut	1,500.00	2,300.00	2,300.00
Grey	750.00	1,150.00	1,150.00
Opaque	300.00	450.00	450.00
Painted white	750.00	1,150.00	1,150.00
Palomino	1,250.00	1,950.00	1,950.00
Rocking horse grey	2,750.00	4,250.00	4,250.00
White	325.00	500.00	500.00

Note: Model with Huntsman wearing a green jacket is known.

Model No. 1516

APPALOOSA
(Spotted Walking Pony)

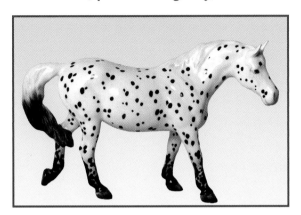

Designer: Arthur Gredington
Height: 5 ¼", 13.3 cm

Colourway	Finish	Intro.	Disc.	U.K. £	U.S. $	Can. $
Brown	Gloss	1958	1967	225.00	350.00	350.00
Chestnut	Gloss	1958	1967	500.00	750.00	750.00
Grey	Gloss	1958	1967	400.00	600.00	600.00
Opaque	Gloss	1958	1967	185.00	300.00	300.00
Painted white	Gloss	1958	1967	550.00	850.00	850.00
Palomino	Gloss	1958	1967	400.00	600.00	600.00
Rocking Horse Grey	Gloss	1958	1962	975.00	1,500.00	1,500.00
Spotted (British)	Gloss	1957	1966	500.00	750.00	750.00

Model No. 1546

H.M. QUEEN ELIZABETH II
ON IMPERIAL

The horse "Imperial' was also available separately as model number 1557.

Designer: Mr. Folkard
Height: 10 ½", 26.7 cm

Colourway	Finish	Intro.	Disc.	U.K. £	U.S. $	Can. $
Chestnut	Gloss	1958	1981	400.00	600.00	600.00

Model No. 1549 / H1549

HORSE
(Head Tucked, Leg Up)

There are two version of model no. 1549, the first has the tail angled towards the off-hind hock, the second has the tail straight down. At the present time the dates cannot be determined as to when the mould was changed.

Model 1549 - First Version

First Version - Tail angled toward off-hind hock

Second Version - Tail straight down

Designer: Pal Zalmen
Height: 7 ½", 19.1 cm

FIRST VERSION: Tail angled towards the off-hind hock

Colourway	Finish	Model	Intro.	Disc.	U.K. £	U.S. $	Can. $
Brown	Gloss	1549	1958	Unknown	60.00	90.00	90.00
Chestnut	Gloss	1549	1958	1967	400.00	600.00	600.00
Grey	Gloss	1549	1961	Unknown	70.00	110.00	110.00
Grey	Matt	1549	1981	Unknown	55.00	85.00	85.00
Opaque	Gloss	1549	1964	1973	175.00	275.00	275.00
Painted white	Gloss	1549	1961	1967	250.00	375.00	375.00
Palomino	Gloss	1549	1961	Unknown	65.00	100.00	100.00
Palomino	Matt	1549	1981	Unknown	65.00	100.00	100.00
Rocking horse grey	Gloss	1549	c.1959	1962	350.00	550.00	550.00
White	Matt	1549	1970	Unknown	55.00	85.00	85.00

SECOND VERSION: Tail is straight down

Colourway	Finish	Model	Intro.	Disc.	U.K. £	U.S. $	Can. $
Brown							
a. Original issue	Gloss	1549	Unknown	1989	30.00	45.00	45.00
b. Reissued	Gloss	H1549	1999	2002	30.00	45.00	45.00
Grey	Gloss	1549	Unknown	1989	40.00	60.00	60.00
Grey	Matt	1549	Unknown	1989	40.00	60.00	60.00
Palomino	Gloss	1549	Unknown	1989	40.00	60.00	60.00
Palomino	Matt	1549	Unknown	1989	40.00	60.00	60.00
White	Matt	1549	Unknown	1982	40.00	60.00	60.00

Model No. 1557

"IMPERIAL"

This horse was used in model no. 1546 with Queen Elizabeth as rider.

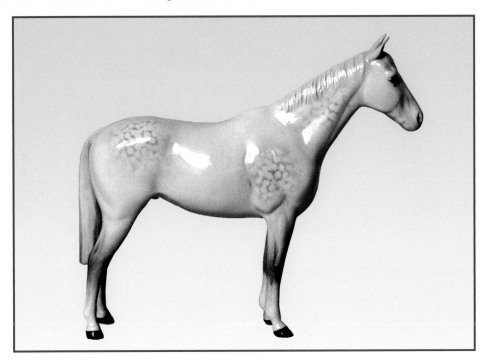

Designer: Albert Hallam and James Hayward
Height: 8 ¼", 21.0 cm

Colourway	Finish	Intro.	Disc.	U.K. £	U.S. $	Can. $
Brown	Gloss	1958	1982	55.00	85.00	85.00
Chestnut	Gloss	1958	1967	275.00	425.00	425.00
Grey	Gloss	1958	1982	60.00	90.00	90.00
Opaque	Gloss	1958	1973	150.00	225.00	225.00
Painted white	Gloss	1958	1967	250.00	375.00	375.00
Palomino	Gloss	1958	1982	50.00	75.00	75.00
Rocking horse grey	Gloss	1958	1962	600.00	900.00	900.00
White	Matt	1970	1982	50.00	75.00	75.00

Model No. 1564　　　　　　　　　**LARGE RACEHORSE**

This is the underlying model for the Connoisseur horse 1564 and the Harnessed version 1564.

Designer:　　Arthur Gredington
Height:　　　11 ¼", 28.5 cm

Colourway	Finish	Intro.	Disc.	U.K. £	U.S. $	Can. $
Brown	Gloss	1959	1982	90.00	135.00	135.00
Chestnut	Gloss	1959	1967	375.00	575.00	575.00
Grey	Gloss	1959	1982	100.00	150.00	150.00
Opaque	Gloss	1959	1973	200.00	300.00	300.00
Painted white	Gloss	1959	1967	550.00	850.00	850.00
Palomino	Gloss	1959	1982	90.00	135.00	135.00
Rocking horse grey	Gloss	1959	1962	1,000.00	1,500.00	1,500.00
White	Matt	1970	1982	75.00	110.00	110.00

　　　　　　SERIES:　Connoisseur Horse

Designer:　　Arthur Gredington
Height:　　　12 ¼", 31.1 cm

Colourway	Finish	Intro.	Disc.	U.K. £	U.S. $	Can. $
Brown	Matt	1970	1981	85.00	130.00	130.00

　　　　　　SERIES:　Harnessed Horses

Height:　　　11 ¼", 28.5 cm

Colourway	Finish	Intro.	Disc.	U.K. £	U.S. $	Can. $
Brown	Gloss	1974	By 1981	125.00	200.00	200.00

Model No. 1588

H.R.H. DUKE OF EDINBURGH
ON ALAMEIN

Designer: Mr. Folkard
Height: 10 ½", 26.7 cm

Colourway	Finish	Intro.	Disc.	U.K. £	U.S. $	Can. $
Light dapple grey	Gloss	1958	1981	400.00	600.00	600.00

Model No. 1624

LIFEGUARD

STYLE ONE: With trumpet

Designer: Arthur Gredington
Height: 9 ½" 24.0 cm

Colourway	Finish	Intro.	Disc.	U.K. £	U.S. $	Can. $
Light dapple grey	Gloss	1959	1977	550.00	850.00	850.00

Model No. 1641

CONNEMARA PONY
"TERESE OF LEAM"

SERIES: Mountain and Moorland Ponies

Designer: Arthur Gredington
Height: 7", 17.8 cm

Colourway	Finish	Intro.	Disc.	U.K. £	U.S. $	Can. $
Grey	Gloss	1961	1984	110.00	175.00	175.00

Model No. 1642

DARTMOOR PONY
"JENTYL" / "WARLORD"

Warlord was commissioned, in a limited edition of 1,500, by P. R. Middleweek & Co. as the first in a series of Dartmoor Ponies.

SERIES: Mountain and Moorland Ponies

Designer: Arthur Gredington
Height: 6 ¼", 15.9 cm

Name	Colourway/Finish	Intro.	Disc.	U.K. £	U.S. $	Can. $
"Jentyl"	Brown/Gloss	1961	1984	135.00	200.00	200.00
"Warlord"	Bay/Gloss	1996	1996	80.00	120.00	120.00

Note: See also The Dartmoor Family page 355.

Model No. 1643

WELSH MOUNTAIN PONY
"COED COCH MADOG"

SERIES: Mountain and Moorland Ponies

First Version: Tail is attached to off-side hind leg

Second Version: Tail hangs loose

Designer: Arthur Gredington
Height: 6 ¼", 15.9 cm

FIRST VERSION: Tail is attached to off-side hind leg.

Colourway	Finish	Intro.	Disc.	U.K. £	U.S. $	Can. $
Grey	Gloss	1961	Unknown	150.00	225.00	225.00

SECOND VERSION: Tail hangs loose.

Colourway	Finish	Intro.	Disc.	U.K. £	U.S. $	Can. $
Grey	Gloss	Unknown	1989	125.00	195.00	195.00

Model No. 1644

HIGHLAND PONY
"MACKIONNEACH"

SERIES: Mountain and Moorland Ponies

Designer: Arthur Gredington
Height: 7 ¼", 18.4 cm

Colourway	Finish	Intro.	Disc.	U.K. £	U.S. $	Can. $
Dun	Gloss	1961	1989	85.00	130.00	130.00
Dark Dun	Gloss	Unknown	Unknown	100.00	150.00	150.00
Light Grey	Gloss	Unknown	Unknown	375.00	600.00	600.00
Opaque	Gloss	Unknown	Unknown		Extremely Rare	

Model No. 1645

EXMOOR PONY
"HEATHERMAN"

SERIES: Mountain and Moorland Ponies

Designer: Arthur Gredington
Height: 6 ½", 16.5 cm

Colourway	Finish	Intro.	Disc.	U.K. £	U.S. $	Can. $
Bay	Gloss	1961	1983	85.00	130.00	130.00

Model No. 1646

NEW FOREST PONY
"JONATHEN 3rd"

SERIES: Mountain and Moorland Ponies

First Version: Tail is attached to the near-side hock

Second Version: Tail hangs loose

Designer: Arthur Gredington
Height: 7", 17.8 cm

FIRST VERSION: Tail is attached to the near-side hock.

Colourway	Finish	Intro.	Disc.	U.K. £	U.S. $	Can. $
Bay	Gloss	1961	Unknown	125.00	195.00	195.00

SECOND VERSION: Tail hangs loose.

Colourway	Finish	Intro.	Disc.	U.K. £	U.S. $	Can. $
Bay	Gloss	Unknown	1984	125.00	195.00	195.00

Model No. 1647

FELL PONY
"DENE DAUNTLESS"

SERIES: Mountain and Moorland Ponies

Designer: Arthur Gredington
Height: 6 ¾", 17.2 cm

Colourway	Finish	Intro.	Disc.	U.K. £	U.S. $	Can. $
Black	Gloss	1961	1982	185.00	285.00	285.00

Model No. 1648

SHETLAND PONY
"ESCHONCHAN RONAY"

SERIES: Mountain and Moorland Ponies

Designer: Arthur Gredington
Height: 4 ¾", 12.1 cm

Colourway	Finish	Intro.	Disc.	U.K. £	U.S. $	Can. $
Brown	Gloss	1961	1989	65.00	100.00	100.00

Note: Examples in opaque gloss and painted white gloss are know to exist.

Model No. 1671

DALES PONY
"MAISIE"

SERIES: Mountain and Moorland Ponies

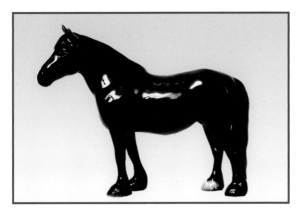

Designer: Arthur Gredington
Height: 6 ½", 16.5 cm

Colourway	Finish	Intro.	Disc.	U.K. £	U.S. $	Can. $
Black	Gloss	1961	1982	175.00	275.00	275.00

Model No. 1730

HUNTSWOMAN

STYLE TWO: Rider and horse stood still

Designer: Arthur Gredington
Height: 8 ¼", 21.0 cm

Colourway	Finish	Intro.	Disc.	U.K. £	U.S. $	Can. $
Brown	Gloss	1960	1975	350.00	550.00	550.00
Grey	Gloss	1960	1995	300.00	450.00	450.00
Opaque	Gloss	1971	1973	400.00	600.00	600.00
Painted white	Gloss	1960	1971	700.00	1,075.00	1,075.00
Rocking horse grey	Gloss	1960	1962	1,500.00	2,300.00	2,300.00
White	Matt	1971	1981	275.00	425.00	425.00

Note: An example is known in black gloss, with the rider wearing a green jacket.

Model No. 1734   **LARGE HUNTER**

FIRST VERSION: The tail hangs straight down, unattached to the leg

Designer: Arthur Gredington
Height: 11 ¼", 28.5 cm

Colourway	Finish	Intro.	Disc.	U.K. £	U.S. $	Can. $
Brown	Gloss	1961	1963	200.00	300.00	300.00
Chestnut	Gloss	1961	1963	750.00	1,150.00	1,150.00
Grey	Gloss	1961	1963	400.00	600.00	600.00
Opaque	Gloss	1961	1963	275.00	425.00	425.00
Painted white	Gloss	1961	1963	600.00	900.00	900.00
Palomino	Gloss	1961	1963	375.00	575.00	575.00
Rocking horse grey	Gloss	1961	1962	875.00	1,350.00	1,350.00

SECOND VERSION: The tail is slightly arched away from the body and is attached to the off-side hock.

Second Version: Arched tail attached to off-side hock

Large Hunter - Connoisseur Horse

Height: 11 ¾", 29.8 cm

Colourway	Finish	Intro.	Disc.	U.K. £	U.S. $	Can. $
Brown	Gloss	1963	1984	70.00	110.00	110.00
Chestnut	Gloss	1963	1967	500.00	750.00	750.00
Grey	Gloss	1963	1984	100.00	150.00	150.00
Opaque	Gloss	1963	1973	200.00	300.00	300.00
Painted white	Gloss	1963	1967	575.00	900.00	900.00
Palomino	Gloss	1963	1983	90.00	135.00	135.00
White	Matt	1970	1982	75.00	120.00	120.00

SERIES: Connoisseur Horses

Height: 12 ¼", 31.1 cm

Colourway	Finish	Intro.	Disc.	U.K. £	U.S. $	Can. $
Grey	Matt	1970	1982	90.00	135.00	135.00

Model No. 1771   ARAB "BAHRAM"

Arab "Bahram"

Arab "Bahram" Connoisseur Horse

Designer: Arthur Gredington
Height: 7 ½", 19.1 cm

Colourway	Finish	Intro.	Disc.	U.K. £	U.S. $	Can. $
Brown	Gloss	1961	1989	45.00	70.00	70.00
Brown	Matt	1980	1989	45.00	70.00	70.00
Chestnut	Gloss	1961	1967	275.00	425.00	425.00
Grey	Gloss	1961	1989	60.00	90.00	90.00
Grey	Matt	1980	1989	60.00	90.00	90.00
Opaque	Gloss	1961	1973	150.00	225.00	225.00
Painted white	Gloss	1961	1967	400.00	600.00	600.00
Palomino	Gloss	1961	1989	75.00	115.00	115.00
Palomino	Matt	1980	1989	45.00	70.00	70.00
Rocking horse grey	Gloss	1961	1962		Extremely Rare	
White	Matt	1970	1982	45.00	70.00	70.00

Note: An example is known in a black satin colourway.

          SERIES: Connoisseur Horses

Height: 8 ¼", 21.0 cm

Colourway	Finish	Intro.	Disc.	U.K. £	U.S. $	Can. $
Grey	Matt	1970	1989	110.00	175.00	175.00

Model No. 1772 / H1772

THOROUGHBRED STALLION
(Large)

Thoroughbred Stallion

Thoroughbred Stallion - Connoisseur Horse

Designer: Arthur Gredington
Height: 8", 20.3 cm

Colourway	Finish	Model	Intro.	Disc.	U.K. £	U.S. $	Can. $
Brown							
a. Original issue	Gloss	1772	1961	1989	50.00	75.00	75.00
b. Reissued	Gloss	H1772	1999	2002	50.00	75.00	75.00
Chestnut	Gloss	1772	1961	1967	275.00	425.00	425.00
Grey	Gloss	1772	1961	1989	60.00	90.00	90.00
Opaque	Gloss	1772	1961	1973	175.00	275.00	275.00
Painted white	Gloss	1772	1961	1967	475.00	750.00	750.00
Palomino	Gloss	1772	1961	1983	125.00	200.00	200.00
Rocking horse grey	Gloss	1772	1961	1962		Extremely Rare	
White	Matt	1772	1970	1982	50.00	75.00	75.00

Note: An example is known in a grey matt colourway.

SERIES: Connoisseur Horses

Height: 8 ¾", 22.2 cm

Colourway	Finish	Intro.	Disc.	U.K. £	U.S. $	Can. $
Bay	Matt	1970	1989	70.00	110.00	110.00

Model No. (A)1772 / (A)H1772   **APPALOOSA STALLION**

Colourway No. 1, More detailed paintwork, striped hooves   Colourway No. 2, Less distinct roan areas, cream hooves

Designer: Arthur Gredington
Height: 8", 20.3 cm

COLOURWAY No. 1.   More detailed paintwork with the head and neck in particular more "mottled."
Striped hooves.

Colourway	Finish	Model	Intro.	Disc.	U.K. £	U.S. $	Can. $
Black and white	Gloss	(A)1772	c.1967	Unknown	125.00	200.00	200.00

COLOURWAY No. 2.   Less distinct roan areas of black on head and neck and brown on lower body quarters.
Cream hooves.

Colourway	Finish	Model	Intro.	Disc.	U.K. £	U.S. $	Can. $
Black and white							
a. Original issue	Gloss	(A)1772	Unknown	1989	95.00	150.00	150.00
b. Re-issue	Gloss	(A)H1772	1999	2002	95.00	150.00	150.00

Model No. 1793

WELSH COB
(Standing)

First Version: Tail hangs straight down

Second Version - Top part of tail arched away from body

Designer: Arthur Gredington
Height: 7 ½", 19.1 cm

FIRST VERSION: Tail hangs straight down.

Colourway	Finish	Intro.	Disc.	U.K. £	U.S. $	Can. $
Brown	Gloss	1962	c.1975/76	75.00	115.00	115.00
Chestnut	Gloss	1962	c.1975/76	625.00	975.00	975.00
Grey	Gloss	1962	c.1975/76	175.00	275.00	275.00
Opaque	Gloss	1962	c.1975/76	200.00	300.00	300.00
Painted white	Gloss	1962	c.1975/76	475.00	750.00	750.00
Palomino	Gloss	1962	1970	400.00	600.00	600.00
Piebald	Gloss	Unknown	Unknown		Very Rare	
White	Matt	1970	c.1975/76	80.00	125.00	125.00

SECOND VERSION: The tail was altered so that the top part (dock) arched away from the body.

Colourway	Finish	Intro.	Disc.	U.K. £	U.S. $	Can. $
Brown	Gloss	c.1975/76	1982	60.00	90.00	90.00
Grey	Gloss	c.1975/76	1982	100.00	150.00	150.00
White	Matt	c.1975/76	1982	60.00	90.00	90.00

Model No. 1811   **MARE AND FOAL**

The mare and foal are available separately as model number 1812 mare and 1813 foal.

Designer: Arthur Gredington
Height: 6", 15.0 cm

Colourway	Finish	Intro.	Disc.	U.K. £	U.S. $	Can. $
Brown mare and chestnut foal	Gloss	1962	1975	175.00	275.00	275.00
Grey mare and black foal	Gloss	1962	1975	225.00	350.00	350.00
Grey mare and brown foal	Gloss	1962	1975	300.00	450.00	450.00

Model No. 1812

MARE
(Facing Right, Head Down)

Model no. 1812 was paired with foal model number 1813 to make model number 1811 "Mare and Foal."

| Designer: | Arthur Gredington |
| Height: | 5 ¾", 14.6 cm |

Colourway	Finish	Intro.	Disc.	U.K. £	U.S. $	Can. $
Brown	Gloss	1962	1989	45.00	70.00	70.00
Brown	Matt	1970	1989	50.00	75.00	75.00
Chestnut	Gloss	1962	1967	375.00	600.00	600.00
Grey	Gloss	1962	1989	75.00	115.00	115.00
Grey	Matt	1970	1989	60.00	90.00	90.00
Opaque	Gloss	1962	1973	150.00	225.00	225.00
Painted white	Gloss	1962	1967	300.00	450.00	450.00
Palomino	Gloss	1962	1989	50.00	75.00	75.00
Palomino	Matt	1970	1983	50.00	75.00	75.00
"Treacle"	Gloss	1992	1992	75.00	115.00	115.00
"Treacle"	Matt	1992	1992	75.00	115.00	115.00
White	Matt	1970	1982	50.00	75.00	75.00

Note: "Treacle" (allover treacle brown gloss or matt finish, no other painted features) seems to have originated from Sinclairs, who offered this piece by mail order in 1992. The figures were sold as brown gloss, but a limited number of these were treacle in colour.

Model No. 1813 / F1813

FOAL
(Larger Thoroughbred Type)

First Version - Fine head and legs

Second Version - Plain head, thicker, less shapely legs

Designer: Arthur Gredington
Height: 4 ½", 11.9 cm

FIRST VERSION: Fine head and legs, off fore leg is placed well behind the near fore leg.

Colourway	Finish	Model	Intro.	Disc.	U.K. £	U.S. $	Can. $
Brown	Gloss	1813	1962	1982	20.00	30.00	30.00
Brown	Matt	1813	1979	1982	20.00	30.00	30.00
Chestnut	Gloss	1813	1962	1967	225.00	350.00	350.00
Grey	Gloss	1813	1962	1982	35.00	55.00	55.00
Opaque	Gloss	1813	1962	1973	90.00	135.00	135.00
Painted white	Gloss	1813	1963	1967	225.00	350.00	350.00
Palomino	Gloss	1813	1962	1982	35.00	55.00	55.00
Piebald	Gloss	1813	Unknown	Unknown	Sold e-Bay August 2004 £1,220.00		
White	Matt	1813	1970	c.1982	35.00	55.00	55.00

SECOND VERSION: Plain head, thicker legs with less shape, off fore leg almost parallel to near fore leg.

Colourway	Finish	Model	Intro.	Disc.	U.K. £	U.S. $	Can. $
Brown							
a. Original issue	Gloss	1813	1982	1982	25.00	40.00	40.00
b. Reissued	Gloss	F1813	1999	1999	25.00	40.00	40.00
Brown	Matt	1813	1982	1989	25.00	40.00	40.00
Grey	Gloss	1813	1982	1989	25.00	40.00	40.00
Palomino	Gloss	1813	1982	1989	25.00	40.00	40.00
Orange bay	Gloss	1813	1982	c.1984	30.00	45.00	45.00
White	Matt	1813	c.1982	1982	30.00	45.00	45.00

Model No. 1816

FOAL
(Smaller Thoroughbred Type, Facing Left)

First Version: Fine head, thin delicate legs

Second Version: Head and legs thicker

Designer: Arthur Gredington
Height: 3 ½", 8.9 cm

FIRST VERSION: Fine head and very thin delicate legs.

Colourway	Finish	Intro.	Disc.	U.K. £	U.S. $	Can. $
Brown	Gloss	1963	1975	30.00	45.00	45.00
Chestnut	Gloss	1963	1967	425.00	650.00	650.00
Grey	Gloss	1963	1975	50.00	75.00	75.00
Opaque	Gloss	1963	1973	80.00	120.00	120.00
Painted white	Gloss	1963	1967	200.00	300.00	300.00
Palomino	Gloss	1963	1975	35.00	55.00	55.00
White	Matt	1970	1975	25.00	40.00	40.00

SECOND VERSION: Head and legs made thicker and less shape to the legs.

Colourway	Finish	Intro.	Disc.	U.K. £	U.S. $	Can. $
Brown	Gloss	1975	1989	20.00	30.00	30.00
Brown	Matt	1979	1989	15.00	25.00	25.00
Grey	Gloss	1975	1983	25.00	40.00	40.00
Palomino	Gloss	1975	1989	25.00	40.00	40.00
White	Matt	1975	1982	20.00	30.00	30.00

Model No. 1817

FOAL
(Smaller Thoroughbred Type, Facing Right)

Designer: Arthur Gredington
Height: 3 ¼", 8.3 cm

Colourway	Finish	Intro.	Disc.	U.K. £	U.S. $	Can. $
Brown	Gloss	1963	1975	25.00	40.00	40.00
Chestnut	Gloss	1963	1967	225.00	350.00	350.00
Grey	Gloss	1963	1975	30.00	45.00	45.00
Opaque	Gloss	1963	1973	100.00	150.00	150.00
Painted white	Gloss	1963	1967	225.00	350.00	350.00
Palomino	Gloss	1963	1975	30.00	45.00	45.00
White	Matt	1970	1975	40.00	60.00	60.00

Model No. 1862

HORSE AND JOCKEY

STYLE TWO: Standing horse and jockey

Designer: Arthur Gredington
Height: 8", 20.3 cm

Colourway	Finish	Intro.	Disc.	U.K. £	U.S. $	Can. $
Brown	Gloss	1963	1984	275.00	425.00	425.00
Light dapple grey	Gloss	1963	1983	400.00	600.00	600.00
Painted white	Gloss	1963	by 1984	700.00	1,075.00	1,075.00

Model No. 1991 / H1991

MARE
(Facing Right, Head Up)

Designer: Arthur Gredington
Height: 5 ½", 14.0 cm

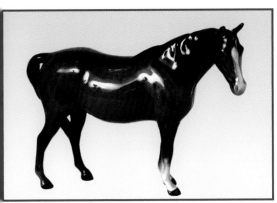

First Version – The end only of the tai attached to the hock

Second Version – Tail attached to the quarters and hock

FIRST VERSION: The end only of the tail is attached to the hock.

Colourway	Finish	Model	Intro.	Disc.	U.K. £	U.S. $	Can. $
Brown	Gloss	1991	1965	Unknown	35.00	50.00	50.00
Brown	Matt	1991	1970	Unknown	35.00	50.00	50.00
Chestnut	Gloss	1991	1965	Unknown	325.00	500.00	500.00
Grey	Gloss	1991	1965	Unknown	60.00	90.00	90.00
Grey	Matt	1991	1970	Unknown	40.00	60.00	60.00
Opaque	Gloss	1991	1965	Unknown	150.00	225.00	225.00
Painted white	Gloss	1991	1965	Unknown	325.00	500.00	500.00
Palomino	Gloss	1991	1965	Unknown	55.00	85.00	85.00
Palomino	Matt	1991	1970	Unknown	50.00	75.00	75.00
White	Matt	1991	1970	Unknown	50.00	75.00	75.00

SECOND VERSION: The tail is attached to the quarters and the hock.

Colourway	Finish	Model	Intro.	Disc.	U.K. £	U.S. $	Can. $
Brown							
a. Original issue	Gloss	1991	Unknown	1989	20.00	30.00	30.00
b. Reissued	Gloss	H1991	1999	2002	20.00	30.00	30.00
Brown	Matt	1991	Unknown	1989	25.00	40.00	40.00
Grey	Gloss	1991	Unknown	1989	35.00	50.00	50.00
Grey	Matt	1991	Unknown	1989	25.00	40.00	40.00
Palomino	Gloss	1991	Unknown	1989	35.00	50.00	50.00
Palomino	Matt	1991	Unknown	1989	25.00	40.00	40.00
White	Matt	1991	Unknown	1982	25.00	40.00	40.00

Model No. 1992 / H1992

THOROUGHBRED STALLION
(Small)

Designer: Arthur Gredington   Height: 5 ½", 14.0.cm

Colourway	Finish	Model	Intro.	Disc.	U.K. £	U.S. $	Can. $
Brown							
a. Original issue	Gloss	1992	1965	1989	30.00	45.00	45.00
b. Reissued	Gloss	H1992	1999	2002	30.00	45.00	45.00
Brown	Matt	1992	1970	1989	30.00	45.00	45.00
Chestnut	Gloss	1992	1965	1967	275.00	425.00	425.00
Grey	Gloss	1992	1965	1989	35.00	55.00	55.00
Grey	Matt	1992	1970	1989	35.00	55.00	55.00
Opaque	Gloss	1992	1965	1973	150.00	225.00	225.00
Painted white	Gloss	1992	1965	1967	275.00	425.00	425.00
Palomino	Gloss	1992	1965	1989	35.00	55.00	55.00
Palomino	Matt	1992	1970	1989	35.00	55.00	55.00
White	Matt	1992	1970	1982	35.00	55.00	55.00

Model No. 2065 / A206   # ARKLE

SERIES: Connoisseur Horses

Designer: Arthur Gredington
Height: 11 7/8", 30.1 cm
Colour: Bay, matt
Issued: a.   Model 2065 – 1970-1989
              b.   Model A2065 – 1999-2002

Description	U.K. £	U.S. $	Can. $
a. Model 2065	115.00	175.00	175.00
b. Model A2065	115.00	175.00	175.00

Model No. 2084

ARKLE
PAT TAAFFE UP

SERIES: Connoisseur Horses

Designer: Arthur Gredington
Height: 12 ½", 21.7 cm

Colourway	Finish	Intro.	Disc.	U.K. £	U.S. $	Can. $
Bay	Matt	1970	1982	300.00	450.00	450.00

Model No. 2186

QUARTER HORSE

Designer: Arthur Gredington
Height: 8 ¼", 21.0 cm

Colourway	Finish	Intro.	Disc.	U.K. £	U.S. $	Can. $
Brown	Gloss	1969	1982	65.00	100.00	100.00
Brown	Matt	1970	1982	65.00	100.00	100.00
Opaque	Gloss	1970	1982	300.00	450.00	450.00
White	Matt	1973	1982	50.00	75.00	75.00

Model No. 2210

HIGHWAYMAN

SERIES: Connoisseur Horses

| Designer: | Albert Hallam |
| Height: | 13 ¾", 34.9 cm |

Colourway	Finish	Intro.	Disc.	U.K. £	U.S. $	Can. $
Bay	Matt	1970	1975	600.00	900.00	900.00

Model No. 2242

ARAB STALLION

This is an authentic rendition of an Arab horse. It is on a pottery (base) stand.

Designer: Albert Hallam
Height: 8 ½", 21.6 cm

Colourway	Finish	Intro.	Disc.	U.K. £	U.S. $	Can. $
Brown	Gloss	1970	1975	300.00	450.00	450.00

Model No. 2269

ARAB STALLION WITH SADDLE

SERIES: Connoisseur Horses

Designer: Albert Hallam
Height: 9 ½", 24.0 cm

Colourway	Finish	Intro.	Disc.	U.K. £	U.S. $	Can.
Dappled grey	Matt	1970	1975	850.00	1,300.00	1,300.00

Model No. 2275

BEDOUIN ARAB

SERIES: Connoisseur Horses

Designer: Albert Hallam
Height: 11 ½", 29.2 cm

Colourway	Finish	Intro.	Disc.	U.K. £	U.S. $	Can. $
Chestnut	Matt	1970	1975	1,400.00	2,175.00	2,175.00

Model No. 2282

NORWEGIAN FJORD HORSE

Designer: Albert Hallam
Height: 6 ½", 16.5 cm

Colourway	Finish	Intro.	Disc.	U.K. £	U.S. $	Can. $
Dun	Gloss	1970	1975	325.00	500.00	500.00

Model No. 2309   **BURNHAM BEAUTY**

Designer: Albert Hallam
Height: 10 ¾", 27.8 cm

Colourway	Finish	Intro.	Disc.	U.K. £	U.S. $	Can. $
Brown	Gloss	1972	1982	75.00	115.00	115.00
White	Matt	1974	1982	75.00	115.00	115.00

SERIES: Connoisseur Horses

Height: 11 ¼", 28.5 cm

Colourway	Finish	Intro.	Disc.	U.K. £	U.S. $	Can. $
Bay	Matt	1971	1982	85.00	130.00	130.00

SERIES: Harnessed Horses

Height: 10 ¾", 27.8 cm

Colourway	Finish	Intro.	Disc.	U.K. £	U.S. $	Can. $
Brown	Matt	1979	1982	125.00	200.00	200.00

Model No. 2340   # CARDIGAN BAY

Two versions of model no. 2340 exist. The first version has only two hooves attached to the base making it unstable and prone to breakage. The base was later redesigned to better support the model and has three legs attached to it.

Designer: Albert Hallam
Height: 9 ¼", 23.5 cm

First Version – Off hind leg is not attached to the base   Second Version – Off hind leg is attached to the base

SERIES: Connoisseur Horses

FIRST VERSION: Two legs attached to the base - off hind leg is not attached to the base.

Colourway	Finish	Intro.	Disc.	U.K. £	U.S. $	Can. $
Brown	Matt	1971	c.1972	600.00	950.00	950.00

SECOND VERSION: Three legs attached to the base - off hind leg is attached to the base.

Colourway	Finish	Intro.	Disc.	U.K. £	U.S. $	Can. $
Brown	Matt	c.1972	1976	475.00	750.00	750.00

Model No. 2345 / A2345

NIJINSKY

SERIES: Connoisseur Horses

Designer: Albert Hallam
Height: 11 ¼", 28.5 cm

Colourway	Finsh	Model	Intro.	Disc.	U.K. £	U.S. $	Can. $
Bay							
a. Original issue	Matt	2345	1971	1989	110.00	175.00	175.00
b. Reissued	Matt	A2345	1999	2002	110.00	175.00	175.00

Model No. 2352

NIJINSKY
LESTER PIGGOTT UP

SERIES: Connoisseur Horses

Designer: Albert Hallam
Height: 12 ½", 31.7 cm

Colourway	Finish	Intro.	Disc.	U.K. £	U.S. $	Can. $
Bay	Matt	1971	1982	300.00	450.00	450.00

Model No. 2421

THE WINNER

Designer: Albert Hallam
Height: 9 ½", 24.0 cm

Colourway	Finish	Intro.	Disc.	U.K. £	U.S. $	Can. $
Brown	Gloss	1973	1982	60.00	90.00	90.00
Brown	Matt	1973	1982	60.00	90.00	90.00
White	Matt	1973	1982	60.00	90.00	90.00

Model No. 2422

MILL REEF

The mahogany bay (gloss) variety was sold through Lawleys, Royal Doulton's retail shops, in the mid 1980s. When Mill Reef was withdrawn from the range at the end of 1989 a white matt variety was sold at the Beswick factory shop.

Designer: Albert Hallam
Height: 9", 22.9 cm

Colourway	Finish	Intro.	Disc.	U.K. £	U.S. $	Can. $
Mahogany bay	Gloss	1985	1988	125.00	200.00	200.00
White	Matt	1989	Unknown	65.00	100.00	100.00

SERIES: Connoisseur Horses

Colourway	Finish	Intro.	Disc.	U.K. £	U.S. $	Can. $
Brown/wooden plinth	Matt	1973	1989	100.00	150.00	150.00

Model No. 2431

MOUNTIE STALLION

SERIES: Connoisseur Horses

Designer: Graham Tongue
Height: 10", 25.4 cm

Colourway	Finish	Intro.	Disc.	U.K. £	U.S. $	Can. $
Black	Gloss	1973	1975	900.00	1,350.00	1,350.00

Model No. 2459

SHIRE MARE
(Lying)

Designer: Unknown
Height: 5", 12.7 cm

Colourways	Finish	Intro.	Disc.	U.K. £	U.S. $	Can. $
Brown	Gloss	1973	Unknown	225.00	350.00	350.00
Grey	Gloss	1973	1976	225.00	350.00	350.00

Model No. 2460

SHIRE FOAL
(Lying)

Designer: Unknown
Height: 3 ½", 8.9 cm

Colourway	Finish	Intro.	Disc.	U.K. £	U.S. $	Can. $
Dark brown	Gloss	1973	1976	75.00	115.00	115.00

Model No. 2464

PERCHERON

SERIES: Harnessed Horses

Designer: Unknown
Height: 9 ¾", 24.7 cm

Colourway	Finish	Intro.	Disc.	U.K. £	U.S. $	Can. $
Dappled grey	Matt	1974	1982	225.00	350.00	350.00

Model No. 2465

CLYDESDALE

SERIES: Harnessed Horses

Designer: Unknown
Height: 10 ¾", 27.8 cm

FIRST VERSION: Working Harness

Colourway	Finish	Intro.	Disc.	U.K. £	U.S. $	Can. $
Chocolate Brown	Matt	1974	1982	130.00	200.00	200.00

SECOND VERSION: Show Harness

Colourway	Finish	Intro.	Disc.	U.K. £	U.S. $	Can. $
Chocolate Brown	Matt	1974	1982	150.00	225.00	200.00

Model No. 2466 / H2466   **BLACK BEAUTY**

This model was used in model number 2466/2536 Black Beauty and Foal, and model number 2703 Spirit of Youth.

Designer: Graham Tongue
Height: 7 ¼", 18.4 cm

Colourway	Finish	Model	Intro.	Disc.	U.K. £	U.S. $	Can. $
Black							
a. Original issue	Matt	2466	1974	1989	40.00	60.00	60.00
b. Reissued	Matt	H2466	1999	2002	40.00	60.00	60.00

Model No. A2466/2536   **BLACK BEAUTY AND FOAL**

A special edition of this model was commissioned by Lawleys by Post to celebrate the centenary of Beswick's Gold Street factory.

Centenary Edition (1898 - 1998)   General Issue

Designer: Graham Tongue
Height: 9 ½", 24.0 cm
Length: 13 ½", 34.3 cm
Series: Connoisseur

Colourway	Finish	Model	Intro.	Disc.	U.K. £	U.S. $	Can. $
Black							
a. Centenary	Matt	A2466/2536	1998	1998	65.00	100.00	100.00
c. General issue	Matt	A2466/2536	1999	2002	65.00	100.00	100.00

Model No. 2467   **LIPIZZANER WITH RIDER**

SERIES: Connoisseur Horses

First Version - Hind legs attached to a circular base   Second Version - Tail and rear legs attached to oval base

Designer: Graham Tongue
Height: 10", 25.4 cm

FIRST VERSION: Hind legs attached to a circular base.

Colourway	Finish	Intro.	Disc.	U.K. £	U.S. $	Can. $
White	Gloss	1974	Unknown	500.00	750.00	750.00

SECOND VERSON: Tail and rear legs attached to an oval base.

Colourway	Finish	Intro.	Disc.	U.K. £	U.S. $	Can. $
White	Gloss	Unknown	1981	500.00	750.00	750.00

Model No. 2505   **STEEPLECHASER**

Designer: Graham Tongue
Height: 8 ¾", 22.2 cm

Colourway	Finish	Intro.	Disc.	U.K. £	U.S. $	Can. $
Dark brown	Gloss	1975	1981	500.00	750.00	750.00

Model No. 2510 / A2510   **RED RUM**

STYLE ONE: Large Size - 12"

SERIES: Connoisseur Horses

Designer: Graham Tongue
Height: 12", 30.5 cm

Colourway	Finish	Model	Intro.	Disc.	U.K. £	U.S. $	Can. $
Bay							
a. Original issue	Matt	2510	1975	1989	115.00	175.00	175.00
b. Reissued	Matt	A2510	1999	2002	115.00	175.00	175.00

Model No. 2511

RED RUM
BRIAN FLETCHER UP

SERIES: Connoisseur Horses

Designer: Graham Tongue
Height: 12 ¼", 31.1 cm

Colourway	Finish	Intro.	Disc.	U.K. £	U.S. $	Can. $
Bay	Matt	1975	1982	275.00	425.00	425.00

Model No. 2535

PSALM
ANN MOORE UP

SERIES: Connoisseur Horses

Designer: Graham Tongue
Height: 12 ¾", 32.4 cm

Colourway	Finish	Intro.	Disc.	U.K. £	U.S. $	Can. $
Brown	Matt	1975	1982	325.00	500.00	500.00

Model No. 2536 / F2536

BLACK BEAUTY FOAL

Designer: Graham Tongue
Height: 6", 15.2 cm

Colourway	Finish	Model	Intro.	Disc.	U.K. £	U.S. $	Can. $
Black							
a. Original issue	Matt	2536	1976	1989	20.00	30.00	30.00
b. Reissued	Matt	F2536	1999	2002	20.00	30.00	30.00
Brown	Matt	2536	1984	Unknown	25.00	40.00	40.00
Chocolate brown	Matt	2536	1984	Unknown	30.00	45.00	45.00
Palomino	Matt	2536	1984	Unknown	35.00	55.00	55.00
White	Matt	2536	1984	Unknown	25.00	40.00	40.00

Model No. 2540

PSALM

SERIES: Connoisseur Horses

Designer: Graham Tongue
Height: 11 ½", 29.2 cm

Colourway	Finish	Intro.	Disc.	U.K. £	U.S. $	Can. $
Brown	Matt	1975	1982	150.00	225.00	225.00

Model No. 2541A

WELSH MOUNTAIN STALLION
"GREDINGTON SIMWNT"

This model of Gredington Simwnt was greatly adapted to produce "The Spirit of Whitfield."

SERIES: Connoisseur Horses

Designer: Graham Tongue
Height: 9", 22.9 cm

Colourway	Finish	Intro.	Disc.	U.K. £	U.S. $	Can. $
Light grey	Matt	1976	1989	400.00	600.00	600.00

Model No. 2548

WHITBREAD SHIRE HORSE

A small number of sample models of the Whitbread Shire Horse were made originally for sale as souvenirs from the Whitbread (Brewery) Shire Horse Farm, Kent, U.K., however they were never put into production.

Designer: Unknown
Height: 6", 15.2 cm

Colourway	Finish	Intro.	Disc.	U.K. £	U.S. $	Can. $
Grey	Gloss	1976	1976	600.00	900.00	900.00
Grey	Matt	1976	1976	600.00	900.00	900.00

Model No. 2558   GRUNDY

> **SERIES:** Connoisseur Horses

Designer: Graham Tongue
Height: 11 ¼", 28.5 cm

Colourway	Finish	Model	Intro.	Disc.	U.K. £	U.S. $	Can. $
Chestnut	Matt	2558	1977	1989	115.00	175.00	175.00

Model No. 2562   LIFEGUARD

> **STYLE TWO:** With Sword

> **SERIES:** Connoisseur Horses

Designer: Graham Tongue
Height: 14 ½", 36.8 cm

Colourway	Finish	Model	Intro.	Disc.	U.K. £	U.S. $	Can. $
Black	Matt	2562	1977	1989	475.00	725.00	725.00

Model No. 2578

SHIRE HORSE
(Large action shire)

Designer: Alan Maslankowski
Height: 8 ¼", 21.0 cm

Colourway	Finish	Intro.	Disc.	U.K. £	U.S. $	Can. $
Brown	Gloss	1980	1982	130.00	200.00	200.00
Brown	Matt	1978	1989	130.00	200.00	200.00
Grey	Gloss	1978	1982	250.00	375.00	375.00
Grey	Matt	1980	1983	200.00	300.00	300.00

SERIES: Harnessed Horses

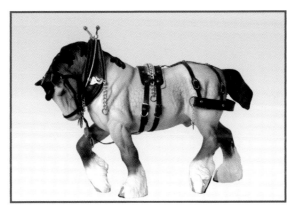

Colourway	Finish	Intro.	Disc.	U.K. £	U.S. $	Can. $
Brown	Matt	1978	1982	175.00	275.00	275.00
Grey	Matt	1978	1982	250.00	375.00	375.00

Model No. 2582   **BLUES AND ROYALS**

SERIES: Connoisseur Horses

Designer: Graham Tongue
Height: 14 ½", 36.8 cm

Colourway	Finish	Intro.	Disc.	U.K. £	U.S. $	Can. $
Black	Matt	1987	1989	350.00	550.00	550.00

Model No. 2605

MORGAN STALLION
" TARRYALL MAESTRO "

SERIES: Connoisseur Horses

Designer: Graham Tongue
Height: 11 ½", 29.2 cm

Colourway	Finish	Intro.	Disc.	U.K. £	U.S. $	Can. $
Black	Matt	1979	1989	150.00	225.00	225.00

Model No. 2608

THE MINSTREL

SERIES: Connoisseur Horses

Designer: Graham Tongue
Height: 13 ¼", 33.6 cm

Colourway	Finish	Intro.	Disc.	U.K. £	U.S. $	Can. $
Chestnut	Matt	1980	1989	150.00	225.00	225.00

Model No. 2671

MOONLIGHT

SERIES: Connoisseur Horses

Designer: Graham Tongue
Height: 11 ¼", 28.5 cm

Colourway	Finish	Intro.	Disc.	U.K. £	U.S. $	Can. $
"Moonlight" - Grey	Matt	1982	1989	115.00	175.00	175.00
"Nightshade" - Black	Matt	1986	1989	130.00	200.00	200.00
"Sunburst" - Palomino	Matt	1986	1989	130.00	200.00	200.00

Model No. 2674

TROY

SERIES: Connoisseur Horses

Designer: Graham Tongue
Height: 11 ¾", 29.8 cm

Colourway	Finish	Intro.	Disc.	U.K. £	U.S. $	Can. $
Bay	Matt	1981	1989	130.00	200.00	200.00

Model No. 2688 / H2688   **SPIRIT OF THE WIND**

Designer: Graham Tongue
Height: 8", 20.3 cm

Colourway	Finish	Model	Intro.	Disc.	U.K. £	U.S. $	Can. $
Brown	Gloss	2688	1982	1989	30.00	45.00	45.00
Brown	Matt	2688	1982	1989	30.00	45.00	45.00
Grey	Gloss	2688	1982	1989	80.00	120.00	120.00
Grey	Matt	2688	1982	1989	80.00	120.00	120.00
Palomino	Gloss	2688	1982	1989	80.00	120.00	120.00
Palomino	Matt	2688	1982	1989	55.00	85.00	85.00

SERIES: On Wooden Plinth

Colourway/Plinth	Finish	Model	Intro.	Disc.	U.K. £	U.S. $	Can. $
Black/Brown	Matt	2688	1986	1989	30.00	45.00	45.00
Brown/Brown							
a. Original issue	Gloss	2688	1986	1989	40.00	60.00	60.00
b. Reissued	Gloss	H2688	1999	2002	40.00	60.00	60.00
Brown/Brown							
a. Original issue	Matt	2688	1986	1989	30.00	45.00	45.00
b. Reissued	Matt	H2688	1999	2002	30.00	45.00	45.00
White/Black	Matt	2688	1982	1989	30.00	45.00	45.00

SERIES: On Ceramic Plinth

Colourway	Finish	Intro.	Disc.	U.K. £	U.S. $	Can. $
Brown	Gloss	c.1987	c.1987	70.00	100.00	100.00

SERIES: Britannia Collection

Colourway	Finish	Intro.	Disc.	U.K. £	U.S. $	Can. $
Bronze	Gloss	1989	1993	70.00	100.00	100.00

Model No. 2689 / H2689   **SPIRIT OF FREEDOM**

Model number 2689 was used together with model number 2353 to become the Spirit of Affection.

Designer: Graham Tongue
Height: 7", 17.8 cm

Colourway	Finish	Model	Intro.	Disc.	U.K. £	U.S. $	Can. $
Brown	Gloss	2689	1982	1989	30.00	45.00	45.00
Brown	Matt	2689	1982	1989	30.00	45.00	45.00
Grey	Gloss	2689	1982	1989	50.00	75.00	75.00
Grey	Matt	2689	1982	1989	50.00	75.00	75.00
Palomino	Gloss	2689	1982	1989	35.00	55.00	55.00
Palomino	Matt	2689	1982	1989	60.00	90.00	90.00

SERIES: On Wooden Plinth

The black and brown versions were mounted on brown wooden plinths and the white version was issued on a black wooden plinth.

Colourway/Plinth	Finish	Model	Intro.	Disc.	U.K. £	U.S. $	Can. $
Black/brown	Matt	2689	1987	1989	25.00	40.00	40.00
Brown/brown							
a. Original issue	Gloss	2689	1986	1989	45.00	70.00	70.00
b. Reissued	Gloss	H2689	1999	2002	45.00	70.00	70.00
Brown/brown0							
a. Original issue	Matt	2689	1986	1989	45.00	70.00	70.00
b. Reissued	Matt	H2689	1999	2002	45.00	70.00	70.00
White/black	Matt	2689	1982	1989	45.00	70.00	70.00

SERIES: On Ceramic Plinth

Colourway	Finish	Model	Intro.	Disc.	U.K. £	U.S. $	Can. $
Brown	Gloss	2689	c.1987	c.1987	30.00	45.00	45.00

Model No. 2689/2536 – H2689/2536   ## SPIRIT OF AFFECTION

The Spirit of Affection is the Spirit of Freedom with the Black Beauty Foal. In all versions but one, the mare and the foal are the same colour. The brown, grey and palomino versions were mounted on a brown wooden plinth and the white version was mounted on a black wooden plinth.

SERIES: On Wooden Plinth

Designer: Graham Tongue
Height: 8", 20.3 cm

Colourway	Finish	Model	Intro.	Disc.	U.K. £	U.S. $	Can. $
Brown	Matt	2689/2536	1982	1989	55.00	85.00	85.00
Grey mare, chocolate brown foal	Matt	2689/2536	1984	1989	80.00	120.00	120.00
Palomino	Matt	2689/2536	1984	1989	80.00	120.00	120.00
White							
a. Original issue	Matt	2689/2536	1982	1989	50.00	75.00	75.00
b. Reissued	Matt	H2689/2536	1999	2002	50.00	75.00	75.00

Model No. 2703 / H2703   **SPIRIT OF YOUTH**

The Spirit of Youth is the same model as 2466 "Black Beauty."

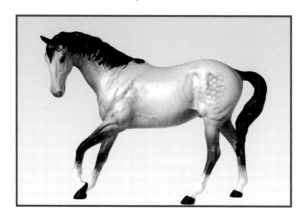

Designer: Graham Tongue
Height: 7", 17.8 cm

Colourway	Finish	Model	Intro.	Disc.	U.K. £	U.S. $	Can. $
Brown	Gloss	2703	1982	1989	35.00	55.00	55.00
Brown	Matt	2703	1982	1989	40.00	60.00	60.00
Grey	Gloss	2703	1982	1989	60.00	90.00	90.00
Grey	Matt	2703	1982	1989	45.00	70.00	70.00
Palomino	Gloss	2703	1982	1989	85.00	130.00	130.00
Palomino	Matt	2703	1982	1989	50.00	75.00	75.00

SERIES: On Wooden Plinth

The black and brown models were issued on a brown wooden plinth and the white model was issued on a black wooden plinth.

Colourway/Plinth	Finish	Model	Intro.	Disc.	U.K. £	U.S. $	Can. $
Black/Brown	Matt	2703	1987	1989	45.00	70.00	70.00
Brown/Brown							
a. Original issue	Gloss	2703	1982	1989	45.00	70.00	70.00
b. Reissued	Gloss	H2703	1999	2002	45.00	70.00	70.00
Brown/Brown	Matt	2703	1986	1989	40.00	60.00	60.00
White/Black	Matt	2703	1982	1989	40.00	60.00	60.00

SERIES: On Ceramic Plinth

Colourway	Finish	Model	Intro.	Disc.	U.K. £	U.S. $	Can. $
Brown	Gloss	2703	c.1987	c.1987	50.00	75.00	75.00

Model No. 2829

SPIRIT OF FIRE

Designer: Graham Tongue
Height: 8", 20.3 cm

Colourway	Finish	Intro.	Disc.	U.K. £	U.S. $	Can. $
Brown	Gloss	1984	1989	40.00	60.00	60.00
Brown	Matt	1984	1989	40.00	60.00	60.00
Grey	Gloss	1984	1989	50.00	75.00	75.00
Grey	Matt	1984	1989	45.00	65.00	65.00
Palomino	Gloss	1984	1989	80.00	120.00	120.00
Palomino	Matt	1984	1989	35.00	55.00	55.00

SERIES: On Wooden Plinth

The black and brown versions were issued on a brown wooden plinth and the white version was issued on a black wooden plinth.

Colourway/Plinth	Finish	Intro.	Disc.	U.K. £	U.S. $	Can. $
Black/Brown	Matt	1986	1989	40.00	60.00	60.00
Brown/Brown	Matt	1986	1989	40.00	60.00	60.00
White/Black	Matt	1984	1989	40.00	60.00	60.00

SERIES: On Ceramic Plinth

Colourway	Finish	Intro.	Disc.	U.K. £	U.S. $	Can. $
Brown	Gloss	c.1987	c.1987	40.00	60.00	60.00

Model No. 2837 / F2837

SPRINGTIME

Designer: Graham Tongue
Height: 4 ½", 11.9 cm

SERIES: Spirited Foals

VARIATION No. 1 Free Standing

Colourway	Finish	Model	Intro.	Disc.	U.K. £	U.S. $	Can. $
Brown	Gloss	2837	1984	1989	15.00	25.00	25.00

VARIATION No. 2 On Wooden Plinth

Colourway/Plinth	Finish	Model	Intro.	Disc.	U.K. £	U.S. $	Can. $
Black/Brown	Matt	2837	1987	1989	20.00	30.00	30.00
Brown/Brown	Matt	2837	1986	1989	20.00	30.00	30.00
White/Black							
a. Original issue	Matt	2837	1984	1989	15.00	25.00	25.00
b. Reissued	Matt	F2837	1999	2002	15.00	25.00	25.00

Model No. 2839   **YOUNG SPIRIT**

Young Spirit was originally illustrated in a catalogue with his ears sticking out slightly. The model was changed to have the ears flat against the foals head, probably due to the potential problem of breakage in shipping. No date has been established for the mould change but it is probably either in the early stages of production, i.e. prototype or shortly after issue.

    SERIES: Spirited Foals

Designer: Graham Tongue
Height: 4 ½", 11.9 cm

VARIATION No. 1   Free Standing

Colourway	Finish	Intro.	Disc.	U.K. £	U.S. $	Can. $
Brown	Gloss	1984	1989	20.00	30.00	30.00

VARIATION No. 2   On Wooden Plinth

Colourway/Plinth	Finish	Intro.	Disc.	U.K. £	U.S. $	Can. $
Black/Brown	Matt	1987	1989	20.00	30.00	30.00
Brown/Brown	Matt	1986	1989	20.00	30.00	30.00
White/Black	Matt	1984	1989	20.00	30.00	30.00

Model No. 2875   **SUNLIGHT**

Designer: Graham Tongue
Height: 4 ½", 11.9 cm

SERIES: Spirited Foals

VARIATION No. 1 Free Standing

Colourway	Finish	Intro.	Disc.	U.K. £	U.S. $	Can. $
Brown	Gloss	1987	1989	20.00	30.00	30.00

VARIATION No. 2 On Wooden Plinth

Colourway/Plinth	Finish	Intro.	Disc.	U.K. £	U.S. $	Can. $
Black/Brown	Matt	1987	1989	20.00	30.00	30.00
Brown/Brown	Matt	1987	1989	20.00	30.00	30.00
White/Black	Matt	1985	1989	20.00	30.00	30.00

Model No. 2876

ADVENTURE

SERIES: Spirited Foals

Designer: Graham Tongue
Height: 4 ½", 11.9 cm

VARIATION No. 1   Free Standing

Colourway	Finish	Intro.	Disc.	U.K. £	U.S. $	Can. $
Brown	Gloss	1987	1989	20.00	30.00	30.00

VARIATION No. 2   On Wooden Plinth

Colourway/Plinth	Finish	Intro.	Disc.	U.K. £	U.S. $	Can. $
Black/Brown	Matt	1987	1989	20.00	30.00	30.00
Brown/Brown	Matt	1987	1989	20.00	30.00	30.00
White/Black	Matt	1985	1989	20.00	30.00	30.00

Model No. 2914   **SPIRIT OF EARTH**

Designer: Graham Tongue
Height: 7 ½", 19.1 cm

Colourway	Finish	Intro.	Disc.	U.K. £	U.S. $	Can. $
Brown	Gloss	1987	1989	70.00	110.00	110.00
Brown	Matt	1987	1989	60.00	90.00	90.00
Grey	Gloss	1987	1989	115.00	175.00	175.00
Grey	Matt	1987	1989	115.00	175.00	175.00

SERIES: On Wooden Plinth

The black and brown versions were issued on a brown wooden plinth and the white version was issued on a black wooden plinth.

Colourway/Plinth	Finish	Intro.	Disc.	U.K. £	U.S. $	Can. $
Black/Brown	Matt	1987	1989	50.00	75.00	75.00
Brown/Brown	Matt	1987	1989	50.00	75.00	75.00
White/Black	Matt	1986	1989	50.00	75.00	75.00

SERIES: On Ceramic Plinth

Colourway/Plinth	Finish	Intro.	Disc.	U.K. £	U.S. $	Can. $
Brown/Ceramic	Gloss	c.1987	c.1987	115.00	175.00	175.00

SERIES: Britannia Collection

Colourway	Finish	Intro.	Disc.	U.K. £	U.S. $	Can. $
Bronze	Gloss	1989	1993	150.00	225.00	225.00

Model No. 2916   **SPIRIT OF PEACE**

Designer: Graham Tongue
Height: 4 ¾", 12.1 cm

Colourway	Finish	Intro.	Disc.	U.K. £	U.S. $	Can. $
Brown	Gloss	1987	1989	35.00	55.00	55.00
Brown	Matt	1987	1989	35.00	55.00	55.00
Grey	Gloss	1987	1989	70.00	110.00	110.00
Grey	Matt	1987	1989	70.00	110.00	110.00
Palomino	Gloss	1987	1989	45.00	70.00	70.00
Palomino	Matt	1987	1989	45.00	70.00	70.00

SERIES: On Wooden Plinth

The black and brown versions were issued on a brown wooden plinth and the white version was issued on a black wooden plinth.

Colourway/Plinth	Finish	Intro.	Disc.	U.K. £	U.S. $	Can. $
Black/Brown	Matt	1987	1989	35.00	55.00	55.00
Brown/Brown	Matt	1987	1989	40.00	60.00	60.00
White/Black	Matt	1986	1989	25.00	40.00	40.00

SERIES: On Ceramic Plinth

Colourway	Finish	Intro.	Disc.	U.K. £	U.S. $	Can. $
Brown	Gloss	c.1987	c.1987	45.00	70.00	70.00

Model No. 2935

SPIRIT OF NATURE

Designer: Graham Tongue
Height: 5 ½", 14.0 cm

Colourway	Finish	Intro.	Disc.	U.K. £	U.S. $	Can. $
Brown	Gloss	1987	1989	30.00	45.00	45.00
Brown	Matt	1987	1989	30.00	45.00	45.00
Grey	Gloss	1987	1989	85.00	130.00	130.00
Grey	Matt	1987	1989	70.00	110.00	110.00
Palomino	Gloss	1987	1989	40.00	60.00	60.00
Palomino	Matt	1987	1989	40.00	60.00	60.00

SERIES: On Wooden Plinth

The black and brown versions were mounted on brown wooden plinths and the white version was mounted on a black wooden plinth.

Colourway/Plinth	Finish	Intro.	Disc.	U.K. £	U.S. $	Can. $
Black/Brown	Matt	1987	1989	35.00	55.00	55.00
Brown/Brown	Matt	1987	1989	50.00	75.00	75.00
White/Black	Matt	1987	1989	50.00	75.00	75.00

SERIES: On Ceramic Plinth

Colourway	Finish	Intro.	Disc.	U.K. £	U.S. $	Can. $
Brown	Gloss	c.1987	c.1987	50.00	75.00	75.00

Model No. 3426 / A234   ## CANCARA – THE BLACK HORSE

Modelled from "Downland Cancara" graded Trakehner stallion famous for advertising Lloyds Bank. Backstamp - "1994 Special Beswick Centenary."

SERIES: Connoisseur Horses

Designer: Graham Tongue
Height: 16 ½", 41.9 cm

Colourway	Finish	Model	Intro.	Disc.	U.K. £	U.S. $	Can. $
Black							
a. Original issue	Matt	3426	1994	1994	350.00	550.00	550.00
b. Reissued	Matt	A234	1999	2002	350.00	550.00	550.00

Model No. A182   **FIRST BORN**

SERIES: Connoisseur

Designer: Amanda Hughes-Lubeck
Height: 7", 17.8 cm

Colourway	Finish	Intro.	Disc.	U.K. £	U.S. $	Can. $
Chestnut mare and foal	Matt	1999	2002	65.00	100.00	100.00

Model No. H183   **SPIRIT OF THE WILD**

Designer: Warren Platt
Height: 12", 30.5 cm

Colourway	Finish	Intro.	Disc.	U.K. £	U.S. $	Can. $
Black	Matt	1999	2002	40.00	60.00	60.00
Brown	Matt	1999	2002	50.00	75.00	75.00
White	Matt	1999	2002	35.00	55.00	55.00

Model No. A184

DESERT ORCHID

SERIES: Connoisseur

Designer: Warren Platt
Height: 7¾", 19.7 cm

Colourway	Finish	Intro.	Disc.	U.K. £	U.S. $	Can. $
Light grey	Matt	1999	2002	115.00	175.00	175.00

Model No. H193

MY FIRST HORSE

Designer: Amanda Hughes-Lubeck
Height: 8 ¼", 21.0 cm

Colourway	Finish	Intro.	Disc.	U.K. £	U.S. $	Can. $
Chestnut	Gloss	1999	2002	60.00	90.00	90.00

Model No. A226   **RED RUM**

STYLE TWO: Small size - 9"

SERIES: Connoisseur

Designer: Amanda Hughes-Lubeck
Height: 9", 22.9 cm

Colourway	Finish	Intro.	Disc.	U.K. £	U.S. $	Can. $
Bay	Matt	1999	2002	80.00	125.00	125.00

Model No. H244   **NEW FOREST PONY**

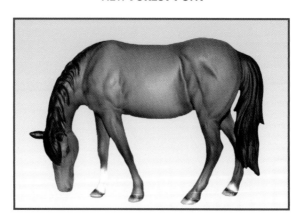

Designer: Shane Ridge
Height: 6", 15.0 cm

Colourway	Finish	Intro.	Disc.	U.K. £	U.S. $	Can. $
Brown	Matt	1999	2002	50.00	75.00	75.00

Model No. A247

WELSH MOUNTAIN PONY/
"CHAMPION WELSH MOUNTAIN PONY"

The Champion Welsh Mountain Pony was the 1999 Beswick Collectors Club "Special." A "Beswick" green rug with yellow binding has BCC99 on the corner, and a red rosette is on the bridle. The Champion Welsh Pony was issued in a limited edition of 580.

In 2000 the Welsh Pony was again chosen as the Beswick Collectors Club "Special." This verson, in white gloss, and issued in a limited dition of 505, has a green rug with yellow binding.

SERIES: Connoisseur

Welsh Mountain Pony (General Issue)

"Champion Welsh Mountain Pony" (Freestanding) (BCC Version)

Designer: Graham Tongue
Height: 8 ¼", 21.0 cm

Colourway	Finish	Intro.	Disc.	U.K. £	U.S. $	Can. $
Black (BCC-1999)	Gloss	1999	Ltd. Ed.	325.00	500.00	500.00
White (BCC-2000)	Gloss	2000	Ltd. Ed.	275.00	425.00	425.00
White (on wooden plinth)	Gloss	1999	2002	175.00	275.00	275.00

Model No. A250

LAMMTARRA

Designer: Warren Platt
Height: 7 ¾", 19.6 cm
Series: Connoisseur

Colourway	Finish	Intro.	Disc.	U.K. £	U.S. $	Can. $
Chestnut	Matt	1999	2002	80.00	125.00	125.00

Model No. H259

PALOMINO

Designer: Shane Ridge
Height: 6 ¾", 17.2 cm

Colourway	Finish	Intro.	Disc.	U.K. £	U.S. $	Can. $
Palomino	Gloss	1999	2002	40.00	60.00	60.00

Model No. H260

HUNTER

Designer: Graham Tongue
Height: 8", 20.3 cm

Colourway	Finish	Intro.	Disc.	U.K. £	U.S. $	Can. $
Black	Gloss	2005	Ltd. Ed.	225.00	350.00	350.00
Grey	Gloss	1999	2002	70.00	110.00	110.00

Model No. H261

HACKNEY PONY

Designer: Martyn Alcock
Height: 6 ¾", 17.2 cm

Colourway	Finish	Intro.	Disc.	U.K. £	U.S. $	Can. $
Bay	Gloss	1999	2002	55.00	85.00	85.00

Model No. A266

ONE MAN

A small quantity of this model were signed in gold pen, on the base, by John Hales, the owner of One Man.

Designer: Martyn Alcock
Height: 7 ½", 19.0 cm
Series: Connoisseur

Colourway	Finish	Intro.	Disc.	U.K. £	U.S. $	Can. $
Light dapple grey	Gloss	1999	2002	85.00	135.00	135.00

Model No. A270

WELSH COB STALLION

SERIES: Connoisseur

Designer: Robert Donaldson
Height: 7 ¼", 18.4 cm

Colourway	Finish	Intro.	Disc.	U.K. £	U.S. $	Can. $
Black	Matt	2000	2002	175.00	275.00	275.00

Model No. A271

DRESSAGE STALLION

Modeller:	Robert Donaldson
Height:	7 ½", 19.0 cm
Series:	Connoisseur

Colourway	Finish	Intro.	Disc.	U.K. £	U.S. $	Can. $
Dark brown	Matt	2000	2002	80.00	125.00	125.00

Model No. A3990

ERISKAY PONY

Designer:	Robert Donaldson
Height:	6", 15.24 cm
Series:	Connoisseur

Colourway	Finish	Intro.	Disc.	U.K. £	U.S. $	Can. $
Light dapple grey	Matt	2000	2002	65.00	100.00	100.00

Note: Produced in association with the Rare Breeds Survival Trust.

Model No. A3998   **CLYDESDALE**

Designer: Robert Donaldson
Height: 8 ½", 21.5 cm
Series: Connoisseur

Colourway	Finish	Intro.	Disc.	U.K. £	U.S. $	Can. $
Bay	Matt	2000	2002	100.00	150.00	150.00

Note: Produced in association with the Rare Breeds Survival Trust.

Model No. A3999   **CLEVELAND BAY**

Designer: Robert Donaldson
Height: 8 ½", 21.5 cm
Series: Connoisseur

Colourway	Finish	Intro.	Disc.	U.K. £	U.S. $	Can. $
Bay	Matt	2000	2002	80.00	125.00	125.00

Note: Produced in association with the Rare Breeds Survival Trust.

Model No. A4000

SUFFOLK PUNCH

Designer:	Robert Donaldson
Height:	8 ½", 21.5 cm
Series:	Connoisseur

Colourway	Finish	Intro.	Disc.	U.K. £	U.S. $	Can. $
Chestnut	Matt	2000	2002	100.00	150.00	150.00

Note: Produced in association with the Rare Breeds Survival Trust.

Model No. H185

SHETLAND PONY / "HOLLYDELL DIXIE"

This Shetland Pony was the 1995 Beswick Collectors Circle "Special." It was decorated to represent Shetland Mare, Supreme Champion "Hollydell Dixie," and was issued in a limited edition of 553 in August 1995. Both the Beswick and BCC backstamps appear on this model.

Designer:	Amanda Hughes-Lubeck
Height:	5 ¼", 13.3 cm

Colourway	Finish	Intro.	Disc.	U.K. £	U.S. $	Can. $
Skewbald (BCC95)	Gloss	1995	Ltd. Ed.	225.00	350.00	350.00
Dapple grey	Gloss	1999	2002	75.00	115.00	115.00

Model No. H4078

SPIRIT OF WISDOM

Designer: Shane Ridge
Height: 9 ½", 24.1 cm

Colourway	Finish	Intro.	Disc.	U.K. £	U.S. $	Can. $
Black	Matt	2001	2002	65.00	100.00	100.00
Brown	Matt	2001	2002	65.00	100.00	100.00
White	Matt	2001	2002	65.00	100.00	100.00

Model No. H4079

SPIRIT OF FLIGHT

Designer: Shane Ridge
Height·   9", 22.9 cm

Colourway	Finish	Intro.	Disc.	U.K. £	U.S. $	Can. $
Black	Matt	2001	2002	65.00	100.00	100.00
Brown	Matt	2001	2002	65.00	100.00	100.00
White	Matt	2001	2002	65.00	100.00	100.00

Wall Ornaments

- Horses

INDEX BY MODEL NUMBER

Photograph not
available
at press time

Photograph not
available
at press time

Model No. 686
HORSE'S HEAD LOOKING LEFT THROUGH A HORSESHOE
First Version - Flat back

Designer:	Mr. Owen
Height:	7 ¼" x 6", 18.4 x 15.0 cm
Colour:	1. Brown - gloss
	2. Dark chestnut - gloss
Issued:	1938-1939
Varieties:	807

Colourway	U.K. £	U.S. $	Can. $
1. Brown	75.00	115.00	115.00
2. Dark chestnut	100.00	150.00	150.00

Model No. 687
HORSE'S HEAD LOOKING RIGHT THROUGH A HORSESHOE
First Version - Flat back

Designer:	Mr. Owen
Height:	7 ¼" x 6", 18.4 x 15.0 cm
Colour:	1. Brown - gloss
	2. Dark chestnut - gloss
Issued:	1939-1939
Varieties:	806

Colourway	U.K. £	U.S. $	Can. $
1. Brown	75.00	115.00	115.00
2. Dark chestnut	100.00	150.00	150.00

Model No. 806
HORSE'S HEAD LOOKING LEFT THROUGH A HORSESHOE
Second Version - Raised back

Designer:	Mr. Owen
Height:	7 ¼" x 6", 18.4 x 15.0 cm
Colour:	Brown - gloss
Issued:	1939-1968
Varieties:	687

Description	U.K. £	U.S. $	Can. $
Gloss	60.00	90.00	90.00

Model No. 807
HORSE'S HEAD LOOKING RIGHT THROUGH A HORSESHOE
Second Version - Raised back

Designer:	Mr. Owen
Height:	7 ¼" x 6", 18.4 x 15.0 cm
Colour:	Brown - gloss
Issued:	1938-1968
Varieties:	686

Description	U.K. £	U.S. $	Can. $
Gloss	60.00	90.00	90.00

Model No. 1382
HUNTER HEAD

Designer:	Arthur Gredington
Height:	4" x 4", 10.1 x 10.1 cm
Colour:	Brown - gloss
Issued:	1955-1969

Description	U.K. £	U.S. $	Can. $
Gloss	40.00	60.00	60.00

Model No. 1384
PALOMINO HEAD

Designer:	Arthur Gredington
Height:	4"x 4", 10.1 x 10.1 cm
Colour:	Palomino - gloss
Issued:	1955-1969

Description	U.K. £	U.S. $	Can. $
Gloss	40.00	60.00	60.00

Model No. 1385
ARAB HEAD

Designer:	Arthur Gredington
Height:	4" x 4", 10.1 x 10.1 cm
Colour:	Dark brown - gloss
Issued:	1955-1969

Description	U.K. £	U.S. $	Can. $
Gloss	40.00	60.00	60.00

Model No. 1505
HUNTSMAN

Designer:	Albert Hallam and James Hayward
Height:	8 ½", 21.6 cm
Colour:	1. Brown - gloss
	2. Copper lustre
Issued:	1958-1962

Colourway	U.K. £	U.S. $	Can. $
1. Brown	150.00	230.00	230.00
2. Copper lustre	85.00	130.00	130.00

Model No. 1513
"TAKING OFF"
Designer: Colin Melbourne
Height: 9", 22.9 cm
Colour: 1.   Brown - gloss
           2.   Copper lustre
Issued: 1958-1962

Colourway	U.K. £	U.S. $	Can. $
1. Brown	150.00	230.00	230.00
2. Copper lustre	85.00	130.00	130.00

Model No. 1514
"LANDING"
Designer: Colin Melbourne
Height: 7 ¾", 19.7 cm
Colour: 1.   Brown - gloss
           2.   Copper lustre
Issued: 1958-1962

Colourway	U.K. £	U.S. $	Can. $
1. Brown	150.00	230.00	230.00
2. Copper lustre	85.00	130.00	130.00

Model No. 1515
"GOING OVER"
Designer: Colin Melbourne
Height: 7 ½", 19.1 cm
Colour: 1.   Brown - gloss
           2.   Copper lustre
Issued: 1958-1962

Colourway	U.K. £	U.S. $	Can. $
1. Brown	150.00	230.00	230.00
2. Copper lustre	85.00	130.00	130.00

Model No. 2699
TROY
Designer: Unknown
Height: 6", 15.0 cm
Colour: Brown - matt
Issued: 1984-1989
Series: Champions All

Description	U.K. £	U.S. $	Can. $
Matt	35.00	55.00	55.00

Model No. 2700
ARKLE

Designer:	Unknown
Height:	6", 15.0 cm
Colour:	Bay - matt
Issued:	1984-1989
Series:	Champions All

Description	U.K. £	U.S. $	Can. $
Matt	35.00	55.00	55.00

Model No. 2701
THE MINSTREL

Designer:	Unknown
Height:	6", 15.0 cm
Colour:	Chestnut - matt
Issued:	1984-1989
Series:	Champions All

Description	U.K. £	U.S. $	Can. $
Matt	35.00	55.00	55.00

Model No. 2702
RED RUM

Designer:	Unknown
Height:	6", 15.0 cm
Colour:	Bay - matt
Issued:	1984-1989
Series:	Champions All

Description	U.K. £	U.S. $	Can. $
Matt	35.00	55.00	55.00

Arab Stallion with Saddle, Model No. 2269

Chapter Eight
WILD ANIMALS

The wild animals in this group have been produced by John Beswick for more than fifty years. Many are authentic and true to life in shape and colour, others are comical.

Beswick wild animals are very popular with collectors. They are less of a minefield for the inexperienced than some of the other series, as the animals are familiar and can be easily identified, since most carry the Beswick backstamp.

As you can see, Beswick produced these animals in a random order. It was not until the late 1930s that realism was created by the use of natural colours, instead of the very popular blue gloss used in earlier days. Around this time, the models were also refined to represent real animals.

The variety of animals is enormous and most animals are represented, ranging from the smallest mouse to the very large African elephant. The powerful bison, the gentle springbok and the elegant giraffe are just some of these superb pieces.

At the time of the introduction of the Connoisseur Series in 1967, most of the items were horses, and it was not until 1973 that three wild animals were absorbed into the series. These were the already existing versions of two elephants, numbers 998 and 1770, both free standing, and a puma on a rock, number 1702. As the name suggests, the Connoisseur Series comprises prestige models, and consequently were and are more expensive than the rest of the animals.

It is interesting to note that Arthur Gredington was the modeller responsible for the majority of the wild animals. Some collectors collect models from one particular designer or modeller, and these would make an excellent choice.

Many of the wild animals are avidly sought after. The search is a challenge, but well worth the effort if you can find your treasured piece.

Model No. 315
SQUIRREL - on pottery base
Designer:	Miss Greaves
Height:	8 ¾", 22.2 cm
Colour:	See below
Issued:	1935-by 1954

Colourway	U.K. £	U.S. $	Can. $
1. Blue - gloss	100.00	150.00	150.00
2. Blue/brown - satin	70.00	110.00	110.00
3. Cream - satin matt	70.00	110.00	110.00
4. Natural - satin	110.00	170.00	170.00

Model No. 316
RABBIT - on pottery base
Designer:	Miss Greaves
Height:	6 ¾", 17.2 cm
Colour:	See below
Issued:	1935-by 1954

Colourway	U.K. £	U.S. $	Can. $
1. Blue , gloss	125.00	195.00	195.00
2. Blue/brown, satin	90.00	140.00	140.00
3. Cream, satin matt	90.00	140.00	140.00
4. Natural, satin	135.00	210.00	210.00

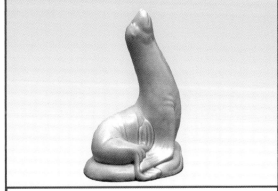

Model No. 368
FROG - on pottery base
Designer:	Miss Greaves
Height:	6 ¾", 16.5 cm
Colour:	See below
Issued:	1936-by 1954

Colourway	U.K. £	U.S. $	Can. $
1. Blue - gloss	100.00	150.00	150.00
2. Blue/brown - satin	70.00	110.00	110.00
3. Cream - satin matt	70.00	110.00	110.00
4. Gold		Rare	
5. Green - satin matt	70.00	110.00	110.00
6. Natural - satin	110.00	170.00	170.00

Model No. 383
SEAL - on pottery base
Designer:	Mr. Owen
Height:	10", 25.4 cm
Colour:	See below
Issued:	1936-by 1954

Colourway	U.K. £	U.S. $	Can. $
1. Blue, gloss	90.00	140.00	140.00
2. Blue/brown, satin	65.00	100.00	100.00
3. Cream, satin matt	65.00	100.00	100.00
4. Natural, satin	100.00	150.00	150.00

Model No. 397
MONKEY - on pottery base

Designer:	Mr. Owen
Height:	7", 17.8 cm
Colour:	See below
Issued:	1936-by 1954

Colourway	U.K. £	U.S. $	Can. $
1. Blue, gloss	100.00	150.00	150.00
2. Blue/brown, satin	90.00	140.00	140.00
3. Cream, satin matt	80.00	120.00	120.00
4. Green, gloss	80.00	120.00	120.00
5. Natural, satin	110.00	170.00	170.00

Model No. 417
POLAR BEAR - on pottery base

Designer:	Mr. Owen
Height:	7", 17.8 cm
Colour:	See below
Issued:	1936-by 1954

Colourway	U.K. £	U.S. $	Can. $
1. Blue, gloss	100.00	150.00	150.00
2. Brown, gloss	150.00	225.00	225.00
3. Cream, satin matt	95.00	150.00	150.00
4. Green, gloss	95.00	150.00	150.00
5. Natural, satin	95.00	150.00	150.00

Model No. 568/569
CHARACTER ELEPHANT

Designer:	Mr. Owen	
Height:	1.	Large - 9", 22.9 cm
	2.	Small - 4 ¾", 12.1 cm
Colour:	See below	
Issued:	1938-by 1954	

Colourway	U.K. £	U.S. $	Can. $
1. Blue, gloss - large	375.00	575.00	575.00
2. Cream, satin - large	350.00	525.00	525.00
3. Cream, gold highlights	375.00	575.00	575.00
4. Blue, gloss - small	225.00	350.00	350.00
5. Cream, satin - small	200.00	300.00	300.00

Model No. 692
ELEPHANT WITH HOWDAH

Designer:	Unknown
Height:	4 ¼", 10.8 cm
Colour:	Blue - gloss
Issued:	1939-by 1954

Colourway	U.K. £	U.S. $	Can. $
Blue	150.00	225.00	225.00

Model No. 696
DEER ON ROCK

Designer:	Arthur Gredington
Height:	8", 20.3 cm
Colour:	See below
Issued:	1939-1954
Set:	721

Colourway	U.K. £	U.S. $	Can. $
1. Blue, gloss	75.00	115.00	115.00
2. Brown, gloss	50.00	75.00	75.00
3. Cream, satin	50.00	75.00	75.00
4. Flambé	200.00	300.00	300.00

Model No. 697
HIPPOPOTAMUS

Designer:	Mr. Watkin
Height:	2 ¼", 5.7 cm
Colour:	1. Blue - gloss
	2. Cream - satin matt
	3. Green - gloss
Issued:	1939-by 1954
Series:	Fun Models

Colourway	U.K. £	U.S. $	Can. $
1. Blue	35.00	55.00	55.00
2. Cream	30.00	45.00	45.00
3. Green	35.00	55.00	55.00

Photograph not available.
Model No. 709 possibly
not put into production.

Model No. 698
GIRAFFE

Designer:	Mr. Watkin
Height:	1. Large - 6", 15.0 cm
	2. Small - 4", 10.1 cm
Colour:	See below
Issued:	1939-by 1954
Series:	Fun Models

Colourway	U.K. £	U.S. $	Can. $
1. Blue, gloss - large	75.00	115.00	115.00
2. Cream, satin - large	60.00	90.00	90.00
3. Blue, gloss - small	50.00	75.00	75.00
4. Cream, satin - small	45.00	70.00	70.00

Model No. 709
BEAVER

Designer:	Mr. Watkin
Height:	Unknown
Colour:	Unknown
Issued:	1939-Unknown

Description	U.K. £	U.S. $	Can. $
Beaver		Possibly not put into production	

Model No. 711
PANDA

Designer:	Mr. Watkin
Height:	4 ½", 11.9 cm
Colour:	See below
Issued:	1939-by 1954

Colourway	U.K. £	U.S. $	Can. $
1. Black/white, gloss	50.00	75.00	75.00
2. Blue, gloss	75.00	115.00	115.00
3. Cream, satin matt	50.00	75.00	75.00

Model No. 720
PANDA CUB

Designer:	James Haywood
Height:	3 ¾", 9.5 cm
Colour:	See below
Issued:	1939-by 1954

Colourway	U.K. £	U.S. $	Can. $
1. Black/white, gloss	55.00	85.00	85.00
2. Blue, gloss	45.00	70.00	70.00
3. Cream, satin matt	45.00	70.00	70.00

Model No. 721
DEER ON BASE

Designer:	Arthur Gredington
Height:	4 ½", 11.9 cm
Colour:	See below
Issued:	1939-by 1954
Set:	696

Colourway	U.K. £	U.S. $	Can. $
1. Blue, gloss	60.00	90.00	90.00
2. Brown, gloss	50.00	75.00	75.00
3. Green, matt	40.00	60.00	60.00
4. White, matt	30.00	45.00	45.00

Model No. 738
PANDA WITH BALL

Designer:	Mr. Watkin
Height:	4 ½", 11.9 cm
Colour:	See below
Issued:	1939-by 1954

Colourway	U.K. £	U.S. $	Can. $
1. Black/white, gloss	55.00	85.00	85.00
2. Blue, gloss	75.00	115.00	115.00
3. Cream, satin matt	55.00	85.00	85.00

Model No. 823
RABBIT - On haunches

Designer:	Arthur Gredington
Height:	3", 7.6 cm
Colour:	1. Blue – gloss
	2. Brown – gloss
Issued:	1. 1940-1954
	2. 1940-1971
Set:	824, 825, 826

Colourway	U.K. £	U.S. $	Can. $
1. Blue, gloss	20.00	30.00	30.00
2. Brown, gloss	10.00	15.00	15.00

Model No. 824
RABBIT - Scratching ear

Designer:	Arthur Gredington
Height:	2 ¼", 5.7 cm
Colour:	1. Blue – gloss
	2. Brown – gloss
Issued:	1. 1940-1954
	2. 1940-1971
Set:	823, 825, 826

Colourway	U.K. £	U.S. $	Can. $
1. Blue, gloss	20.00	30.00	30.00
2. Brown, gloss	10.00	15.00	15.00

Model No. 825
RABBIT - Crouching

Designer:	Arthur Gredington
Height:	1 ½", 3.8 cm
Colour:	1. Blue – gloss
	2. Brown – gloss
Issued:	1. 1940-1954
	2. 1940-1971
Set:	823, 824, 826

Colourway	U.K. £	U.S. $	Can. $
1. Blue, gloss	20.00	30.00	30.00
2. Brown, gloss	10.00	15.00	15.00

Model No. 826
RABBIT - Seated

Designer:	Arthur Gredington
Height:	2", 5.0 cm
Colour:	1. Blue – gloss
	2. Brown – gloss
Issued:	1. 1940-1954
	2. 1940-1971
Set:	823, 824, 825

Colourway	U.K. £	U.S. $	Can. $
1. Blue, gloss	20.00	30.00	30.00
2. Brown, gloss	10.00	15.00	15.00

Model No. 828
ELEPHANT

Designer: Mr. Owen
Colour: 1. Blue - gloss
              2. Cream - satin matt
              3. Pale grey - gloss
Issued: 1940-by 1954

Description	Colourway	Height	U.K. £	Price U.S. $	Can. $
Large	Blue	6", 15.0 cm	150.00	225.00	225.00
Large	Cream	6", 15.0 cm	125.00	200.00	200.00
Large	Pale grey	6", 15.0 cm	125.00	200.00	200.00
Medium	Blue	4 ½", 11.9 cm	100.00	150.00	150.00
Medium	Cream	4 ½", 11.9 cm	85.00	130.00	130.00
Medium	Pale grey	4 ½", 11.9 cm	85.00	130.00	130.00
Small	Blue	3", 7.6 cm	75.00	115.00	115.00
Small	Cream	3", 7.6 cm	65.00	100.00	100.00
Small	Pale grey	3", 7.6 cm	65.00	100.00	100.00

Model No. 830
LIZARD

Designer:	Miss Joachim
Height:	Unknown
Colour:	Green - gloss
Issued:	1940-Unknown

Colourway	U.K. £	U.S. $	Can. $
Green		Extremely Rare	

Model No. 841
LEOPARD - Seated

Designer:	Arthur Gredington
Height:	6 ¼", 15.9 cm
Colour:	See below
Issued:	1940-by 1954

Colourway	U.K. £	U.S. $	Can. $
1. Tan brown/black - gloss	450.00	700.00	700.00
2. Cream - satin matt	400.00	600.00	600.00

Model No. 845A
ZEBRA
First Version - Tan with black stripes

Designer:	Arthur Gredington
Height:	7 ¼", 18.4 cm
Colour:	Tan with black stripes - gloss
Issued:	1940-Unknown

Colourway	U.K. £	U.S. $	Can. $
Tan/black	350.00	550.00	550.00

Model No. 845B
ZEBRA
Second Version - White with black stripes

Designer:	Arthur Gredington
Height:	7 ¼", 18.4 cm
Colour:	White with black stripes - gloss
Issued:	Unknown-1969

Colourway	U.K. £	U.S. $	Can. $
White/black	115.00	175.00	175.00

Model No. 853
GIRAFFE - Small

Designer:	Arthur Gredington
Height:	7 ¼", 18.4 cm
Colour:	Natural - gloss
Issued:	1940-1975

Colourway	U.K. £	U.S. $	Can. $
Natural	65.00	100.00	100.00

Note: Also known in white gloss.

Model No. 954
STAG - Lying

Designer:	Arthur Gredington
Height:	5 ½", 14.0 cm
Colour:	Light brown - gloss
Issued:	1941-1975

Colourway	U.K. £	U.S. $	Can. $
Light brown	50.00	75.00	75.00

Note: Earlier models appear with a red-brown colour.

Model No. 974
ELEPHANT - Trunk stretching - small

Designer:	Arthur Gredington
Height:	4 ¾", 12.1 cm
Colour:	Grey - gloss or matt
Issued:	1. Gloss - 1943 -1996
	2. Matt - 1985-1988

Description	U.K. £	U.S. $	Can. $
1. Gloss	50.00	75.00	75.00
2. Matt	50.00	75.00	75.00

Note: Also known in satin matt

Model No. 981
STAG - Standing

Designer:	Arthur Gredington
Height:	8", 20.3 cm
Colour:	See below
Issued:	1a. Gloss - 1942-1997
	1b. Matt - 1985-1988
	2. Satin - 1989-1992
Series:	2. Britannia Collection

Colourways	U.K. £	U.S. $	Can. $
1a. Light brown, gloss	60.00	90.00	90.00
1b. Light brown, matt	60.00	90.00	90.00
2. Bronze, satin	65.00	100.00	100.00

Model No. 998
ELEPHANT - Trunk stretching - large

Designer:	Arthur Gredington
Height:	10 ¼", 26.0 cm
Colour:	Natural - gloss or satin matt
Issued:	1. Gloss - 1943-1975
	2. Satin matt - 1970-1973
Series:	Model in satin matt finish was transferred to Connoisseur Series in 1973.

Description	U.K. £	U.S. $	Can. $
1. Gloss	125.00	185.00	185.00
2. Satin matt	125.00	185.00	185.00

Model No. 999A
DOE

Designer:	Arthur Gredington
Height:	6", 15.0 cm
Colour:	1. Light brown - gloss
	2. Light and dark brown - matt
Issued:	1. Gloss - 1943-1997
	2. Matt - 1985-1988

Description	U.K. £	U.S. $	Can. $
1. Gloss	25.00	40.00	40.00
2. Matt	25.00	40.00	40.00

Note: Earlier models appear with a red-brown colour.

Model No. 999B
DOE AND FAWN - on ceramic plinth

Designer:	Arthur Gredington
Height:	7", 17.8 cm
Colour:	Light brown - gloss
Issued:	1993-1996

Colourway	U.K. £	U.S. $	Can. $
Light brown	50.00	75.00	75.00

Note: Doe is no. 999, Fawn is no. 1000B.

Model No. 1000A
FAWN
First Version - tail up

Designer:	Arthur Gredington
Height:	3 ½", 8.9 cm
Colour:	Light brown - gloss
Issued:	1943-1955

Colourway	U.K. £	U.S. $	Can. $
Light brown	60.00	90.00	90.00

Note: Earlier models appear with a red-brown colour.

Model No. 1000B
FAWN
Second Version - tail down

Designer:	Arthur Gredington
Remodelled:	Mr. Orwell
Height:	3 ½", 8.9 cm
Colour:	Light brown - gloss or matt
Issued:	1. Gloss - 1955-1997
	2. Matt - 1985-1988

Description	U.K. £	U.S. $	Can. $
1. Gloss	20.00	30.00	30.00
2. Matt	20.00	30.00	30.00

Model No. 1003
FAWNIE

Designer:	Arthur Gredington
Height:	5 ¼", 13.3 cm
Colour:	See below – gloss
Issued:	1944-1967
Series:	Fun Models

Colourway	U.K. £	U.S. $	Can. $
1. Green	50.00	75.00	75.00
2. Grey-brown	60.00	90.00	90.00

Model No. 1005
KANGARINE

Designer:	Arthur Gredington
Height:	5", 12.7 cm
Colour:	1. Blue with white markings - gloss
	2. Brown - gloss
Issued:	1944-1966
Series:	Fun Models

Colourway	U.K. £	U.S. $	Can. $
1. Blue	90.00	135.00	135.00
2. Brown	65.00	100.00	100.00

Model No. 1007
SQUIRREL - Standing

Designer:	Arthur Gredington
Height:	2 ¼", 5.7 cm
Colour:	Tan - gloss
Issued:	1944-c.1963
Set:	1008, 1009
Series:	Fun Models

Colourway	U.K. £	U.S. $	Can. $
Tan	15.00	25.00	25.00

Note: Makes a set of three with model numbers 1008 and 1009. For Model 1009 see "Beswick Collectables"

Model No. 1008
SQUIRREL - Lying

Designer:	Arthur Gredington
Height:	1 ¾", 4.5 cm
Colour:	Tan - gloss
Issued:	1944-c.1963
Set:	1007, 1009
Series:	Fun Models

Colourway	U.K. £	U.S. $	Can. $
Tan	15.00	25.00	25.00

Note: Makes a set of three with model numbers 1007 and 1009. For Model 1009 see "Beswick Collectables"

Model No. 1016A
FOX - Standing

Designer:	Arthur Gredington
Height:	5 ½", 14.0 cm
Colour:	Red-brown and white - gloss or matt
Issued:	1. Gloss - 1945-1997
	2. Matt - 1985-1988
Varieties:	1016B

Description	U.K. £	U.S. $	Can. $
1. Gloss	50.00	75.00	75.00
2. Matt	60.00	90.00	90.00

Model No. 1016B
FOX - Standing - on ceramic base

Designer:	Arthur Gredington
Height:	6 ¾", 17.2 cm
Colour:	Red-brown and white - gloss
Issued:	1993-1996
Varieties:	1016A

Colourway	U.K. £	U.S. $	Can. $
Red-brown/white	60.00	90.00	90.00

Model No. 1017
FOX - Curled

Designer:	Arthur Gredington
Height:	1 ¾", 3.2 cm
Colour:	Red brown - gloss or matt
Issued:	1. Gloss - 1945 -1996
	2. Matt - 1985-1988

Description	U.K. £	U.S. $	Can. $
1. Gloss	40.00	80.00	80.00
2. Matt	60.00	90.00	90.00

Model No. 1019
BISON

Designer:	Arthur Gredington
Height:	5 ¾", 14.6 cm
Colour:	Dark brown - gloss
Issued:	1945-1973

Colourway	U.K. £	U.S. $	Can. $
Dark brown	90.00	135.00	135.00

Model No. 1021
STOAT

Designer:	Arthur Gredington
Height:	5 ½", 14.0 cm
Colour:	1. Tan (summer coat) - gloss
	2. White (winter coat) - gloss
Issued:	1945-1963

Colourway	U.K. £	U.S. $	Can. $
1. Tan	350.00	550.00	550.00
2. White	350.00	550.00	550.00

Model No. 1024
HARE - Running

Designer:	Arthur Gredington
Height:	5 ¼", 12.7 cm
Colour:	Tan - gloss
Issued:	1945-1963

Colourway	U.K. £	U.S. $	Can. $
Tan	350.00	550.00	550.00

Note: As a pair with model number 1025.

Model No. 1025
HARE - Seated

Designer:	Arthur Gredington
Height:	7", 17.8 cm
Colour:	Tan - gloss
Issued:	1945-1963

Colourway	U.K. £	U.S. $	Can. $
Tan	350.00	550.00	550.00

Note: As a pair with model number 1024.

Model No. 1038
KOALA BEAR

Designer:	Arthur Gredington
Height:	3 ½", 8.9 cm
Colour:	Grey - gloss
Issued:	1945-1971
Set:	1039, 1040

Colourway	U.K. £	U.S. $	Can. $
Grey	30.00	45.00	45.00

Model No. 1039
KOALA BEAR - On branch

Designer:	Arthur Gredington
Height:	2 ¼", 5.7 cm
Colour:	Grey - gloss
Issued:	1945-1973
Set:	1038, 1040

Colourway	U.K. £	U.S. $	Can. $
Grey	30.00	45.00	45.00

Model No. 1040
KOALA BEAR

Designer:	Arthur Gredington
Height:	2 ¼", 5.7 cm
Colour:	Grey - gloss
Issued:	1945-1973
Set:	1038, 1039

Colourway	U.K. £	U.S. $	Can. $
Grey	30.00	45.00	45.00

Model No. 1043
CAMEL FOAL

Designer:	Arthur Gredington
Height:	5", 12.7 cm
Colour:	Light and dark brown - gloss
Issued:	1946-1971
Set:	1044

Colourway	U.K. £	U.S. $	Can. $
Brown	80.00	120.00	120.00

Model No. 1044
CAMEL

Designer:	Arthur Gredington
Height:	7", 17.8 cm
Colour:	Light and dark brown - gloss
Issued:	1946-1973
Set:	1043

Colourway	U.K. £	U.S. $	Can. $
Brown	80.00	120.00	120.00

Model No. 1048
SPRINGBOK

Designer:	Arthur Gredington
Height:	7 ¼", 18.4 cm
Colour:	Tan and white - gloss
Issued:	1946-1963

Colourway	U.K. £	U.S. $	Can. $
Tan/white	300.00	450.00	450.00

Model No. 1082
LEOPARD

Designer:	Arthur Gredington
Height:	4 ¾", 12.1 cm
Colour:	1. Golden brown with black markings - gloss
	2. Black - satin
Issued:	1946-1975

Description	U.K. £	U.S. $	Can. $
1. Gloss	75.00	115.00	115.00
2. Satin	125.00	200.00	200.00

Model No. 1089
KOALA BEAR - With fruit

Designer:	Miss Jones
Height:	3 ½", 8.9 cm
Colour:	Grey - gloss
Issued:	1947-1971

Colourway	U.K. £	U.S. $	Can. $
Grey	20.00	30.00	30.00

Model No. 1160
KANGAROO

Designer:	Arthur Gredington
Height:	5 ¾", 14.6 cm
Colour:	Brown - gloss
Issued:	1949-1966

Colourway	U.K. £	U.S. $	Can. $
Brown	75.00	115.00	115.00

Model No. 1308
SKUNK

Designer:	Arthur Gredington
Height:	2 ¾", 7.0 cm
Colour:	Black and white - gloss
Issued:	1953-1963
Set:	1309, 1310

Colourway	U.K. £	U.S. $	Can. $
Black/white	50.00	75.00	75.00

Model No. 1309
SKUNK

Designer:	Arthur Gredington
Height:	1 ½", 3.8 cm
Colour:	Black and white - gloss
Issued:	1953-1963
Set:	1308, 1310

Colourway	U.K. £	U.S. $	Can. $
Black/white	50.00	75.00	75.00

Model No. 1310
SKUNK

Designer:	Arthur Gredington
Height:	2", 5.0 cm
Colour:	Black and white - gloss
Issued:	1953-1963
Set:	1307, 1309

Colourway	U.K. £	U.S. $	Can. $
Black/white	50.00	75.00	75.00

Model No. 1313
BEAR - Standing

Designer:	Arthur Gredington
Height:	2 ½", 6.4 cm
Colour:	Black or brown - gloss
Issued:	1953-1966
Set:	1314, 1315

Colourway	U.K. £	U.S. $	Can. $
1. Black	75.00	115.00	115.00
2. Brown	75.00	115.00	115.00

Model No. 1314
BEAR - On hind legs

Designer:	Arthur Gredington
Height:	4 ½", 11.9 cm
Colour:	Black or brown - gloss
Issued:	1953-1966
Set:	1313, 1315

Colourway	U.K. £	U.S. $	Can. $
1. Black	50.00	75.00	75.00
2. Brown	50.00	75.00	75.00

Model No. 1315
BEAR CUB - Seated

Designer:	Arthur Gredington
Height:	2 ¼", 5.7 cm
Colour:	Black or brown - gloss
Issued:	1953-1966
Set:	1313, 1314

Colourway	U.K. £	U.S. $	Can. $
1. Black	40.00	60.00	60.00
2. Brown	40.00	60.00	60.00

Model No. 1440
FOX - Standing

Designer:	Arthur Gredington
Height:	2 ½", 6.4 cm
Colour:	Red-brown and white - gloss or matt
Issued:	1. Gloss - 1956-1997
	2. Matt - 1985-1988

Description	U.K. £	U.S. $	Can. $
1. Gloss	30.00	45.00	45.00
2. Matt	30.00	45.00	45.00

Note: The early version had no white tip on tail. The tail with the white tip was from 1967 onwards.

Model No. 1486
TIGRESS

Designer:	Colin Melbourne
Height:	4 ¼", 10.8 cm
Colour:	1. Black - satin matt
	2. Tan with black stripes and markings - gloss
Issued:	1957-1975

Colourway	U.K. £	U.S. $	Can. $
1. Black - matt	140.00	215.00	215.00
2. Tan/black stripes - gloss	110.00	170.00	170.00

Model No. 1506
LION - Facing right

Designer:	Colin Melbourne
Height:	5 ¼", 13.3 cm
Colour:	Golden brown - gloss
Issued:	1957-1967
Set:	1507, 1508

Colourway	U.K. £	U.S. $	Can. $
Golden brown	55.00	85.00	85.00

Model No. 1507
LIONESS - Facing left

Designer:	Colin Melbourne
Height:	4 ¾", 12.1 cm
Colour:	See below
Issued:	1957-1967
Set:	1506, 1508

Colourway	U.K. £	U.S. $	Can. $
1. Black satin - matt	125.00	200.00	200.00
2. Golden brown - gloss	50.00	75.00	75.00

Note: The black satin matt colourway was probably considered a panther.

Model No. 1508
LION CUB - Facing right

Designer:	Colin Melbourne
Height:	4", 10.1 cm
Colour:	See below
Issued:	1957-1967
Set:	1506, 1507

Colourway	U.K. £	U.S. $	Can. $
1. Black satin - matt	125.00	200.00	200.00
2. Golden brown - gloss	50.00	75.00	75.00

Note: The black satin matt colourway was probably considered a panther.

Model No. 1532
HIPPOPOTAMUS

Designer:	Colin Melbourne		
Height:	3 ½", 8.9 cm		
Colour:	Dark grey with pink underneath - gloss		
Issued:	1958-1966		

Colourway	U.K. £	U.S. $	Can. $
Dark grey	125.00	195.00	195.00

Model No. 1533
POLAR BEAR

Designer:	Arthur Gredington		
Height:	4 ¾", 12.1 cm		
Colour:	White - gloss		
Issued:	1958-1966		

Colourway	U.K. £	U.S. $	Can. $
White	175.00	275.00	275.00

Model No. 1534
SEAL

Designer:	Arthur Gredington		
Length:	5 ¾", 14.6 cm		
Colour:	Grey - gloss		
Issued:	1958-1966		

Colourway	U.K. £	U.S. $	Can. $
Grey	100.00	150.00	150.00

Model No. 1551
CHAMOIS

Designer:	Pal Zalmen		
Height:	4", 10.1 cm		
Colour:	Fawn or grey - gloss		
Issued:	1958-1971		
Series:	Fun Models		

Colourway	U.K. £	U.S. $	Can. $
1. Fawn	30.00	45.00	45.00
2. Grey	30.00	45.00	45.00

Model No. 1597
GIRAFFE

Designer:	J. Lawson
Height:	4 ¼", 10.8 cm
Colour:	Tan with dark patches - gloss
Issued:	1959-1971
Series:	Fun Models

Colourway	U.K. £	U.S. $	Can. $
Tan	50.00	75.00	75.00

Model No. 1615A
BABYCHAM
First Version - Large eyes

Designer:	Albert Hallam
Height:	4", 10.1 cm
Colour:	Yellow - gloss
Issued:	1960-1975
Series:	Fun Models

Description	U.K. £	U.S. $	Can. $
Large eyes	90.00	135.00	135.00

Model 1615B
BABYCHAM
Second Version - Small eyes, name on ribbon

Designer:	Albert Hallam
Height:	4", 10.1 cm
Colour:	Yellow - gloss
Issued:	Unknown
Series:	Fun Models

Description	U.K. £	U.S. $	Can. $
Small eyes	80.00	120.00	120.00

Model No. 1631
GIRAFFE - Large

Designer:	J. Lawson
Height:	12", 30.5 cm
Colour:	Light brown with dark brown patches - gloss
Issued:	1959-1975

Colourway	U.K. £	U.S. $	Can. $
Brown	225.00	350.00	350.00

Note: Pattern and colour varies.

Model No. 1678
MOUSE

Designer: Albert Hallam
Height: 2 ½", 6.4 cm
Colour: Brown - gloss
Issued: 1960-1997

Colourway	U.K. £	U.S. $	Can. $
Brown	10.00	15.00	15.00

Note: Produced in white for model number 4677.

Model No. 1688
REINDEER

Designer: J. Lawson
Height: 3 ¾", 9.5 cm
Colour: 1. Fawn - gloss
2. Grey - gloss
Issued: 1960-1971
Series: Fun Models

Colourway	U.K. £	U.S. $	Can. $
1. Fawn	40.00	60.00	60.00
2. Grey	40.00	60.00	60.00

Model No. 1702
PUMA ON ROCK
Style One

Designer: Arthur Gredington
Height: 8 ½", 21.6 cm
Colour: 1. Black - gloss
2. Tawny - gloss or matt
Issued: 1. Black
 a. Gloss - 1960-1973
Reissued: b. Gloss - 1979-1983
Issued: 2. Tawny
 a. Gloss - 1960-1975
 b. Matt - 1970-1973
 c. Satin matt - 1973-1989
Reissued: d. Gloss - 1979-1983
Series: 2c. Connoisseur Series

Colourway	U.K. £	U.S. $	Can. $
1. Black			
a. Gloss	120.00	185.00	185.00
b. Reissued	120.00	185.00	185.00
2. Tawny			
a. Gloss	70.00	110.00	110.00
b. Matt	70.00	110.00	110.00
c. Satin matt	70.00	110.00	110.00
d. Reissued, gloss	70.00	110.00	110.00

Model No. 1720
ELEPHANT AND TIGER

Designer:	Arthur Gredington		
Height:	12", 30.5 cm		
Colour:	Grey, tan with black stripes - gloss		
Issued:	1960-1975		

Description	U.K. £	U.S. $	Can. $
Gloss	400.00	600.00	600.00

Note: The elephant is the same model as used in 1770.

Model No. 1733
COMICAL FOX

Designer:	Harry Sales		
Height:	3 ¼", 8.3 cm		
Colour:	Red-brown and white - gloss		
Issued:	1961-1968		
Series:	Fun Models		

Description	U.K. £	U.S. $	Can. $
Gloss	40.00	60.00	60.00

Model No. 1748
FOX - Seated

Designer:	Arthur Gredington		
Height:	3", 7.6 cm		
Colour:	Red-brown and white - gloss or matt		
Issued:	1. Gloss - 1961-1997		
	2. Matt - 1985-1988		

Description	U.K. £	U.S. $	Can. $
1. Gloss	25.00	40.00	40.00
2. Matt	25.00	40.00	40.00

Model No. 1770
ELEPHANT - Trunk in salute

Designer:	Arthur Gredington		
Height:	12", 30.5 cm		
Colour:	Grey - gloss or satin matt		
Issued:	1. Gloss - 1961-1975		
	2. Satin matt - 1970-1973		

Description	U.K. £	U.S. $	Can. $
1. Gloss	225.00	350.00	350.00
2. Satin matt	225.00	350.00	350.00

Note: Satin matt transferred to Connoiseur Series in 1973.
Elephant same model as used in 1720.

Model No. 1815
PANDA CUB

Designer:	Albert Hallam
Height:	2 ¼", 5.7 cm
Colour:	Black and white - gloss or matt
Issued:	1. Gloss - 1962-1997
	2. Matt - 1985-1988

Description	U.K. £	U.S. $	Can. $
1. Gloss	20.00	30.00	30.00
2. Matt	20.00	30.00	30.00

Model No. 1823
PUMA ON ROCK
Style Two

Designer:	Arthur Gredington
Height:	6", 15.0 cm
Colour:	1. Black - gloss
	2. Tawny - gloss
Issued:	1. Black - 1962-1973
	2. Tawny - 1962-1975

Colourway	U.K. £	U.S. $	Can. $
1. Black	90.00	140.00	140.00
2. Tawny	70.00	110.00	110.00

Model No. 1943
BEAVER ON LOG - Facing left

Designer:	Albert Hallam
Height:	2 ½", 6.4 cm
Colour:	Tan - gloss
Issued:	1964-1967

Colourway	U.K. £	U.S. $	Can. $
Tan	100.00	150.00	150.00

Model No. 2089
LION - Facing left

Designer:	Graham Tongue
Height:	5 ½", 14.0 cm
Colour:	Golden brown - gloss
Issued:	1967-1984

Colourway	U.K. £	U.S. $	Can. $
Golden brown	40.00	60.00	60.00

Note: Makes a set of three with model numbers 2097 and 2098

Model No. 2090
MOOSE

Designer:	Arthur Gredington
Height:	6 ¼", 15.9 cm
Colour:	Dark brown - gloss or satin matt
Issued:	1967-1973

Description	U.K. £	U.S. $	Can. $
1. Gloss	500.00	750.00	750.00
2. Satin matt	500.00	750.00	750.00

Model No. 2096
TIGER

Designer:	Graham Tongue
Height:	7 ½", 19.1 cm
Colour:	Tan with black stripes - gloss or matt
Issued:	1. Gloss - 1967-1990
	2. Matt - 1985-1988

Description	U.K. £	U.S. $	Can. $
1. Gloss	75.00	115.00	115.00
2. Matt	75.00	115.00	115.00

Note: Example known in black satin matt - very rare.

Model No. 2097
LIONESS - Facing right

Designer:	Graham Tongue
Height:	5 ¾", 14.6 cm
Colour:	Golden brown - gloss
Issued:	1967-1984

Colourway	U.K. £	U.S. $	Can. $
Golden brown	50.00	75.00	75.00

Note: Makes a set of three with model numbers 2089 and 2098.

Model No. 2098
LION CUB - Facing left

Designer:	Graham Tongue
Height:	4", 10.1 cm
Colour:	Golden brown - gloss
Issued:	1967-1984

Colourway	U.K. £	U.S. $	Can. $
Golden brown	30.00	45.00	45.00

Note: Makes a set of three with model numbers 2089 and 2097.

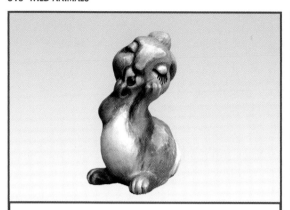

Model No. 2131
RABBIT

Designer:	Albert Hallam, Graham Tongue
Height:	3", 7.6 cm
Colour:	Light brown and white - gloss
Issued:	1967-1973
Series:	Fun Models

Colourway	U.K. £	U.S. $	Can. $
Brown/white	30.00	45.00	45.00

Model No. 2132
RABBIT Holding Baby

Designer:	Albert Hallam
Height:	3", 7.6 cm
Colour:	Light brown and white - gloss
Issued:	1967-1971
Series:	Fun Models

Colourway	U.K. £	U.S. $	Can. $
Brown/white	30.00	45.00	45.00

Model No. 2194
RACOON ON LOG

Designer:	Albert Hallam
Height:	4 ¼", 10.8 cm
Colour:	Dark grey - gloss
Issued:	1968-1972

Colourway	U.K. £	U.S. $	Can. $
Dark grey	100.00	150.00	150.00

Model No. 2195
BEAVER ON LOG - Facing right

Designer:	Albert Hallam
Height:	4 ½", 11.9 cm
Colour:	Brown - gloss
Issued:	1968-c.1973

Colourway	U.K. £	U.S. $	Can. $
Brown	100.00	150.00	150.00

Model No. 2237
BABYCHAM WALL PLAQUE

Designer:	Graham Tongue
Height:	3" x 6 ¼", 7.6 x 15.9 cm (Concave)
Colour:	Unknown - gloss
Issued:	c.1970-c.1975
Series:	Wall Plaques

Description	U.K. £	U.S. $	Can. $
Gloss	75.00	115.00	115.00

Model No. 2253
HEDGEHOG

Designer:	Harry Sales
Height:	3 ½" 8.9 cm
Colour:	1. Blue - gloss
	2. Brown - gloss
Issued:	1969-1971
Series:	Moda Range

Colourway	U.K. £	U.S. $	Can. $
1. Blue	175.00	275.00	275.00
2. Brown	175.00	275.00	275.00

Photograph not available.
Model No. 2302 possibly
not put into production.

Model No. 2302
MOUSE

Designer:	Albert Hallam
Height:	1 ¾", 8.9 cm
Colour:	Unknown
Issued:	1969-Unknown

Description	U.K. £	U.S. $	Can. $
Mouse		Possibly not put into production

Model No. 2312
KANGAROO

Designer:	Albert Hallam
Height:	5", 12.7 cm
Colour:	Light and dark brown - gloss
Issued:	1970-1973

Description	U.K. £	U.S. $	Can. $
Gloss	125.00	195.00	195.00

Model No. 2348
FOX

Designer:	Graham Tongue
Height:	12 ½", 31.7 cm
Colour:	Red-brown and white - gloss
Issued:	1970-1984
Series:	Fireside Model

Description	U.K. £	U.S. $	Can. $
Gloss	350.00	525.00	525.00

Model No. 2554A
LION ON ROCK

Designer:	Graham Tongue
Height:	8 ¼", 21.0 cm
Colour:	Golden brown - satin matt
Issued:	1975-1984
Varieties:	2554B (standing)
Series:	Connoisseur

Description	U.K. £	U.S. $	Can. $
Satin matt	85.00	130.00	130.00

Model No. 2554B
LION - Standing

Designer:	Graham Tongue
Height:	6 ¾", 17.2 cm
Colour:	Golden brown - gloss
Modelled:	1975
Issued:	1987-1995

Description	U.K. £	U.S. $	Can. $
Gloss	65.00	100.00	100.00

Model No. 2613
PANDA "CHI CHI"
First Version - With bamboo shoot

Designer:	Unknown
Height:	3 ¾", 9.5 cm
Colour:	Black and white - gloss
Issued:	1978-c.1980
Varieties:	2944

Description	U.K. £	U.S. $	Can. $
Gloss	125.00	195.00	195.00

Note: This model was produced for the British Museum, backstamp reads BM (NH).

Model No. 2629
STAG

Designer:	Graham Tongue
Height:	13 ½", 34.3 cm
Colour:	1. Golden brown - satin matt
	2. Bronze with black shading - satin
Issued:	1. 1978-1989
	2. 1989-1992
Series:	1. Connoisseur
	2. Britannia

Colourway	U.K. £	U.S. $	Can. $
1. Golden brown	100.00	150.00	150.00
2. Bronze/black shading	100.00	150.00	150.00

Model No. 2686
OTTER

Designer:	David Lyttleton
Height:	2 ¼", 5.7 cm
Colour:	Grey - matt
Issued:	1985-1985

Description	U.K. £	U.S. $	Can. $
Matt	35.00	50.00	50.00

Note: Part of a trial run in 1985 but never put into general production.

Model No. 2687
BADGER

Designer:	David Lyttleton
Height:	3", 7.6 cm
Colour:	Black - matt
Issued:	1985-1985

Description	U.K. £	U.S. $	Can. $
Matt	35.00	50.00	50.00

Note: Part of a trial run in 1985 but never put into general production.

Model No. 2693
SEAL

Designer:	Graham Tongue
Height:	3 ½", 8.9 cm
Colour:	Grey - matt
Issued:	1985-1985

Description	U.K. £	U.S. $	Can. $
Matt	35.00	50.00	50.00

Note: Part of a trial run in 1985 but never put into general production.

Model No. 2725
CHEETAH ON ROCK

Designer: Graham Tongue
Height: 6 ½", 16.5 cm
Colour: Pale brown with dark spots - satin finish
Issued: 1981-1989
Series: Connoisseur

Description	U.K. £	U.S. $	Can. $
Satin finish	175.00	275.00	275.00

Note: Transferred to R.D. backstamp as The Watering Hole (DA 39), 08/89, with model modifications.

Model No. 2944
PANDA "CHI CHI"
Second Version - Without bamboo shoot

Designer: Unknown
Height: 3 ¾", 9.5 cm
Colour: Black and white - matt
Issued: 1985-1985
Varieties: 2613

Description	U.K. £	U.S. $	Can. $
Matt	50.00	75.00	75.00

Note: Part of a trial run in 1985 but did not go into general production.

Model No. 3009
CHEETAH - Standing

Designer: Graham Tongue
Height: 5", 12.7 cm
Colour: Golden brown with dark spots - gloss
Issued: 1986-1995

Description	U.K. £	U.S. $	Can. $
Gloss	65.00	100.00	100.00

Model No. 3392
BADGER CUB

Designer: Amanda Hughes-Lubeck
Height: 2", 5.0 cm
Colour: Black and white - gloss
Issued: 1992-1997
Set: 3393, 3394

Description	U.K. £	U.S. $	Can. $
Gloss	35.00	50.00	50.00

Model No. 3393
BADGER - Male

Designer:	Amanda Hughes-Lubeck
Height:	2", 5.0 cm
Colour:	Black and white - gloss
Issued:	1992-1997
Set:	3392, 3394

Description	U.K. £	U.S. $	Can. $
Gloss	35.00	50.00	50.00

Model No. 3394
BADGER - Female

Designer:	Amanda Hughes-Lubeck
Height:	2", 5.0 cm
Colour:	Black and white - gloss
Issued:	1992 -1997
Set:	3392, 3393

Description	U.K. £	U.S. $	Can. $
Gloss	35.00	50.00	50.00

Model No. 3397
HARVEST MOUSE

Designer:	Martyn Alcock
Height:	2 ¼", 5.7 cm
Colour:	Brown - gloss
Issued:	1992-1997

Description	U.K. £	U.S. $	Can. $
Gloss	20.00	30.00	30.00

Model No. 3399
WOODMOUSE

Designer:	Martyn Alcock
Height:	3 ¼", 8.3 cm
Colour:	Brown - gloss
Issued:	1992-1997

Description	U.K. £	U.S. $	Can. $
Gloss	20.00	30.00	30.00

Puma on Rock, Style One, Model No. 1702

WILD ANIMAL
WALL PLAQUES

Model No. 2933
LION'S HEAD

Designer:	Graham Tongue
Height:	6", 15.0 cm
Colour:	Golden brown - matt
Issued:	1985-1989

Description	U.K. £	U.S. $	Can. $
Matt	20.00	30.00	30.00

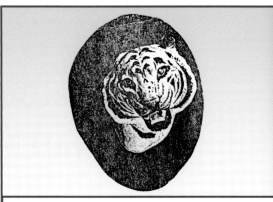

Model No. 2934
TIGER'S HEAD

Designer:	Arthur Gredington
Height:	6", 15.0 cm
Colour:	Tan - matt
Issued:	1985-1989

Description	U.K. £	U.S. $	Can. $
Matt	20.00	30.00	30.00

Model No. 2936
STAG'S HEAD

Designer:	Graham Tongue
Height:	6", 15.0 cm
Colour:	Light brown - matt
Issued:	1985-1989

Description	U.K. £	U.S. $	Can. $
Matt	20.00	30.00	30.00

Chapter Nine

THE CM SERIES

This unique series of models, all created by Colin Melbourne, evokes great emotion amongst collectors; it is either loved or hated there are no half measures here. The models were called "contemporary" when they were in production during the late 1950s. They reflected the mood of the time, both in style and in decoration. None of the decorations are realistic, and all are stylized, some to a greater extent than others.

The decoration for the models in this section fall into two categories:

Series 1. Issued 1956-1962

This series is sub-divided in three groups:

1. Colour combinations—charcoal grey/red/white gloss
2. Spotted colour combinations—yellow/shaded charcoal/black
3. Solid colours—grey/brown/green blue/white

Series 2. Issued 1962-1966

This was called the chalk design. The background colour was white and the decorations in geometric shapes or floral designs appeared in a variety of colourways.

INDEX BY MODEL NUMBER

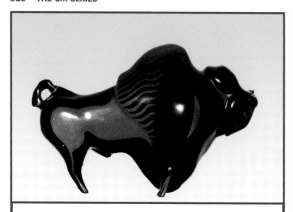

Model No. 1409
BISON - Large

Designer:	Colin Melbourne
Length:	7 ½" x 10 ½", 19.1 x 26.7 cm
Colour:	For colour combinations and varieties see page 327
Issued:	1956-by 1963

Description	U.K. £	U.S. $	Can. $
Series 1	250.00	400.00	400.00
Series 2	275.00	425.00	425.00

Model No. 1410
COW

Designer:	Colin Melbourne
Height:	5", 12.7 cm
Colour:	For colour combinations and varieties see page 327
Issued:	1956-by 1963

Description	U.K. £	U.S. $	Can. $
Series 1	250.00	400.00	400.00

Model No. 1411
HORSE

Designer:	Colin Melbourne
Height:	8 ½", 21.6 cm
Colour:	For colour combinations and varieties see page 327
Issued:	1956-by 1966

Description	U.K. £	U.S. $	Can. $
Series 1	500.00	750.00	750.00
Series 2	500.00	750.00	750.00

Model No. 1412
CAT - Large

Designer:	Colin Melbourne
Height:	9 ½", 24.0 cm
Colour:	For colour combinations and varieties see page 327
Issued:	1956-by 1966

Description	U.K. £	U.S. $	Can. $
Series 1	225.00	350.00	350.00
Series 2	250.00	400.00	400.00

Model No. 1413
DOVE

Designer:	Colin Melbourne
Height:	5 ¼", 12.7 cm
Colour:	For colour combinations and varieties see page 327
Issued:	1956-by 1965

Description	U.K. £	U.S. $	Can. $
Series 1	200.00	300.00	300.00
Series 2	225.00	350.00	350.00

Model No. 1414
BISON - Medium

Designer:	Colin Melbourne
Length:	5 ½" x 8 ¾", 14.0 x 22.2 cm
Colour:	For colour combinations and varieties see page 327
Issued:	1956-by 1966

Description	U.K. £	U.S. $	Can. $
Series 1	450.00	700.00	700.00
Series 2	525.00	800.00	800.00

Model No. 1415
BIRD

Designer:	Colin Melbourne
Height:	3", 7.6 cm
Colour:	For colour combinations and varieties see page 327
Issued:	1956-by 1965

Description	U.K. £	U.S. $	Can. $
Series 1	150.00	235.00	235.00
Series 2	200.00	300.00	300.00

Model No. 1416
COCK - Small

Designer:	Colin Melbourne
Height:	5", 12.7 cm
Colour:	For colour combinations and varieties see page 327
Issued:	1956-by 1965

Description	U.K. £	U.S. $	Can. $
Series 1	300.00	450.00	450.00
Series 2	350.00	525.00	525.00

Model No. 1417
CAT
Designer: Colin Melbourne
Height: 5 ½", 14.0 cm
Colour: For colour combinations and varieties
              see page 327
Issued: 1956-by 1966

Description	U.K. £	U.S. $	Can. $
Series 1	125.00	200.00	200.00
Series 2	225.00	350.00	350.00

Model No. 1418
FOX - Small
Designer: Colin Melbourne
Length: 2" x 8", 5.0 x 20.3 cm
Colour: For colour combinations and varieties
              see page 327
Issued: 1956-by 1966

Description	U.K. £	U.S. $	Can. $
Series 1	225.00	350.00	350.00
Series 2	225.00	350.00	350.00

Model No. 1419
LION
Designer: Colin Melbourne
Height: 4 ¾", 12.1 cm
Colour: For colour combinations and varieties
              see page 327
Issued: 1956-by 1963

Description	U.K. £	U.S. $	Can. $
Series 1	200.00	300.00	300.00

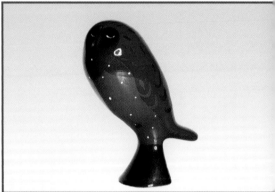

Model No. 1420
OWL - Small
Designer: Colin Melbourne
Height: 4 ¾", 12.1 cm
Colour: For colour combinations and varieties
              see page 327
Issued: 1956-by 1965

Description	U.K. £	U.S. $	Can. $
Series 1	225.00	350.00	350.00
Series 2	225.00	350.00	350.00

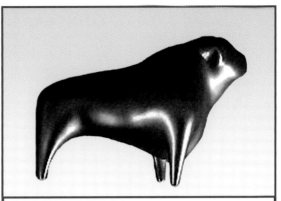

Model No. 1462
OWL - Large

Designer:	Colin Melbourne	
Height:	8 ¼", 21.0 cm	
Colour:	For colour combinations and varieties see page 327	
Issued:	1956-by 1965	

Description	U.K. £	U.S. $	Can. $
Series 1	200.00	300.00	300.00
Series 2	225.00	350.00	350.00

Model No. 1463
BULLDOG

Designer:	Colin Melbourne	
Height:	Unknown	
Colour:	For colour combinations and varieties see page 327	
Issued:	1956-1970	

Description	U.K. £	U.S. $	Can. $
Series 1	175.00	275.00	275.00

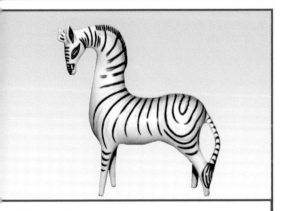

Model No. 1465
ZEBRA

Designer:	Colin Melbourne	
Height:	6", 15.0 cm	
Colour:	For colour combinations and varieties see page 327	
Issued:	1956-by 1966	

Description	U.K. £	U.S. $	Can. $
Series 1	250.00	375.00	375.00
Series 2	275.00	425.00	425.00

Model No. 1467
COCK - Large

Designer:	Colin Melbourne	
Height:	11 ¾", 29.8 cm	
Colour:	For colour combinations and varieties see page 327	
Issued:	1956-by 1963	

Description	U.K. £	U.S. $	Can. $
Series 1	250.00	375.00	375.00
Series 2	275.00	425.00	425.00

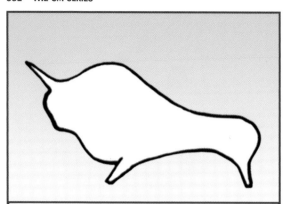

Model No. 1468
BISON - Small

Designer:	Colin Melbourne
Height:	Unknown
Colour:	For colour combinations and varieties see page 327
Issued:	1956-by 1966

Description	U.K. £	U.S. $	Can. $
Series 1	200.00	300.00	300.00
Series 2	250.00	400.00	400.00

Model No. 1469
DACHSHUND

Designer:	Colin Melbourne
Length:	7", 17.8 cm
Colour:	For colour combinations and varieties see page 327
Issued:	1957-1970

Description	U.K. £	U.S. $	Can. $
Series 1	150.00	225.00	225.00
Series 2	200.00	300.00	300.00

Model No. 1470
CLOWN ON HORSE - Small

Designer:	Colin Melbourne
Height:	5 ¾", 14.6 cm
Colour:	For colour combinations and varieties see page 327
Issued:	1957-by 1966

Description	U.K. £	U.S. $	Can. $
Series 1	225.00	350.00	350.00
Series 2	275.00	425.00	425.00

Model No. 1471
GOOSE

Designer:	Colin Melbourne
Height:	3 ½", 8.9 cm
Colour:	For colour combinations and varieties see page 327
Issued:	1957-by 1962

Description	U.K. £	U.S. $	Can. $
Series 1	175.00	275.00	275.00

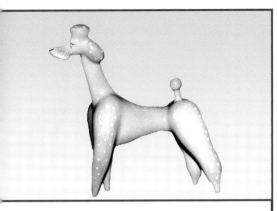

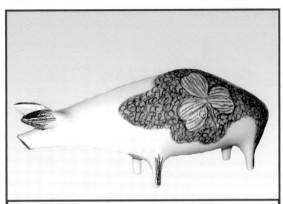

Model No. 1472
POODLE

Designer: Colin Melbourne
Height: 5 ¾", 14.6 cm
Colour: For colour combinations and varieties
              see page 327
Issued: 1957-1962

Description	U.K. £	U.S. $	Can. $
Series 1	225.00	350.00	350.00

Model No. 1473
PIG

Designer: Colin Melbourne
Length: 2 ½" x 6", 6.4 x 15.0 cm
Colour: For colour combinations and varieties
              see page 327
Issued: 1957-by 1965

Description	U.K. £	U.S. $	Can. $
Series 1	500.00	750.00	750.00
Series 2	500.00	750.00	750.00

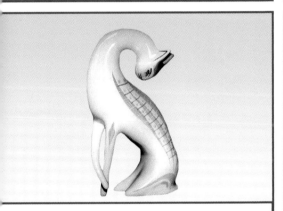

Model No. 1474
CAT

Designer: Colin Melbourne
Height: 5 ¼", 13.3 cm
Colour: For colour combinations and varieties
              see page 327
Issued: 1957-by 1966

Description	U.K. £	U.S. $	Can. $
Series 1	200.00	300.00	300.00
Series 2	225.00	350.00	350.00

Model No. 1475
FOX - Large

Designer: Colin Melbourne
Length: 10 ½", 26.7 cm
Colour: For colour combinations and varieties
              see page 327
Issued: 1957-by 1966

Description	U.K. £	U.S. $	Can. $
Series 1	200.00	300.00	300.00
Series 2	225.00	350.00	350.00

Model No. 1476
CLOWN ON HORSE - Large

Designer: Colin Melbourne
Height: 8 ½", 21.6 cm
Colour: For colour combinations and varieties
              see page 327
Issued: 1957-by 1966

Description	U.K. £	U.S. $	Can. $
Series 1	675.00	1,000.00	1,000.00
Series 2	600.00	900.00	900.00

Model No. 1481
REINDEER

Designer: Colin Melbourne
Height: 5 ½", 14.0 cm
Colour: For colour combinations and varieties
              see page 327
Issued: 1957-by 1966

Description	U.K. £	U.S. $	Can. $
Series 1	225.00	350.00	350.00
Series 2	250.00	375.00	375.00

Model No. 1482
PEACOCK

Designer: Colin Melbourne
Height: 3 ½", 8.9 cm
Colour: For colour combinations and varieties
              see page 327
Issued: 1957-by 1965

Description	U.K. £	U.S. $	Can. $
Series 1	200.00	300.00	300.00
Series 2	225.00	350.00	350.00

Chapter Ten
LITTLE LIKEABLES

When introduced in 1985 this collection of animal models was a departure from the usual Beswick pieces since they were produced in bone china, all white with a minimum of gold and pastel coloured decoration.

Despite their obvious charm they had been withdrawn by January 1987.

INDEX BY MODEL NUMBER

LL1
FAMILY GATHERING™
(Hen and Two Chicks)

Designer:	Diane Griffiths
Height:	4 ½", 11.9 cm
Colour:	White hen and chicks with yellow beaks and gold comb on hen - gloss
Issued:	1985 - 1987

Description	U.K. £	U.S. $	Can. $
Gloss	25.00	40.00	40.00

LL2
WATCHING THE WORLD GO BY™
(Frog)

Designer:	Robert Tabbenor
Height:	3 ¾", 9.5 cm
Colour:	White frog, black and green eyes - gloss
Issued:	1985-1987

Description	U.K. £	U.S. $	Can. $
Gloss	25.00	40.00	40.00

Note: Also known in a green colourway.

LL3
HIDE AND SEEK™
(Pig and Two Piglets)

Designer:	Robert Tabbenor
Height:	3 ¼", 8.3 cm
Colour:	White pigs with pink noses, ears and tails - gloss
Issued:	1985-1987

Description	U.K. £	U.S. $	Can. $
Gloss	25.00	40.00	40.00

LL4
MY PONY™
(Pony)

Designer:	Diane Griffiths
Height:	7 ¼", 18.4 cm
Colour:	White pony with blue highlights in mane and tail - gloss
Issued:	1985-1987

Description	U.K. £	U.S. $	Can. $
Gloss	30.00	45.00	45.00

LL5
ON TOP OF THE WORLD™
(Elephant)

Designer:	Diane Griffiths
Height:	3 ¾", 9.5 cm
Colour:	White elephant with black eyes and gold nails - gloss
Issued:	1985-1987

Description	U.K. £	U.S. $	Can. $
Gloss	25.00	40.00	40.00

LL6
TREAT ME GENTLY™
(Fawn)

Designer:	Diane Griffiths
Height:	4 ½", 11.9 cm
Colour:	White fawn with black and brown eyes, black nose and gold hoof - gloss
Issued:	1985-1987

Description	U.K. £	U.S. $	Can. $
Gloss	20.00	30.00	30.00

LL7
OUT AT LAST™
(Duckling)

Designer:	Robert Tabbenor
Height:	3 ¼", 8.3 cm
Colour:	White duck with black and brown eyes and gold beak - gloss
Issued:	1985-1987

Description	U.K. £	U.S. $	Can. $
Gloss	20.00	30.00	30.00

LL8
CATS CHORUS™
(Cats)

Designer:	Robert Tabbenor
Height:	4 ¾", 12.1 cm
Colour:	Two white cats with black and green eyes, black nose, pink ears and mouth - gloss
Issued:	1985-1987

Description	U.K. £	U.S. $	Can. $
Gloss	20.00	30.00	30.00

Chapter Eleven

STUDIO SCULPTURES

The series of Studio Sculptures made a very brief appearance, most for a maximum of two years, and some for only six months, between 1984 and 1985. When the collection was launched, Harry Sales, Beswick's Design Manager, explained "The new bonded ceramic body gives us endless opportunities to capture every minute detail of the subject and bring the sculptures to life."

The models in this new medium formed four groups, of which two are relevant to this book. These are: the "Countryside Series" which consists of fourteen models and includes birds, a squirrel, dogs, and rabbits, and the "Young Friends Series" which contained four different models, two of which are in two colourways, of pet cats and dogs. None of the models were "free standing" for the model incorporated a base, and some had an additional wooden plinth.

The Studio Sculptures were completely different in style and detail because of the different medium used. They were also different in price! In 1985 their prices ranged from £13.95 to £59.00 and they were considerably more than models in earthenware. For example the Studio Sculpture Wren "Early Bird" retailed at £15.95 whilst the Beswick Wren (993) was £4.95 quite a difference. Therefore it was not too surprising to find that overall the series was not the expected commercial success and so it was not listed in the 1986 price list.

INDEX BY MODEL NUMBER

For other figurines in the Studio Sculpture Series see "Storybook Figurines: Royal Doulton, Beswick, Royal Albert (A Charlton Standard Catalogue).

Beatrix Potter Series- SS1, SS2, SS3, SS4, SS11, SS26, SS27 Thelwell Series - SS7, SS12; SS23-25 not allocated.

SS5
PUPPY LOVE (Two puppies)

Height:	4 ½", 11.9 cm
Colour:	1. One brown/white, one black/white - satin matt
	2. One black/white, one white with black patches - satin matt
Issued:	1984-1986
Series:	Young Friends

Colourway	U.K. £	U.S. $	Can. $
1. Brown/black	20.00	30.00	30.00
2. Black/white	20.00	30.00	30.00

SS6
I SPY
(Two kittens)

Height:	4 ½", 11.9 cm
Colour:	1. Two white cats - satin matt
	2. One tabby, one ginger - satin matt
Issued:	1984-1986
Series:	Young Friends

Colourway	U.K. £	U.S. $	Can. $
1. White	20.00	30.00	30.00
2. Tabby/ginger	20.00	30.00	30.00

SS8
CONTENTMENT
(Dutch Rabbits)

Length:	4 ¾", 12.1 cm
Colour:	1. Brown and white - satin matt
	2. Black and white - satin matt
Issued:	1984-1986
Series:	Countryside

Colourway	U.K. £	U.S. $	Can. $
1. Brown/white	10.00	15.00	15.00
2. Black/white	10.00	15.00	15.00

SS9
BRIGHT EYES
(Dutch Rabbit)

Length:	4 ½", 11.9 cm
Colour:	1. Brown and white - satin matt
	2. Black and white - satin matt
Issued:	1984-1986
Series:	Countryside

Colourway	U.K. £	U.S. $	Can. $
1. Brown/white	10.00	15.00	15.00
2. Black/white	10.00	15.00	15.00

SS10
MIND HOW YOU GO
(Goose and goslings)

Length:	5 ¼", 13.3 cm		
Colour:	White goose and yellow goslings - satin matt		
Issued:	1984-1986		
Series:	Countryside		

Description	U.K. £	U.S. $	Can. $
Satin matt	20.00	30.00	30.00

SS13
HAPPY LANDINGS
(Swan on wooden base)

Height:	5", 12.7 cm		
Colour:	White - satin matt		
Issued:	1984-1986		
Series:	Countryside		

Description	U.K. £	U.S. $	Can. $
Satin matt	40.00	60.00	60.00

SS14
THE CHASE
(Dogs on wooden base)

Height:	4", 10.1 cm		
Colour:	Shaded brown and white - satin matt		
Issued:	1984-1986		
Series:	Countryside		

Description	U.K. £	U.S. $	Can. $
Satin matt	40.00	60.00	60.00

SS15
HIDE AND SEEK
(Dogs on wooden base)

Height:	4 ½", 11.9 cm		
Colour:	Shaded brown - satin matt		
Issued:	1984-1986		
Series:	Countryside		

Description	U.K. £	U.S. $	Can. $
Satin matt	40.00	60.00	60.00

SS16
MENU FOR TODAY
(Spaniel puppy with kitten)

Height:	3 ½", 8.9 cm
Colour:	1. Brown puppy, white kitten - satin matt
	2. Brown puppy, tabby kitten - satin matt
Issued:	1984-1986
Series:	Young Friends

Colourway	U.K. £	U.S. $	Can. $
1. Brown/white	15.00	25.00	25.00
2. Brown/tabby	15.00	25.00	25.00

SS17
SHARING
(German Shepherd puppy with kitten)

Height:	3 ½", 8.9 cm
Colour:	Black and brown dog, white kitten
	- satin matt
Issued:	1984-1986
Series:	Young Friends

Description	U.K. £	U.S. $	Can. $
Satin matt	15.00	25.00	25.00

SS18
PLANNING AHEAD
(Squirrel)

Height:	3", 7.6 cm
Colour:	Red - satin matt
Issued:	1984-1986
Series:	Countryside

Description	U.K. £	U.S. $	Can. $
Satin matt	10.00	15.00	15.00

SS19
EARLY BIRD
(Wren)

Height:	2 ½", 6.4 cm
Colour:	Dark and light brown - satin matt
Issued:	1984-1986
Series:	Countryside

Description	U.K. £	U.S. $	Can. $
Satin matt	10.00	15.00	15.00

SS20
GOLDEN RETRIEVER
Height: 5", 12.7 cm
Colour: Golden brown - satin matt
Issued: 1984-1986
Series: Countryside

Description	U.K. £	U.S. $	Can. $
Satin matt	35.00	50.00	50.00

SS21
POINTER
Height: Unknown
Colour: White and brown - satin matt
Issued: 1984-1986
Series: Countryside

Description	U.K. £	U.S. $	Can. $
Satin matt	35.00	50.00	50.00

SS22
ENGLISH SETTER
Height: 8", 20.3 cm
Colour: White and liver - satin matt
Issued: 1984-1986
Series: Countryside

Description	U.K. £	U.S. $	Can. $
Satin matt	35.00	50.00	50.00

SS28
ROBIN
Height: 3", 7.6 cm
Colour: Brown and red - satin matt
Issued: 1985-1986
Series: Countryside

Description	U.K. £	U.S. $	Can. $
Satin matt	15.00	25.00	25.00

SS29
BLUE TIT

Height:	2 ½", 6.4 cm
Colour:	Yellow, green and white - satin matt
Issued:	1985-1986
Series:	Countryside

Description	U.K. £	U.S. $	Can. $
Satin matt	15.00	25.00	25.00

SS30
CHAFFINCH

Height:	2 ¼", 5.7 cm
Colour:	Brown, ochre, grey, black - satin matt
Issued:	1985-1986
Series:	Countryside

Description	U.K. £	U.S. $	Can. $
Satin matt	15.00	25.00	25.00

Chapter Twelve
WHISKY FLASKS

INDEX BY MODEL NUMBER

Model No. 2051
LOCH NESS MONSTER (NESSIE)

Designer:	Albert Hallam
Height:	3", 7.6 cm
Colour:	Grey-green - gloss
Issued:	1965-1986

Description	U.K. £	U.S. $	Can. $
1. Head stopper	10.00	15.00	15.00
2. Base stopper	10.00	15.00	15.00

Model No. 2104
EAGLE

Designer:	Graham Tongue
Height:	4", 10.1 cm
Colour:	Brown - gloss
Issued:	1967-1986

Description	U.K. £	U.S. $	Can. $
Gloss	10.00	15.00	15.00

Model No. 2281A
EAGLE
First Version – Fixed Head

Designer:	Graham Tongue
Height:	10 3/8", 27.3 cm
Colour:	Light and dark brown - gloss
Issued:	1969 - Unknown

Description	U.K. £	U.S. $	Can. $
Fixed Head	30.00	45.00	45.00

Note: Model no. 2281A was first issued with a fixed head. See opposite for movable head varieties.

Model No. 2281B
EAGLE
Second Versions – Moveable Head
a. Without lugs at neck
b. With small lugs at neck

Designer:	Graham Tongue
Height:	10 3/8", 27.3 cm
Colour:	Light and dark brown - gloss
Issued:	Unknown - 1980

Description	U.K. £	U.S. $	Can. $
1. Without lugs	30.00	45.00	45.00
2. With small lugs	30.00	45.00	45.00

Model No. 2350
HAGGIS BIRD

Designer: James Haywood
Remodelled: Albert Hallam
Height: 2 ½", 6.4 cm
Colour: Brown - gloss
Issued: 1971-1986

Description	U.K. £	U.S. $	Can. $
Gloss	10.00	15.00	15.00

Model No. 2561
GROUSE

Designer: David Lyttleton
Height: 9", 22.9 cm
Colour: Brown and red - gloss
Issued: 1976-1984

Description	U.K. £	U.S. $	Can. $
Gloss	70.00	110.00	110.00

Note: Model no. 2561 was remodelled with a removable head stopper.

Model No. 2583
OSPREY

Designer: David Lyttleton
Height: 7 ¾", 19.7 cm
Colour: Browns and white - gloss
Issued: 1977-1986

Description:	U.K. £	U.S. $	Can. $
Gloss	30.00	45.00	45.00

Model No. 2636
SQUIRREL

Designer: David Lyttleton
Height: 3 ½", 8.9 cm
Colour: Red-brown - gloss
Issued: 1978-1986

Description	U.K. £	U.S. $	Can. $
Gloss	10.00	15.00	15.00

Model No. 2639
KESTREL

Designer:	Graham Tongue
Height:	6 ½", 16.5 cm
Colour:	Dark grey and white - gloss
Issued:	1979-1986

Description	U.K. £	U.S. $	Can. $
Gloss	60.00	90.00	90.00

Model No. 2640
BUZZARD

Designer:	Graham Tongue
Height:	6 ½", 16.5 cm
Colour:	Dark brown and grey - gloss
Issued:	1979-1986

Description	U.K. £	U.S. $	Can. $
Gloss	45.00	70.00	70.00

Model No. 2641
MERLIN

Designer:	Graham Tongue
Height:	6 ½", 16.5 cm
Colour:	Dark grey and white - gloss
Issued:	1979-1986

Description	U.K. £	U.S. $	Can. $
Gloss	50.00	75.00	75.00

Model No. 2642
PEREGRINE FALCON

Designer:	Graham Tongue
Height:	6 ½", 16.5 cm
Colour:	Dark grey and white - gloss
Issued:	1979-1986

Description	U.K. £	U.S. $	Can. $
Gloss	50.00	75.00	75.00

Model No. 2678
EAGLE
Third Version – Moveable Head, Large Lugs
Designer: Graham Tongue
Height: 10 ½", 26.7 cm
Colour: Light and dark brown - gloss
Issued: 1980- 1987

Description	U.K. £	U.S. $	Can. $
Large lugs	45.00	70.00	70.00

Note: The head locking mechanism on this model has large
lugs on a wider, full-bodied bird.

Model No. 2686
OTTER
Designer: David Lyttleton
Height: 2 ¼", 5.7 cm
Colour: Grey and brown - gloss
Issued: 1981-1986

Description	U.K. £	U.S. $	Can. $
Gloss	10.00	15.00	15.00

Model No. 2687
BADGER
Designer: David Lyttleton
Height: 3", 7.6 cm
Colour: Black and white - gloss
Issued: 1981-1986

Description	U.K. £	U.S. $	Can. $
Gloss	10.00	15.00	15.00

Model No. 2693
SEAL
Designer: Graham Tongue
Height: 3 ½", 8.9 cm
Colour: Grey - gloss
Issued: 1980-1986

Description	U.K. £	U.S. $	Can. $
Gloss	10.00	15.00	15.00

Model No. 2781
TAWNY OWL

Designer:	Graham Tongue
Height:	6 ¼", 15.9 cm
Colour:	Brown - gloss
Issued:	1982-1987

Description	U.K. £	U.S. $	Can. $
Gloss	30.00	45.00	45.00

Model No. 2798
GROUSE

Designer:	David Lyttleton
Height:	9 ½", 24.0 cm
Colour:	Brown and red - matt
Issued:	1982-1987

Description	U.K. £	U.S. $	Can. $
Matt	50.00	75.00	75.00

Model No. 2809
BARN OWL

Designer:	Graham Tongue
Height:	6 ¾", 17.2 cm
Colour:	Tan-brown and white - gloss
Issued:	1983-1987

Description	U.K. £	U.S . $	Can. $
Gloss	50.00	75.00	75.00

Model No. 2825
SHORT-EARED OWL

Designer:	Graham Tongue
Height:	6 ¾", 17.2 cm
Colour:	Dark and light brown - gloss
Issued:	1983-1987

Description	U.K. £	U.S. $	Can. $
Gloss	50.00	75.00	75.00

Model No. 2826
SNOWY OWL

Designer:	Graham Tongue
Height:	1. 6 ½", 16.5 cm
	2. 5 ¾", 14.6 cm
Colour:	White - gloss
Issued:	1983-1987

Description	U.K. £	U.S. $	Can. $
1. Large	70.00	110.00	110.00
2. Small	60.00	90.00	90.00

Model 2281 Eagle Whiskey Flask, Second and Third Versions

Model No. 2281B-b	Model No. 2678	Model No. 2281B-b	Model No. 2678
Second Version	Third Version	Second Version	Third Version
Narrow Body	Wide Body	Small lugs at neck	Large lugs at neck

Chapter Thirteen

COMMISSIONED

MODELS

During the early 1990s Beswick used some of its current freestanding models and attached them to either a ceramic base or to a wooden base with a brass name plate bearing a descriptive title.

Various companies, including British Coal, one of the major home shopping networks and a direct mail corporation, seem to be the largest commissioners of these items.

Little is known about these models, for they are not listed in the Beswick product line.

INDEX BY MODEL NUMBER

ALSATIAN "ULRICA OF BRITTAS"
- on ceramic base
Model No.:	969
Designer:	Arthur Gredington
Height:	6 ¾". 17.2 cm
Colour:	Black and light brown - gloss
Issued:	Unknown
Comm. by:	British Coal, Home Shopping Network

Description	U.K. £	U.S. $	Can. $
Gloss	50.00	75.00	75.00

ANOTHER STAR
Model No.:	Unknown
Designer:	Warren Platt
Height:	2 ¼", 6.4 cm
Colour:	Light brown - gloss
Issued:	1998 in a limited edition of 1,500
Comm. by:	P.R. Middleweek & Co.

Description	U.K. £	U.S. $	Can. $
Gloss	65.00	95.00	95.00

BULLDOG "BASFORD BRITISH MASCOT"
- on ceramic base
Model No.:	965
Designer:	Arthur Gredington
Height:	6 ½", 16.5 cm
Colour:	Brindle - gloss
Issued:	Unknown
Comm. by:	British Coal, Home Shopping Network

Description	U.K. £	U.S. $	Can. $
Gloss	60.00	90.00	90.00

COCKER SPANIEL "HORSESHOE PRIMULA"
- on ceramic base
Model No.:	967
Designer:	Arthur Gredington
Height:	6 ¾", 17.1 cm
Colour:	Golden brown - gloss
Issued:	Unknown
Comm. by:	British Coal, Home Shopping Network

Description	U.K. £	U.S. $	Can. $
Gloss	50.00	75.00	75.00

THE DARTMOOR FAMILY

Model No.:	Unknown
Designer:	Arthur Gredington, Graham Tongue and Warren Platt
Height:	7 ¼", 18.4 cm
Colour:	**Another Bunch** and **Warlord** - red bay, **Another Star** - light brown - gloss
Issued:	1999 in a limited edition of 150
Comm. by:	P.R. Middleweek & Co.

Description	U.K. £	U.S. $	Can. $
Gloss	300.00	450.00	450.00

Note: See also Dartmoor Pony, page 222.

"EWE AND I" - on ceramic plinth

Model No.:	3071/1765
Designer:	Unknown
Height:	4 ½", 11.9 cm
Base:	7 ½", 19.1 cm
Colour:	Black and white - gloss
Issued:	Unknown

Colourway	U.K. £	U.S. $	Can. $
Black/white	50.00	75.00	75.00

Note: Ram is no. 3071; Sheep is no. 1765. Produced as a special commission.

"GOOD FRIENDS" - on ceramic base

Model No.:	2950/1436
Designer:	Colin Melbourne
Height:	6", 15.2 cm
Colour:	White and tan dog, ginger kitten - gloss
Issued:	Unknown
Comm. by:	British Coal, Home Shopping Network

Description	U.K. £	U.S. $	Can. $
Gloss	40.00	60.00	60.00

"HORSES GREAT AND SMALL" - on ceramic base

Model No.:	818/1034
Designer:	Arthur Gredington
Height:	10", 25.4 cm
Colour:	Dark brown and white - gloss
Issued:	Unknown

Description	U.K. £	U.S. $	Can. $
Gloss	90.00	140.00	140.00

MEERKAT - Seated

Model No.:	3568		
Designer:	Martyn Alcock		
Height:	3", 7.6 cm		
Colour:	Grey and brown - gloss		
Issued:	1996 in a limited edition of 1,250		
Comm. by:	UKI Ceramics		

Description	U.K. £	U.S. $	Can. $
Gloss	10.00	15.00	15.00

MEERKAT - Standing

Model No.:	3571		
Designer:	Martyn Alcock		
Height:	3 ½", 8.9 cm		
Colour:	Grey and brown - gloss		
Issued:	1996 in a limited edition of 1,250		
Comm. by:	UKI Ceramics		

Description	U.K. £	U.S. $	Can. $
Gloss	10.00	15.00	15.00

"PLAYTIME" - on ceramic base

Model No.:	1886/3093		
Designer:	Albert Hallam		
Height:	5", 12.7 cm		
Colour:	White kitten with pink or lemon ball of wool - gloss		
Issued:	Unknown		
Comm. by:	British Coal, Home Shopping Network		

Description	U.K. £	U.S. $	Can. $
Gloss	25.00	40.00	40.00

**ST. BERNARD "CORNA GARTH STROLLER"
- on ceramic base**

Model No.:	2221		
Designer:	Albert Hallam		
Height:	6 ¾", 17.1 cm		
Colour:	Dark brown, tan and white - gloss		
Issued:	Unknown		
Comm. by:	British Coal, Home Shopping Network		

Description	U.K. £	U.S. $	Can. $
Gloss	50.00	75.00	75.00

"SHARING" - on ceramic base

Model No.:	1436/1460
Designer:	Arthur Gredington and Colin Melbourne
Height:	4 ¾", 12.1 cm
Colour:	Grey cat, brown dog - gloss
Issued:	Unknown
Comm. by:	British Coal, Home Shopping Network

Description	U.K. £	U.S. $	Can. $
Gloss	40.00	60.00	60.00

SOLID FRIENDSHIP - on wooden plinth

Model No.:	4677
Designer:	Albert Hallam and Warren Platt
Height:	5 ½", 14.0 cm
Colour:	White mouse, black and white cat, and white dog with brown patches - gloss
Issued:	1993
Comm. by:	British Coal, Home Shopping Network

Description	U.K. £	U.S. $	Can. $
Gloss	75.00	115.00	115.00

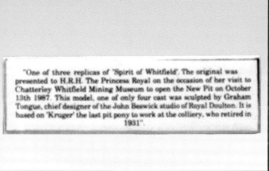

"One of three replicas of 'Spirit of Whitfield'. The original was presented to H.R.H. The Princess Royal on the occasion of her visit to Chatterley Whitfield Mining Museum to open the New Pit on October 13th 1987. This model, one of only four cast was sculpted by Graham Tongue, chief designer of the John Beswick studio of Royal Doulton. It is based on 'Kruger' the last pit pony to work at the colliery, who retired in 1931".

Photograph of ceramic plaque

SPIRIT OF WHITFIELD

Model No.:	Unknown
Designer:	Graham Tongue
Height:	9", 22.9cm
Colour:	Brown - matt
Issued:	1987
Comm. by:	Chatterley Whitfield Mining Museum

Description	U.K. £	U.S. $	Can. $
Matt	Auction sale 1994, £2,750.00		

Note: This model of "Kruger" was commissioned by the Chatterley Whitfield Minign Museum. Only four models exist.

Model No. 3464

TALLY HO!

This model was made exclusively for the mail order company Grattans. The horse and rider, from the model "Rearing Huntsman," with three hounds are on a natural effect base (all gloss). This model stands on a wooden plinth which is topped with green baise and has a brass plaque on the front. Backstamp – "Beswick Ware Made in England Tally ho! Beswick Centenary 1894-1994 © 1944 Royal Doulton."

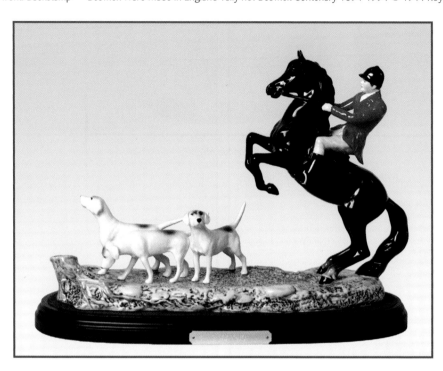

Designer: Unknown
Height: 11" x 14", 27.9 x 35.5 cm
Colour: Horse: Brown
                  Dogs: White, tan and black
                  Rider: Red riding habit, white jodhpurs, black hat - gloss
Comm. by: Grattans (Mail Order Company)

Model No.	Finish	Intro.	Disc.	U.K. £	U.S. $	Can. $
3464	Gloss	1994	1994	750.00	1,150.00	1,150.00

"THAT'S MY BOY" - on wooden plinth

Model No.:   3351
Designer: Warren Platt
Height: 5 ½", 14.0 cm
Colour: White and tan
Issued: 1993
Comm. by: British Coal, Home Shopping Network

Description	U.K. £	U.S. $	Can. $
Gloss	40.00	60.00	60.00

"WATCH IT" - on ceramic base

Model No.:   1558/1678
Designer: Albert Hallam and Pal Zalmen
Height: 8 ¾", 22.2 cm
Colour: Chocolate point cat, grey mouse - gloss
Issued: Unknown

Description	U.K. £	U.S. $	Can. $
Gloss	35.00	55.00	55.00

WARLORD'S MARE "ANOTHER BUNCH"

Model No.:   Unknown
Designer: Graham Tongue
Height: 6", 15.1 cm
Colour: Bay-brown; red, white and blue sash - gloss
Issued: 1997 in a special edition of 1,500
Comm. by: P.R. Middleweek & Co.

Description	U.K. £	U.S. $	Can. $
Gloss	65.00	100.00	100.00

T'ang Horse (small), Model No. 2137

Chapter Fourteen

MISCELLANEOUS

INDEX BY MODEL NUMBER

Model No. 2093
OLD STAFFORDSHIRE LION

Designer: Graham Tongue
Height: 5 ¾", 14.6 cm
Colour: Grey, cream, green - gloss
Issued: 1967-1971

Description	U.K. £	U.S. $	Can. $
Gloss	275.00	425.00	425.00

Model No. 2094
OLD STAFFORDSHIRE UNICORN

Designer: Graham Tongue
Height: 6", 15.0 cm
Colour: Grey, cream, green - gloss
Issued: 1967-1971

Description	U.K. £	U.S. $	Can. $
Gloss	275.00	425.00	425.00

Model No. 2137
T'ANG HORSE - Small

Designer: Graham Tongue
Height: 8", 20.3 cm
Colour: Green/bronze - gloss
Issued: 1967-1972

Description	U.K. £	U.S. $	Can. $
Gloss	400.00	600.00	600.00

Model No. 2182
HERALDIC UNICORN ON BASE

Designer: Graham Tongue
Height: 8 ½", 21.6 cm
Colour.   Unknown
Issued: 1968 - Unknown

Description	U.K. £	U.S. $	Can. $
Gloss		Extremely Rare	

Note: Model 2182 may not have been put into production.

Model No. 2205
T'ANG HORSE- Large

Designer: Graham Tongue
Height: 13", 33.0 cm
Colour: Green/bronze - gloss
Issued: 1968-1972

Description	U.K. £	U.S. $	Can. $
Gloss	500.00	750.00	750.00

Model No. 2222
LION (CAERNARVON 1969)

Designer: Mrs. Elliot
Height: 4", 10.1 cm
Colour: Cream, red lettering - matt
Issued: 1968-1969
Series: Pair with 2223

Description	U.K.£	U.S.$	Can.$
Matt		Only one example known	

Note: 1. Issued to commemorate the investiture of Prince of Wales, Caernarvon, 1969.
2. Models 2222 and 2223 sold as a pair, Lot 482, Bonhams, October 28, 2003, for £700.00

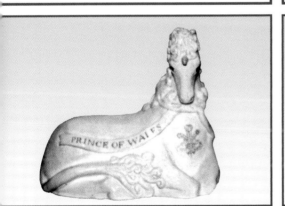

Model No. 2223
UNICORN (PRINCE OF WALES)

Designer: Mrs. Elliott
Height: 4", 10.1 cm
Colour: Cream, red lettering - matt
Issued: 1968-1969
Series: Pair with 2222

Description	U.K. £	U.S. $	Can. $
Matt		Only one example known	

Note: 1. Issued to commemorate the Investiture of the Prince of Wales, Caernarvon, 1969.
2. Models 2222 and 2223 sold as a pair, Lot 482, Bonhams, October 28, 2003, for £700.00

Model No. 2514
"WHITE HORSE WHISKY"

Designer: Alan Maslankowski
Height: 6 ¾", 17.2 cm
Colour: White - gloss
Issued: 1974
Series: Advertising

Description	U.K. £	U.S. $	Can. $
Gloss	350.00	525.00	525.00

Model No. 3021   **UNICORN**

Designer: Graham Tongue
Height: 9", 2.9 cm
Series: Britannia Collection

Colourway	Finish	Intro.	Disc.	U.K. £	U.S. $	Can. $
1. Cream	Matt	1989	Unknown	225.00	350.00	350.00
2. Bronze	Gloss	1989	1992	225.00	350.00	350.00

Indices

2186 Quarter Horse; 1772 Connoisseur Thoroughbred
818 Shire; 1812 Mare; 1261 Palomino
2875 Sunlight Foal; 1407 Arab Foal

INDEX OF MODEL NUMBERS

368 INDEX OF MODEL NUMBERS

Model No.	Name	Page No.
828	Elephant	300
830	Lizard	301
832	Pig	154
833	Piglet - Running	155
834	Piglet - Trotting	155
836	Foal - Large, stretched	183
841	Leopard - Seated	301
845A	Zebra - First Version	301
845B	Zebra - Second Version	301
849	Pheasant on Base - Flying upwards	9
850	Pheasant on Base - Settling	9
853	Giraffe - Small	302
854	Hereford Calf	135
855/1090	Stocky Jogging Mare	184
862	Fantail Pigeon	10
868	Huntsman (On rearing horse)	186
897	Donkey Foal	155
899	Hereford Cow - First Version	135
901A	Hereford Calf - First Version	135
901B	Hereford Calf - Second Version	135
902	Mallard Duck - Standing	10
907	Dog With Ladybird on Tail	89
915/F915	Foal - Lying	187
917	Three Puppies	89
919A	Duck - Large	10
919B	Duck - Medium	10
919C	Duck - Small	11
922	Seagull - Style Two, Wings up, together - Wall plaques	49
925	American Blue Jays	11
926	Baltimore Orioles	11
927	Cardinal	11
928	Tanager	12
929	Chickadee	12
930	Parakeet	12
935	Sheep	155
936	Lamb	156
937	Lamb	156
938	Lamb	156
939	Girl on Jumping Horse	187
941	Foxhound - First Version	89
942	Foxhound - First Version	89
943	Foxhound - First Version	90
944	Foxhound - First Version	90
946/F946	Foal - Grazing	188
947/F946	Foal - Large, head down	189
948	Hereford Cow - Second Version	136
949	Hereford Bull	136
950	Donkey Foal	156
951	Shire Foal - Large	190
953	Mare and Foal on Base	191
954	Stag - Lying	302
961	Dalmatian "Arnoldene" - Large	90
962	Airedale Terrier "Cast Iron Monarch"	90
963	Wired-Haired Terrier "Talavera Romulus"	91
964	Smooth-Haired Terrier "Endon Black Rod"	91
965	Bulldog "Basford British Mascot" - Large	91
965	Bulldog "Basford British Mascot" - on ceramic plinth	354
966	Irish Setter "Sugar of Wendover"	91
967	Cocker Spaniel "Horseshoe Primula"	92
967	Cocker Spaniel "Horseshoe Primula" - on plinth	354
968	Great Dane "Ruler of Oubourgh"	92
969	Alsatian "Ulrica of Brittas" - Large	92
969	Alsatian "Ulrica of Brittas" - on ceramic plinth	354
970	Bull Terrier "Romany Rhinestone" - Large	93
971	Sealyham "Forestedge Foxglove"	93
972	Greyhound "Jovial Roger"	93
973	English Setter "Bayldone Baronet"	93
974	Elephant - Trunk stretching - Small	302
975/H975	Cantering Shire	193
976	Mare - Facing left	194
980A	Robin - First Version	12
980B	Robin - Second Version	13
981	Stag - Standing	302
982	Huntswoman, Style One	195
991A	Chaffinch - First Version	13
991B	Chaffinch - Second Version	13
992A	Blue Tit - First Version	13
992B	Blue Tit - Second Version	14
993A	Wren - First Version	14
993B	Wren - Second Version	14
994	Shelldrake - Rising (beak closed)	14
995	Shelldrake - Settling (beak open)	15
996	Foal - Small, gambolling left	195
997/F997	Foal - Small, stretched, facing left	196
998	Elephant - Trunk stretching - large	303
999A	Doe	303

1501 Huntsman; 1730 Huntswoman
1812 Mare; 1085 Foal; 1862 Horse and Jockey; 1197 Pony (Head Up)

ALPHABETICAL INDEX